The Gift of the Circle

The Gift of the Circle

Carolyn Martin Graham

MOUNTAIN ARBOR
PRESS *an Imprint of BookLogix*
Alpharetta, GA

The author has tried to recreate events, locations, and conversations from her memories of them. The author has made every effort to give credit to the source of any images, quotes, or other material contained within and obtain permissions when feasible.

ISBN: 978-1-63183-674-9 - Paperback
eISBN: 978-1-63183-675-6 - ePub
eISBN: 978-1-63183-676-3 - mobi

Printed in the United States of America   0 9 0 9 2 0

⊗ This paper meets the requirements of ANSI/NISO Z39.48-1992 (Permanence of Paper)

Graphic rendition of The Wee Tiny Sparrow™ by Sage Art & Design, LLC

The Wee Tiny Sparrow™ is a registered trademark of the author (2015).

DEDICATED TO:

Janet Graham Chalmers,

my sister,

who inspired me to live

with her steadfast love.

Brenda Iller Stockdale,

my therapist,

whose luminosity

revealed my pathway

to

mental and physical health.

IN MEMORIAM

With gratitude for my parents,

Ethel Martin Graham

and

James Harlow Graham,

for endowing me with their talents,

their imperfections,

and the legacy of my ancestors.

Contents

Welcome to the Circle

Fellow Seekers:

So, you've come to spend time with me.

Welcome!

In the mysterious way that Divine Orchestration works, we're meant to be together, traveling on an intimate journey with a story wrought from my soul.

The Gift of the Circle will draw you close to me as I course through the landscape of my inner world, refusing to harbor secrets.

When Lyme disease sets off an avalanche of disasters that bury me in sorrow and fear, you'll be alongside me. When I open up for the first time about being sexually exploited, we'll be side by side. And you'll be walking close at hand while I heal myself from a troubled mind and a sick body to become freedom's child, my beloved.

Best of all, you'll witness Destiny's majestic hand when, in the final moments of my journey, I reach the pinnacle of my healing.

I've imagined your comforting or joyful presence beside me many times when I was writing, pathing my way through pain and triumph.

While you read *The Gift of the Circle*, know that I honor your life's journey, and I'm thankful to be a part of your soul's passage on the earth.

May we both be blessed by our time together.

And may my message of hope and healing touch you and come to radiate Light upon those who come within your circle of inspiration.

Namaste!

Carolyn Martin Graham

PART I
RIPENING

The darkest events in one's life have the potential to ripen the soul,
seeding growth and the flowering of wisdom.

THE WATCHER

Before this story moves forward, I want to introduce myself, an aspect of Carolyn Martin Graham, the author. I've known her since she was born. Maybe even before then.

People theorize about my existence, yet they may never find out exactly where I come from. Seems to me, I'm partially from the Aethers of Infinite Wisdom. And partially from experiential conditioning by events and people. No one will ever really know.

I'm known by some as The Observer, by others as The Knower; Carolyn now calls me The Watcher. There are as many names for me as there are cultures that cultivate knowledge of me.

My presence isn't always apparent. To become part of someone's awareness, a relationship with me must be cultivated and nourished using mindfulness meditation. Once I've become apparent to someone, then I have the capacity to reveal what's going to be said before words are uttered. More importantly, I make known motivations behind thoughts and actions. Thus, I make possible wise choices for actions.

I'm not judgmental about the author or anyone else. I merely notice what's going on, maintaining a neutral stance regarding conclusions.

I'm different from someone's conscience. A conscience is molded by the ethics and mores of a culture. I exist apart from that. I'm insight and wisdom—unbiased and available to all who seek me. When I'm well-seated in a relationship with someone, I speak the universal language of compassion. In fact, all sentient beings benefit from my empathy.

In short, I'm profoundly powerful. So much so I could be the ultimate source of peace on the planet.

One other thing about my nature: Once a relationship has been cultivated with me, I have the potential to work as a deep-water keel, keeping one's behavior true to wise counsel. Acting outside of nobility becomes difficult—like swimming against a strong current. In an odd sense, the freedom from emotional turmoil I offer establishes boundaries. Ulterior motives fray around the edges and lose their sway.

I'm found only when one seeks me in mindful stillness. After that, my most powerful influence surfaces in the pauses—between thoughts when actions are chosen.

While beginning to practice mindfulness meditation during the 1980s, Carolyn discovered my presence. She started calling me her "whisper voice." I wasn't a well-developed part of her then, yet she heard me "whispering in her ear" letting her in on her motivations during that pause between thoughts and action; as new as our relationship was, I sometimes inspired her to steer away from unwise behavior.

Yet during the early 1990s, she squeezed meditation out of her schedule, ignoring my promising influence.

She seemed obsessed then, ever on the move: working on the tree house where she lived; rescuing cats and dogs; training her donkey; spending time with her mother—every Sunday and more—managing a cat-companion project for elderly people living in a retirement village; training her dog Forest; taking her therapy dog, Dreamer, for visits to a nursing home; biking long distances; cramming in time to be with her friends; and working a full-time, demanding job. Phew!

She didn't understand why she was crowding her schedule so, why she kept herself perpetually revved up, or why she was out of control. And I couldn't help her.

As I said, I'm nothing without stillness.

That quiet place where I'm found is stirring up a lot of excitement.

Why?

Training the mind to be still can be used to induce relaxation for stress management. A calm mind is a calm body. A calm body invites optimal immune-system functioning.

Carolyn didn't know all that when she created that hectic schedule of hers, excluding time to nurture her relationship with me.

She didn't know that one day she'd seek me out again. Later, I'll say more about that.

For now, though, I'll step aside, be still and watch . . .

FROLICKING
IN THE FRINGES

Off-grid.

That's me.

Eccentric. Creative.

Strangers often ask if I'm an artist.

I am, although not in the conventional sense.

My living environment, clothing choices, and many other aspects of my life reflect independent thinking. Frolicking in the fringes of cultural norms is my modus operandi.

No surprise that I'm androgynous.

Nature? Nurture?

Who knows.

When I was a kid, no one restricted my selection of toys. If I begged long enough, my parents were as likely to buy me a model car kit as they were to purchase a life-sized baby doll. I wore fluffy, pink tutus or my mother's high-heeled shoes, lipstick, and hats, and just as often I strapped on two cap guns to play cowboys and Indians.

As a fifty-year-old adult, my childhood tendency to focus on what I want to do rather than what gender expectations say I should has still guided the direction of my leisure-time activities.

Basically, if I think I can do something, I'll try.

I've hung ceiling fans. Crocheted intricate doilies, using the finest-gauge thread and smallest of steel hooks. Once in a while, I've cut down a tree branch with a chainsaw. Knitting, sewing, or quilting, I've made garments or piecework for myself or for gifts.

Neither a screwdriver nor hammer threatens me. Working with them is as easy as using a pencil for making lists or a block knife for mincing garlic.

Secretly, I'm proud of my vast array of talents.

Yet in public I speak only of my "feminine" skills.

What's up with that?

I'm afraid of being labeled "butch."

Even though I don't look the part, that's insinuated. Too much.

A waiter, someone behind a customer service desk, a grocery store clerk—all can sometimes make me squirm:

"May I help you, sir?"

"Thank you, sir."

"Can I help you find something, sir?"

Inside, I cringe.

Worse, whoever slips invariably does a double take and then apologizes, eyes cast downward.

A good thing, because my face is sure to be crimson with embarrassment, even shame.

Despite my long hair, orchestrated into feminine styles, and ample breasts that proclaim my certain native gender, my secret is on display.

Am I referring to my sexual preferences?

Yes.

I'm bisexual. That's not the end of the story, though.

As a young child, I was beaten and mentally abused by my father, creating a fear that taints my relationships with men. And when I was a sophomore in high school, I was exploited by a sexual predator who served in the lofty, self-appointed role of a sexual mentor.

Before my brain was fully developed, I was emotionally twisted—sexually distorted.

So, I'll never know if I was born with a genetic sexual predisposition.

In practical terms, that doesn't matter much.

Why not?
Right now, I'm celibate . . .

———

Picture a Mother Earth type wearing a bustier. The image doesn't compute.

Eighteen years ago, when I was thirty-two, I served as the director of a counseling department in a high school. My wardrobe was full of trendy, professional clothing made from scratchy, synthetic fabrics, fabrics that sometimes felt like moistened plastic wrap plastered against my skin. Toe pain communicated the insanity of wearing high-heeled, pointed-toe shoes that matched my outfits and purse. And all of my undergarments complemented my outer clothing.

Tight panty hose made for stick people pinched my waist, leaving a red ring of irritation every time I wore a pair. If they were new, I seldom kept them whole for even a day, inevitably taking scissors to the torturing elastic.

A life-altering experience changed all that madness one weekend at a workshop led by Dr. Sidney Simon. My interest was roused as he read from his book *Values Clarification*: "Every day, every one of us meets life situations that call for thought, decision making, and action. Some of these situations are familiar, some novel; some are casual and some are of extreme importance. Everything we do, every decision we make and course of action we take, is based on our consciously or unconsciously held beliefs, attitudes and values."[1]

Somehow, that one sentence rattled my consciousness, awakening a hidden part of me, pointing to my true nature that hadn't matured. When I arrived home after the workshop, unlocking my apartment was a surreal experience. Although I was housed in the same body, I felt more authentic, more myself, than the person who'd left only two days before.

A certain urgency about acting on the dynamic changes,

ringing with integrity, prompted me to step up to the plate and get real. I figured one of the quickest and surest ways to begin my journey to authenticity was to change my entire professional wardrobe.

With vigor, I threw all of my synthetic, stilted clothing into large, black plastic trash bags. My pointed-toe shoes too. While bidding them "good riddance" I paused, taking a close look at a pair long enough to wonder how I could have been masochistic enough to have worn them.

After filtering, all that was left in my closet was comfortable cotton clothing.

Denim became my fabric of choice—especially stone-washed denim—no matter my pursuit. My body experienced the relief of breathing freely under one-hundred-percent cotton comforting my skin.

More importantly, denim began conveying a unique and individualistic message: "You are welcome to approach. I've no need to be more powerful than you. I'm trustworthy. I won't be boxed."

Except for funerals, when I wore a pair of black, rounded-toe stacked heels, flat-heeled sandals became my shoe style of choice. And as the weather cooled each year, I initiated what became a long-standing seasonal ritual of loosening the straps to accommodate thick, warm socks.

I stopped curling my hair on prickly, hard rollers for a stylish look. Instead I transitioned into wearing my chestnut-brown hair in a Gibson Girl bun, hair poofed around my face or in a single French braid with a scrunchie at the end.

Ankle-length skirts became my norm. Often, I added a unique touch, wearing a slightly longer off-white slip I had made. Sometimes I tied a knot in a skirt's hemline to reveal the slip's lace.

Draping tops with uneven hemlines and pockets in unexpected places began speaking of my taste for the creative.

My color preferences?

Besides faded blue denim, I chose mostly off-white, olive greens, rusts, and other shades of brown. Sometimes black.

The underwear thing?

Matching undergarments lost appeal. In fact, when wearing skirts, I figured there wasn't a need to wear panties at all unless I was having my period.

So, I didn't.

I took a stance on makeup too. Very little, if any, proclaimed: "I'm innately beautiful."

As I displayed my curvy, soft body cloaked with welcoming authenticity and harmonious resonance, to many I appeared to be the perfect bohemian Mother Earth.

I figured I might pay a professional price for this comfortable, laid-back style of dress, yet I was and still am determined to be real and sensible. To make my way professionally, I've counted on demonstrating a strong work ethic and my capacity for skillful execution of professional expectations.

After my awakening to a certain authenticity, I succumbed twice to the dress-for-success pressure. Reverting to my uptight dress style, I sought positions offering lots more money than I was making, and tons more responsibility too.

In both cases, I was rejected for promotion even though my interview performances were stellar. Stellar!

Maybe my well-known, pre-promotion-seeking casual dress style had something to do with that.

Or something else.

Who knows?

After suffering the sting of rejection, and the realization that I wasn't going to have the luxuries I'd fantasized about nor the status, I took stock of the direction I wanted to take with my career.

While probing my values and taking care to avoid rationalizing, I paid close attention to those around me with the high levels of pay and responsibility I was seeking. My eyes opened to the stress they endured, to the compromises exerted on their personal lives.

I decided that my day-to-day peace of mind was critical. That

I wanted to be a model employee while at work and leave my job behind when I went home.

Once I came to terms with that reality, I relaxed into my comfortable dress style, feeling comforted by the certainty that I had enough: Enough responsibility. Enough money. And enough of pretense.

———

I've been married twice. And divorced twice.

I've never had children, nor have I ever wanted any.

That doesn't sound much like Mother Earth, but that's the way things went down for me.

My first husband was a darling, a prince yearning to love me. After two years of a troubled marriage, I ran from him as fast as my twenty-three-year-old legs could go, not understanding why I wasn't capable of sustaining physical and emotional intimacy.

After divorcing my first husband, I engaged in many short-term relationships. Some were with men, some with women. Eventually, I tired of hiding my feelings and of the judgment targeting same-sex relationships, so I gave up the women. Since I knew I was sexually attracted to both men and women, I decided to take the path of least resistance.

Ten years later, soon after the time my dress style changed, I married someone who seemed to be dealing well with life's challenges. He was magnetic. A tall, charming, olive-skinned man who hid for a while his penchant for binge drinking and physical abuse. After five years of reeling from the effects of my husband's unpredictable behavior, I divorced him too.

Then, for a time, I saw a married man, believing I could justify my deceitfulness because his wife was a semiconscious alcoholic. In the end, hiding our relationship nauseated me. The fear of being caught corrupted the pleasure of our trysts.

After ending that affair, I took a much-needed hiatus from physical relationships.

Six years later, on the eve of my forty-seventh birthday, I began hungering for another man in my life.

I knew one would show up. Good or bad, one always had when I was ready.

And what a yummy one arrived in my landscape!

He was rich and artistic. His self-designed home was unique, contemporary, standing apart from his neighborhood's traditional styles. Conversations with him were captivating and thought provoking. He also had an impressive social conscience, manifesting in volunteer work. Like me, classical music was his preference.

And I couldn't help but notice his lavish shock of gray, curly hair and ample genitalia snugged into gray sweatpants when I first met him at an art show. Jumping his bones became my fantasy.

Not long after meeting, I fell in love with him and his vast repertoire of interests.

In an odd twist, our sexual relationship was difficult: Although I was attracted to him, he was a reticent lover, taking forever to become aroused. Sometimes he'd even fall asleep in the midst of foreplay. Intercourse was rare.

When I wanted sex, I had to ask. Even though I had to break through awkwardness to express my needs, I did so. My efforts were well-rewarded, for he was an expert at pleasure making. One lazy Saturday afternoon, I called him from my home to invite him to make love. Although we hadn't made love in weeks, he accused me of being a sex addict.

"Asking to have sex once a month is *not* being an addict," I exploded.

He heard me. I got my way. And I remained in the relationship even though navigating the physical aspects was challenging and called on me to be assertive.

A few months after the "addict" incident, my gynecologist recommended that I have a complete hysterectomy, a radical solution for endometriosis. Six weeks after the surgery my gynecologist cleared me for sexual activity, as was customary.

For some reason, I thought my partner would be as thrilled about that as I was. So, I asked him to take me somewhere romantic, somewhere special.

I was amazed when he soon invited me to join him for a weekend at a bed-and-breakfast located in a nearby seaside town. As I hugged him, exuberant with happiness, he whispered in my ear in a husky voice, "Bring black heels and black, seamed stockings."

When preparing for our time together, innocent of what was coming, I scrounged around in my closet, finding my black, rounded-toe funeral shoes with one-and-a-half-inch stacked heels.

Acquiring the black, seamed hose wasn't easy, but after searching, I finally found a pair in a sleazy lingerie shop. I placed them in my wicker suitcase along with everything else for our weekend getaway . . .

———

Our room is beautiful. A cream-colored matelassé spread covers the four-poster, walnut bed. Four poofy pillows with matching shams speak of luxury. Centered in front of the pillows, a sea-glass-green bolster, monogrammed and piped to match the spread, adds panache. Two pieces of dark chocolate placed on the bedside table and a bottle of wine chilling in a ceramic glacette create the final touch.

A picture window overlooks purple-flowered bougainvillea draping a lattice archway. An expansive green lawn invites my eyes to linger then to meander westward into the lapping, sparkling ripples of the Intracoastal Waterway, framed by the warm glows of sunset.

On a cushiony, velvety couch foreplay is leisurely. Expectant.

Suddenly, my partner pulls away.

My eyes question him. He lifts his index finger to his lips, shushing my protest, then stands and walks to his suitcase. Returning, he extends his hands, grinning, eyes sparkling, offering me a beautifully wrapped package.

With care, I unwrap and open a white, embossed box. Mauve tissue paper hints of something decidedly feminine. Not wanting to rush this special moment, I slowly lift the folded paper, first one side, then the other.

Something black and lacy greets me. With both hands, I unhurriedly lift the garment from the box, savoring the experience.

Holy shit! A bustier.

Suddenly, I understand.

Confusion rages against my need to keep my weekend unspoiled. The last thing I want to do is repel sexual interest that's so hard to come by. Yet I struggle with my need to be real. My need to be natural.

In the end, I wimp, suppressing my discomfort. My authenticity. My outrage at the insinuation that my body isn't naturally alluring.

Although my libido has taken a huge hit, I charade into nakedness while my partner looks on. After sizing up my new lingerie, shrugging, I step into the elasticized black lace. Tugging and pulling the too-snug beauty, I finally inch the black, wired bra up to breast height. (I guess my friend was fantasizing about my size as well as my taste for dressed-up sex.) I proceed, adjusting my breasts, making certain they're well-positioned into the bustier's cups.

Cleavage erupts. I don't care. By now, I feel just plain weird, the top part of me bolted in and sweating, the bottom part cold, bulging, and squeezed out of a too-tight fit. I can't help myself. I squirm: *This damn thing is scratchy as hell!*

No matter. I move onward, unbelievably irritated. No telling what my face is saying. I don't bother to check on my partner. I'm too preoccupied with struggling to be a chameleon. I don't search my psyche, either, to understand why I'm willing to be a fake.

Rote as a drone, I proceed.

What about the hose?

I'd never worn seamed hose. They're a real piece of work.

I've seen enough porn to know there are ways for me to invite drooling and more when donning hose. I can't go there.

I don't even get close: The seams in the hose are impossible to get straight. After fiddling with them over and over, I give up.

So they're crooked. So what.

What comes next is even worse.

My legs have never been shapely. As a scrawny-legged, knobby-kneed seven-year-old child, my best friend's father called me "Toothpicks." Years later, the black high school students where I worked as a counselor just after finishing graduate school dubbed me "Big Bird." That was and still is me—a lavishly appointed torso with gawky, skinny limbs like the Sesame Street character.

So, I'm unable to fill the hose to their full length so they'll lie smoothly. They're made for longer legs than mine.

I've no alternative except to bunch the tops into the garters.

Now for my rounded-toe, stacked-heel shoes.

Looking at them, I flush with embarrassment.

Once they're on, my feet are certain they're walking in the wrong place.

My sex drive?

Snuffed.

I'm sure my partner is a goner too.

Should I keep going with this charade? I'm naturally beautiful— aren't I?

I know I'm expected to parade myself—and more.

Confusion freezes me. But not for long.

Off comes the tight, scratchy bustier, bunched-up hose, and frumpy heels. I throw them into my wicker suitcase and don my nightgown and bathrobe.

I've no wish to go somewhere for a late dinner like we'd planned. I'm hungry only for escape into comfort, my inner world.

There's no ensuing conversation about what's just happened. Just lame small talk and a restless night's sleep.

The Protestant, Anglo-Saxon boa constrictor's voice-choking grip, obstructing speech about procreating, copulating, and masturbating, doesn't loosen until years later.

Celibacy reigns through a long night, rattling with unanswered questions.

What happens to the costume?

I throw the hose in the trash before leaving the bed-and-breakfast. The bustier winds up in a thrift store. My stacked-heel shoes go back in my closet—to be worn at funerals.

———

Strangely enough, my relationship with the "bustier" man continued for three more years. I hung on long and hard, hoping something in our relationship would change, leading to a rational permanence.

The ending came two years ago when my guard was down: my partner told me he didn't love me—in front of a group of people—at a weekend personal-growth retreat he'd invited me to attend.

Although that experience was excruciating, that's not the reason for what I'm about to say.

That breakup was merely one of many, involving my walking away from someone or the other way around. Men and women alike.

I was thinking about all that one afternoon, standing at my kitchen sink doing dishes.

Pausing, resting my hand on the counter, I began some soul searching.

I faced up to the fact that I'm lousy at navigating sexual partnerships. I didn't try figuring out why. I just knew I'd experienced more sexually intimate relationships than I stopped to count. Going down that road again seemed pointless unless I was willing to engage in therapy. And there was no telling how long my rehabilitation would take, nor the outcome. The investment in time, energy, and money didn't seem worth the trouble when framed by what I came to understand . . .

I thrive in friendships rich with psychological intimacy. Deep, long-lasting friendships spanning decades. My happiest times have been when I've been single. Free. Engaged with others, yet unfettered and able to pursue my life in peace—bolstered by emotional balance.

Looking up to gaze out the kitchen window onto my backyard garden full of bright-colored zinnias, I knew what was coming.

Standing tall, I planted my feet shoulder's width apart to feel secure. Determined.

Taking in a deep breath, and then stomping my foot, I set my sexual course: "Celibacy will reign from now on. From now on!"

Occasionally, especially during the holidays, I've found myself yearning for someone to hold my hand, escort me to an intimate, romantic, candlelit restaurant—and more. So far, I've been able to come to my senses before allowing myself to be seduced by fantasy into certain mayhem. My life continues to be rich with nourishing friendships. I love my job. Many of those I work with have become my family. Best of all, my life is peaceful. Without chaos. I'm happy.

My decision to be celibate still stands.

THE NAKED TRUTH

When I'm challenging myself, rigorously partnering my body and mind to achieve a goal, I often remember a Mount Everest climber's remark in a *National Geographic* article titled "At My Limit": "There's more than precipice and storm between you and your Everest."[1]

There's the marriage of my mind and body, my mind urging my body. I seek opportunities to push against and burst open boundaries of limitations—despite my fears—by engaging in physical challenges, using my athletic proclivity. I often feel an urge to grow, imagining myself responding to a light that beckons me to flower. Beckons me to engage the power of mind-body communication to push against limits so that I experience a roomier presence in this world.

My growth challenges are carefully chosen, weighing my fears against emotional and physical readiness—so I pick tasks that promise success, which will, at the same time, challenge me some and take me to a new frontier.

What's the payoff?

Every time I grow a little, I stoke my personal power, my prowess, a bit, whittling away at unrealistic fears shackling me. And every time I cross a finish line after exerting extraordinary effort, I'm rewarded by the thrill of knowing I can soar a little higher into the realm of freedom.

Seeking my Everest, I've ridden a bicycle from Charleston to central Florida along the eastern shore, using my mind to urge my body to keep going. Especially so when my new bicycle seat was eating my labia alive, or when I had to pedal up the Route 17 sky-high bridge spanning the Savannah River, muscles on fire with exertion.

When I boarded my houseboat for the first time, intending to live there, my fear of sinking while asleep frazzled my sanity; realizing I was in trouble, I summoned my mind into action, coaxing my body to creep across the deck one step at a time and enter my living quarters. And later I called up my reasoning power to halt my body's urge to repeatedly check the bilge to make certain there were no leaks. When I haven't used my mind and body to grow myself for a while, I feel stale. Adventure becomes a magnetic, alluring teacher I welcome.

Just when I was feeling wrapped too tight into sameness, a friend invited me and six others to go with her and her husband, Joe Kenner, on an excursion to Moab, Utah, for a fifty-mile canoe trip on the Green River in the Canyonlands wilderness.

When I got my first good look at the river, engorged with spring runoff from the Rockies, fear shriveled my big need for challenge into the size of a pea. While imagining myself teeny-tiny paddling a canoe on the fast-running current, sweat burst on my brow in terror. *What were you thinking?* my mind shrieked.

Looking back and forth between the canoe, packed with gear and ready for launch, and the river, I struggled: *What now? Should I go on the river? Or retreat to Moab?*

At that critical moment there was more than the Green River threatening me. My fears were ignoring my expertise with the paddle, my swimming ability, and Joe's vast experience as an outdoorsman and guide. Also, other groups and individuals were preparing to launch, revealing the safety for someone like me.

Had I not taken charge of my fears, opting to proceed, I would have missed out on a gift that has become one of Joe Kenner's legacies. As things turned out, just eighteen months after my first Green River adventure, Joe died of lung cancer.

Yet he's remained alive in my heart, for I've returned to Moab and the Green River four times to challenge myself, twice with a different friend each time, and twice I've soloed.

Every time I've gone there, I've been stunned by the landscape of vivid colors: terracotta canyons, bright-green vegetation growing along the banks of the river, and unblemished cerulean-blue sky, reflected in the ribbon of water my canoe glided over.

I've been lulled by the pristine beauty and profound silence.

Most of the time.

There have also been high winds that rocked the canoe, threatening to capsize me; an entire day of freezing rain that chilled me into hypothermia, mandating that I stop, pitch my tent, and warm up in my sleeping bag; roasting high temperatures; and other natural phenomena that have called upon me to use my prowess to thrive in the wilderness.

There's been an engaging spiritual quality on the Green River, filling me with breathtaking awe, and an opportunity to let go of the norm to experience the mysteries of creative expression, seeming to embrace me: rotund rocks, stacked upon one another, morphing into people, prompting me to name them people rocks. Along the top of canyon rims, they've seemed to be conducting committee meetings. Or they've appeared to be merely greeting me by twos and threes.

Once, when I was lying on a gray, funneled rock surface, smoothed by eons of water swirling into a milky blue pool at the base of the canyon, boulders on the high rim above became Native American chiefs, feathered headdresses touching the sky. While spellbound, I was certain a canyon wren trilled to bless me.

As I opened to the dimensions of infinite possibilities under a limitless blue sky, the mystical became as much of my reality as the hard rock I lay upon. Although I couldn't be certain, I believed that same wren blessing me in the canyon later accompanied me the last ten miles of that journey, trilling assurance.

On my first fifty-mile solo excursion, I spoke with ravens cawing in the wind and saw a rattlesnake sip water from the river beside where my canoe was tied. And, as always, I battled fear. When I reached the end of that Green River adventure, the thrill of knowing I'd edged my way just a little farther into the realm of limitless freedom, the wilderness, showered me with sparkling inspiration and the need to return.

Besides seeking adventure to grow myself, curiosity lures me into the mysterious.

I'm prone to explore: an offshore island, a winding country road, a forest trail, and anything else that seems sensible to me.

I'm a lot like my father. Though I'm not mean like he was, I tend to think outside the box like he did, especially where propriety is concerned . . .

Once, a man I'd been dating drummed up the courage to share his penchant for visiting a nudist colony in nearby Orlando where he was a member. Judging by the way he leaned his head to the side when talking, I don't think he was certain how I'd take his revelation. When I didn't recoil, he went on to extol the virtues of nudity, piquing my curiosity.

Listening, I began feeling highly evolved. And knowing my thirty-year-old body parts were in close-to-nubile positioning, I was eager to investigate, figuring he would ask me to go there. I didn't see harm in nakedness in certain situations: European beaches, indigenous cultures dressing for climate while framed by acceptability, or on the Green River in the wilderness.

Nudity in a nudist colony?

That worked for me.

So, I accepted his invitation to spend a day naked in the sun and fresh air.

———

On a Saturday morning, my male friend and I take off for a memorable adventure.

Upon arriving at the nudist colony, we pull up to a black iron gate.

My friend presses a call button, then identifies himself; since males aren't permitted to enter unaccompanied by a female, and no one is allowed to proceed unannounced, he declares my presence.

Slowly, the heavy gates swing open. We drive through the entrance and park, then amble to the registration building, still fully clothed.

On the way I glance around the grounds. Everyone I see is sunning themselves, either sitting in beach chairs or lying on blankets spread on the ground, stark naked.

Unaccustomed to such nonplussed nudity, I quickly decide to keep my eyes modestly cast downward, wanting to remain noninvasive while wondering if that's even possible. What seemed so sensible before we arrived feels a bit intimidating now. Besides, I'm afraid curiosity about others' body parts, especially their genitalia, will tempt me to stare, revealing my naiveté.

Once inside, we're attended by a nude female.

Standing at the counter, filling out a form she has handed me, I hear the main door open, proclaiming the arrival of someone else. The wood floor creaks on my right; I feel a presence nearby. Glancing downward, the only "safe" way to proceed, I notice large feet donned with sparkling-clean white socks and tennis shoes.

I make the assumption that wearing shoes probably means wearing clothes too.

So I raise my eyes, preparing to offer a greeting, although cautiously.

When they're halfway up my neighbor's body, heat reddens my face: a penis as large as the feet in tennis shoes declares a vibrant spirit by nodding a bit.

Stammering, I introduce myself to the gentleman beside me, shaking his hand while mustering every ounce of aplomb I can manifest in order to appear nonchalant. Reluctantly I turn back to the counter, fighting my urge to investigate more of what my eyes merely glanced over.

After that, my friend and I return to our car and strip. We then position ourselves on a quilt laid over a patch of grass.

As the day of nudity progresses, I relax into an easy camaraderie, visiting with those who come to connect. Parents with children, married and single couples, day visitors like us, and those staying in cottages on the grounds wander by to chat.

Like me, everyone I meet rivets their eyes to faces, at least while being observed.

Nothing overtly improper disrupts the park-like setting. Who knows what's happening cloaked in the privacy of our fellow nudists' minds.

When returning home from spending the entire day bathing naked in the sun, I feel calm, comfortable, and gratified that I'd had the opportunity to go au naturel, even with others present.

So, I return frequently to the nudist colony for more of the same.

Once, I even take sailing lessons there. The instructor is a tall, broad-shouldered man with bulging biceps. I can't help wondering if the size of his manhood matches the rest of his massive body, so I sneak a peek.

I jerk my head up, my face full of undisguised questions about the pinky-sized penis shocking my senses. My eyes lock with the instructor's, unspoken feelings pulsing between us. Our expressions freeze into neutral at warp speed. Charades. An odd juxtaposition to the naked truth just revealed.

In between my ever-interesting visits to the nudist colony, my conventional mint-green and rose-pink mother visits me.

Before she arrives at my apartment, I clean with vigor. On my sparkling glass-top coffee table, I deliberately place a book expounding the merits of nudity, baiting my mother's strong sense of self-righteous propriety, planning to exert my authority over boundaries I've long hated.

My mother's eyes latch onto the book within seconds after she's seated in my living room. They bulge and cross, a sure signal that she's roiling inside. Yet she can't hold back her voyeuristic compulsion to know more, nor her desire to appear open. So the inevitable, predictable questions erupt as if she's asking about weather.

I pull my shoulders back and lift my chin, securing myself in cerebral sophistication as I gear up to proceed.

I tell my mother about my visits to the nudist colony, extoling the virtues of my skin breathing free from the hindrances of clothing. I tell her that seeing lots of naked people helps me realize that each one of us is most certainly physically unique. And imperfect.

While waxing eloquent I feel citified. Justifiably arrogant, acting like a perfect twit.

My ever-dignified mother is dead quiet during my entire rant.

When I finish my monologue, I realize I've gone too far. My bravado deflates in the face of my mother's imposing, indignant figure, so I abruptly change the topic to a piece of knitting lying on an end table.

In her wisdom, my mother switches gears too.

Our emotions drag anchor, though, making conversation awkward for a while.

In an unspoken agreement, the topic of nudity becomes off limits from then on.

I continue to visit the nudist colony even after my relationship with the man who first took me there ends, entertaining my friends with stories of my experiences there.

On my last visit, I take a male friend from Atlanta who's highly intrigued by the notion of experiencing public nudity.

Getting ready for a day's outing in the sun, we pack tennis rackets, a new can of tennis balls, and a picnic lunch.

Not long after signing in, we strip, leaving our clothes in the car. Toting our gear, we stride toward the tennis courts. Once inside we go to opposite ends of a court. While we're taking our rackets out of their zipped coverings, spectators gather outside the surrounding fence.

My friend soon sets me into a bona fide tizzy: he reaches into his duffle bag and takes out a chalk-white device unlike anything I've ever seen.

After stepping into this contraption, made more noticeable by contrasting with his dark skin, he adjusts attached elastic straps around his hips. Then the worst thing I can imagine happens: he positions a rigid plastic cup around his genitals, being especially careful to protect his one remaining testicle, the other having been removed after a diving accident.

I'm mortified, wondering how I'll endure being seen with someone wearing something weird looking that draws attention straight to his crotch.

Somehow I pull myself together and pursue a competitive game of tennis, chasing balls stark naked, my ample breasts flopping this way and that. I feel exhilarated by the competition at hand, unaffected by even the slightest twinge of embarrassment.

Other than being piqued by my companion's rude attire, my greatest emotional challenge comes from straining to appear demure and to protect my dignity, despite all.

What's up with that?

I'm ungainly. I always have been. So I dread retrieving tennis balls from the ground while naked. Squatting is awkward, an emotional and physical challenge with great import. To ensure that I'm perceived as classy, I first must make certain my knees are held tightly together and to the side; then I bend my legs to bring my right arm close enough to the ground to reach the ball, while keeping my chest and head upright. No easy feat.

Yet the entire process is worth every ounce of effort to be certain I don't upend my buttocks and flash the spectators.

Go figure.

Now, when my nudist colony experiences parade in my memory, I find humor in my colorful, opinionated youth—and some sorrow at the way I baited my mother.

I'm chock-full of memories. They have a way of informing me these days.

Sometimes they make me laugh, or they make me feel too human. Once in a while, they inspire me to keep living life in my own way, facing the naked truth of my choices to grow or to grieve, or to just plain dance with them as a celebration of life.

ETHEL. MOTHER. MOM.

My ninety-year-old mother is resilient, aging with grace.

An introvert, she makes herself happy doing handwork or reading. Her daily luncheon outing with friends in the cafeteria of the retirement community where she lives or an occasional bridge game is enough socializing for her.

She gave up driving after a policeman, car bristling with flashing signals, pulled her over when she ran a red light. When mother rolled down her window, preparing for the worst, the policeman barked, "Lady, do you know what you're supposed to do when a traffic light is yellow?"

"Yes sir! Gun the engine and hope the light doesn't turn red before you pass."

Her reply undid the officer, turning him into a trembling mass of stifled laughter. He threw up his hands, got in his car, and pulled away with no more ado.

Soon afterward, Mother handed me her car keys, declaring that she was through driving. Feeling grateful I didn't have to pressure her to stop, and believing she knew what she was doing, I didn't argue.

Mother and I spend Sundays together these days. We have since my father died in 1992, nine years ago . . .

Early one morning I drove him and Mother to a hospital for surgery to remove a grossly enlarged prostate gland.

After my father checked in and was prepped for his operation, Mother and I chatted with him until surgical nurses arrived with a gurney. While they waited, he walked us to the door of his room, wearing a blue hospital gown, cap, and slippers. First, Mother hugged my father tight to her chest. Afraid to show him how much I cared about him, and fearing he'd shove me away like he always had whenever I'd attempted to be close, I wrapped my arms around him lightly, merely touching his shoulders.

Before we'd turned our backs, my father's face turned beet red. Then he began sobbing.

I'd heard him cry only twice—over the phone. Seeing him weep was a first.

My heart ached, yet I sought to appear unaffected for my mother's sake.

Although she said nothing, I'm certain she was deeply moved too. Even so, neither she nor I chose to say anything, knowing there was nothing honest we could offer as reassurance. He was a high-risk surgical patient with complicated heart issues; surgery was his only option.

After my father was helped onto the gurney, Mother and I trudged toward the surgical waiting room, my father's sobs haunting the early-morning silence.

Late that afternoon, I began to fear something was wrong; too much time had passed since our goodbyes. When I checked at the nearby nurses' station, I knew there was trouble: the nurse who called the recovery room for a status report couldn't lift her eyes to meet mine as she reported, "He's still being worked on."

Soon afterward the surgeon appeared, addressing my mother. "I'm sorry. So sorry. We did everything we could. Your husband came through the surgery fine. But he suffered a heart attack just when we were preparing to release him from the recovery room. He's still alive, but his condition isn't promising. He's a very sick man. You'll be able to see him soon in ICU for a few minutes. Someone will call for you when he's ready for visitors . . ."

In the early evening hours, Mother held my father's still-warm hand while he lay in the ICU, hooked up to a respirator and other monitors. When preparing to leave for the night, she squeezed his hand, and he squeezed hers, a hopeful sign.

His eyes flickered when I bent down and kissed him on the forehead, saying good night.

A few days later, he was declared brain-dead.

Mother, my sister, our Aunt Nita, and I stood beside my father's cold body while the respirator was disconnected.

Within minutes he was gone.

With him went stories of his past. The reasons he was violent, unpredictable, and unable to be affectionate with me or my sister.

A dream of mine died when he did. An unrealistic dream that had survived decades, yet somehow buffered my visits home on holidays.

I'd fantasized that one day we'd to get to know each other. That my family could somehow find a way to be a unified whole. That we'd come to affirm each other, to share emotions and go beneath the skeletal surface of the made-safe-by-silence relationship that had defined our moments together.

With my father's last sucking, gasping breaths, he swallowed my silly hope for normalcy.

A few days before that, when I was certain that disconnecting the life-support machines was imminent, I visited my father alone—on a mission.

Holding his hand, I leaned close to his left ear. "Dad, this is Carolyn. I'm by myself. I came to tell you something important. In case you're concerned, I want you to know I'll take care of Mother."

Then I said something that was part of his belief system, rather than my own: "You can let go. You can let go to be with Jesus now."

With that, monitors signaling input from my father's systems flashed and beeped into the space that had been still.

I was spellbound, imbued with awe, grateful my father had heard me.

Then something astounding happened. When the monitors quieted, an angel appeared, every bit as real as my father's still, cold body. With loving grace, the angel bent over and lifted my father, draping him over his forearms like Michelangelo's *Pietà*. The angel then turned and carried my wounded father into a bright, white light.

Was that vision merely a Jungian archetype manifesting? Wishful thinking? I've never felt compelled to decide. Either way, the experience was stunning.

Once my father was gone, true to my promise, I began assuming the responsibility for managing Mother's finances and other practical needs not taken care of by the continuing-care retirement community where she lives.

That was the honorable thing to have done.

———

Every Sunday, I drive the short distance between Mother's place and mine to spend the day with her. I've done that for the last nine years, except for the few times I've been traveling.

Why do I single out Sundays?

I'm crazy busy with an intense full-time job. When my work-days are finished, I usually spend time training my donkey to ride, visiting the home of someone interested in adopting a cat or dog I've rescued, running, or eating dinner with a friend. On Saturdays I work with a couple who is helping me build a cottage in the not-too-distant woods where I'll be moving soon; somehow I squeeze in doing laundry and other household chores.

Giving Sundays to my mother feels like the best way to be certain I'll honor my promise to my father. And to be certain I have boundaries around my time to protect myself from being swallowed by her needs.

I can't protect myself from spending hours and hours in an emergency room with her. The stakes are too high for making a mistake in judgment I don't want on my conscience: Too often, a nurse calls from the village where my mother lives. I'm called at work, in the middle of the night, or who knows when to be told

Mother's being transported to the hospital by ambulance, blood pressure at stroke level, her heart rate threatening attack.

Although I always believe at the outset an anxiety attack is causing Mother's symptoms, I can never be certain. Even so, I'm not hard-hearted enough to abandon her. So I feel compelled to go to her.

Inevitably, by the time I arrive at the emergency room, she's recovered, showing no signs of trouble. Test results, when they come back hours later, are always negative.

Although that peeves me to no end, especially when I've spent late-night hours in the emergency room and have to work the next day, I spare my mother from my tirades. There's no point in spouting off.

I've made more than one unsuccessful attempt to get her to ask her doctor for a prescription for anxiety.

I take an antidepressant to keep my own manageable. A genetic gift from my mother, I was diagnosed with anxiety disorder when I turned forty. In fact, I can't imagine what life would be like without the antidepressant I've taken for decades to spare me from rampaging, unrealistic fears.

Even though I don't rant at my mother about her inconvenient, too-frequent emergency room visits, I'm not compassionate. In general, while my mother's living, I fail to feel empathy for her. I fail to recognize her worth, her goodness, and my profound connection and love for her.

Even though my mother's company is sought by many, for reasons I've never understood, I don't like her much. That dislike is long-standing, going back as far as kindergarten.

So most of the time I'm with my mother, the hours hang heavy.

I act out my commitment to my father in a rote, duty-bound sort of way, maintaining distance, all the while feeling discontent about the differences between me and my mother rather than appreciating our common ground.

Her regard and my disregard for decorum is and always has been a contentious issue. On one of our Sunday outings a few years ago, Mother and I found ourselves face to face with circumstances having many tendrils into the great divide between us.

―――

I'm struggling to push my eighty-eight-year-old, two-hundred-fifty pound, well-dressed and neatly coiffed, pearled mother across soft carpeting that mires the wheelchair, making progress tedious.

I'm piqued at the imposition: My mother isn't sick. Her hips and knees are painful when she tries to walk. They can't bear her weight. I can't bear the thought that she's eaten herself into a wheelchair, her hips pushing out the sides of the seat fabric that rubs against the wheels, breaking them worse than the carpeting.

My irritation at her makes me feel guilty, yet I can't seem to stop myself. Nor am I aware of or even concerned about her feelings at what's happening.

Blithely, I push Mother up and down the carpeted aisles containing displays of hosiery, vainly searching through one selection after another for the *right* brand.

My intestines, though, begin grumbling in protest. Lightning bolts of pain soon shoot across my abdomen. Suddenly, I feel nauseous and faint. Cold sweat beads on my forehead.

Yet I say nothing.

A sales lady, noticing us from several aisles over, approaches. She's immaculately costumed in a pink-flowered, shirtwaist dress. Her complementing high-heeled shoes are a deep shade of rose. Blond, teased hair frames the face of a woman in her midsixties.

She seems tense. The lines in her face clench stress. She doesn't act tight, though. After listening to our request for assistance, with grace and an imposing dignity, she leads us to the merchandise we've come for.

Sorting through sizes and colors of hosiery, she politely talks to Mother while my brain mumbles that I'd rather be outside walking my dog or something else easier to tolerate.

Without warning, unbidden gas escapes from the dark recesses of my butt cheeks with an audible sound. (To my horror, my anus is sometimes an independent thinker—unable to keep secrets, leaking the truth when my tongue is silent.)

Noxious odor fogs the air, wafting around my nostrils with the pungent message of discontent.

I chameleon into the perfect actress, feigning innocence, masking my face with the blank look of a dead person.

With the talent of an award-winning Broadway actress, I dress myself in the character of purity, leaning my head coyly to the side while gazing at things around me, offering up a Mona Lisa smile. Feigning interest, I reach for a scarf on display, then examine the print and texture.

I'm desperate, hoping no one is smelling the dense fumes rising and burning my nostrils.

I feel like a little girl who's made a huge mistake. At some level I'm afraid my mother will yell at me.

Instead, she and the genteel saleswoman are mute, their expressions indicating nothing awry. They, too, are "in character"—a role authored by Victorian propriety.

In retrospect, I realize their generation erased the existence of any organ or body existing between the navel and the top of the thighs. Openly acknowledging anything exuding from the "privates" or "down there" is prohibited by an unspoken agreement.

While still in the department store, I'm not thinking about all that, so their silence over the matter at hand deludes me into thinking I'm escaping retaliation.

Besides, I figure the saleswoman's probably thinking there's something dreadfully wrong with that old lady in the wheelchair, that she must be dying.

I'm shameless as I push Mother, following the quick-stepping clerk toward the cash register, eager to be on the way home and forget the whole ordeal.

Although I'm close to escaping retribution for my unbidden issue, I'm not as free of trouble as I'd hoped.

As I reach to pay for the hose with a credit card, once again my anus speaks, voicing the remnants of annoyance that won't be suppressed. The screaming odor rises—again—accentuating my need to escape from bondage. Again, no one voices discontent. The caustic flaws of impropriety are being coated with decorum.

So, I believe my escape without retribution is still eminent.

As we're leaving the mall, my intestines relax as if to say, "You're done with that responsibility, at least for now."

With those soothing messages in mind, I'm driving Mother home, meandering on winding country roads, feeling satisfied with my clever responses to potentially hazardous conditions.

Mother is sitting in the front passenger seat.

Suddenly, I become aware that the barometric pressure inside the car has plummeted.

A deadly stillness threatens trouble.

With the angry crispness of a starched, scratchy collar, Mother growls my name, inflecting the last syllable: "Carolyn?"

I mask my emotions, a reaction learned in childhood. Inside, though, my stomach is churning. Fear of my mother's ire has turned me into a seven-year-old.

When I tentatively turn to look at Mother, I attempt to disarm what I see with my deadpan expression.

She's implacable.

My seven-year-old self feels the heat of a massive, fire-breathing Komodo dragon with eyes as taut as a hunter's bow. I'm clearly her intended target.

At that impressive threat, my eyes fill my face. Lightning quick, I morph into the well-rehearsed character of an innocent child.

Indignant that I haven't answered the call to my name and her implied indictment, my mother again growls, "Carolyn?"

Tilting my head to appear puzzled and lilting my voice, I reply, "What, Mother?"

From deep in her throat she roars, "Did you smell that vile odor when we were in the store?"

I know not to further stoke her ire with the truth and get myself burned: "Why, no, Mother."

"Well," she huffs, "I did. Twice!"

Getting only a quizzical, coy look from me, Mother swallows and turns away, having failed to indict me.

———

Mother was silenced by my theatrics.

And perhaps something else.

Although I can't be certain, at times like those indecorous moments in the department store, I think my mother can't face the reality of my humanity, my imperfection. So she withdraws into denial to protect her fantasy of me as her perfect child.

And to protect myself from abandonment, I outwardly become the daughter with tightly squeezed boundaries, leaving little space to express myself.

I sometimes yearn for Mother and I to be friends. I would so like to be with her like I am with them: authentic and unjudged.

Once, I even started calling my mother by her first name, Ethel, hoping we could find our way to having a relationship less superficial.

At the time, I didn't understand that overlaying my desire to find friendship with my mother was and is my need to be accepted by her. My need for her to embrace me for who I really am. My need for her to embrace all of me.

Am I asking of her something I can't do for myself?

Probably.

———

Then there's Mom.

We do share some good times.

Spending a weekend at a seaside town or a quaint bed-and-breakfast.

Going to a marina in New Smyrna on my father's birthday, a place he liked. Eating fried fish and potatoes at a picnic table on the shore of the Inland Waterway. Feeding gulls. Remembering.

Dining in the shade of an oak tree at a restaurant in Daytona Beach, eating fat, juicy hamburgers, fries, and sweet coleslaw, and watching boats come and go through the nearby inlet. Remaining in comfortable silence, two introverts drifting in our own worlds.

Eating crispy, Southern-fried chicken at a motorcyclists' dive perched on the shore of the St. John's River, finding pleasure in joining with others there in the revelry over *fine* dining.

Reading and doing handwork together in her apartment, me using skills she taught me when I was a child.

That's where we find common ground.

And laughter.

Mom's laughter is infectious.

We are together when we laugh together.

Moments of shared belly laughs are glued to my heart: When I was an adolescent and much discord separated us, we were digging up a shrub in the backyard for transplanting. Grunting we dug soil, pried roots, dug more soil, pried roots again and again trying to force a pee wee plant free. That such a small life-form would cause both of us so much trouble struck my mother as hilarious, prompting her to let go with spasms of laughter I mimicked with abandon.

Once, more recently, when I was helping Mom get out of my car, we couldn't free her left leg. She laughed. I laughed. We both had tears running down our faces, sharing the ironic comedy over so much struggle to do something that should have been simple.

Years from now, at the end of a long, healing journey, I'll read something written by a family therapist that will solve the mystery of my dislike for my mother.

With that revelation, there'll be more than laughter drawing me close to her.

And I'll yearn to speak with her.

Yet I'll only be able to sense her presence, feeling her heart reach beyond the great divide between life and death.

311 MAIN STREET

In a little while I'll be leaving 311 Main Street to drive twenty miles into the backwoods of Central Florida, where I built a small cabin that's situated on top of a white sandy hill, part of five acres of otherwise densely wooded land bordering a nature preserve. Cool breezes on this Friday of 2001, the day after Thanksgiving, energize me. Not that I need much help. I'm pumped over what I know will be an adventure.

A red, flatbed trailer hitched to my white station wagon is loaded with the stuff I'm taking with me. Forest, my ninety-pound red mastiff mix, is watching, poised at the gate of the chain-link fence surrounding the backyard, hoping I'll call him to go for a ride too.

And then there is Buttercup, a thirteen-hand, cream-colored donkey with taupe spots. I bought her after she was weaned at six months. She is boarded across from a wildlife preserve on a lake where we've spent hours walking amidst wildflowers and sago palm trees. With the help of a friend, I've trained her to ride so we can go on long camping excursions after she joins me in the woods.

My three cats have no idea they'll soon be placed in crates and then loaded into the station wagon for the journey to our new home.

———

When I bought 311 Main Street in 1983, eighteen years ago, a rusted, pitted mailbox stood sentinel on the northeast corner. Budzinski, the last name of Bill, my now-deceased friend and former property owner, remained displayed in bold, black letters on both sides for many years after I purchased his house.

How come?

That was my way of paying tribute to the relationship we developed when we were neighbors sharing a finger pier at a nearby marina, living on houseboats. After someone surprised me, replacing my treasured artifact with a shiny new thing for a birthday present, I repurposed the old one into an interior design piece: a storage container for knitting needles.

Besides the mailbox, only a nine-hundred-square-foot, yellow cement-block house stood on the rectangular plot of land located next door to Enterprise Elementary School, named after the Florida township where I'd come to live. Chickens sometimes pecked in the dirt beneath two giant live oak trees that were festooned with lacy, gray Spanish moss. White blossoms of wild ginger, thriving in a patch of black muck at the far end of the backyard, perfumed the air with a spicy scent. And, after I moved in, every school-day morning I awoke to the sound of school cafeteria workers sliding open a squeaky gate, my signal to start my day too.

Living in only part of what I came to call the Little House, worked for me. Having come straight from occupying fewer than three hundred square feet for three years on my houseboat, I found no need to use all the space that was mine. So, from the beginning, I spent most of my time in the one large room at the front that included the kitchen, living room, and foyer, sleeping on a daybed that also served as a couch. Because I didn't use the back part of the house, others lived there, sharing my home.

Books, mostly nonfiction, were everywhere: on the scaly-barked cedar-plank fireplace mantle, on six-inch rough-sawn cedar slats positioned over doorways, and close at hand by one end of the daybed on the bookshelf I built. At the other end, a small, round table displayed a candle and timer I used for my daily twenty-minute mindfulness meditation practice that was steady and sure for ten years. Then I began cramming my time with an urgency I didn't understand, squeezing stillness out of my schedule.

A desk and built-in bunk in the brown-tiled foyer, a square wood dining table with chairs, a swiveling brown wicker rocker with my jute basket at the side containing crocheting or knitting projects, and a wood gliding bench were my only other pieces of furniture.

A tiny bedroom, located across the hall from the one bathroom, served as a closet and utility room. Before Bill died, he built me a combination bunk bed with an enclosed closet underneath for hanging things and storing this and that. Peach crates purchased from a grocery store for two dollars each held folded clothes.

The tiny bathroom was shared—without complications—by all who lived with me in the Little House. Because I thought the process of struggling to put a new toilet paper roll on a spring-loaded rod unnecessarily troublesome, I built a roll-wide shelf that I mounted near the toilet on the wooden bathroom cabinet. A road sign I found buried in leaves when I'd paused to pee on a six-mile run was mounted on the wall over the toilet. Rusted and pitted with bullet holes, in faded red capital letters the work of art read: "No dumping allowed."

A large bedroom at the far end, about one-third of the entire house, having a door to the outside, was routinely occupied by renters or guests. First, a woman in her thirties rented the space, one she could call her own while she adjusted to living with her new boyfriend. Then came a young man who had graduated penniless from college. He stayed with me just long enough to secure work and save money to pay for an apartment.

Deana and Bob, two college students, were next. Shortly after Deana began renting, with eyes pleading, she asked permission for her newfound boyfriend, Bob, to join her. Although I felt iffy when I gave the okay, the three of us lived together seamlessly while they finished up some undergraduate courses, worked, and saved money so they could move to Boulder. I grew to adore the two of them, and a year after our living arrangement began, I officiated at their marriage that took place on the lawn of Bob's parents' lakeside home. When they moved so Bob could attend Naropa University, sadness filled me to the brim.

Others came and went, too, all leaving a cache of fondness to savor.

Trek, my high-end, metallic, gunmetal-gray touring bicycle, named after her purpose and the manufacturer, was also a fine companion in the Little House. In the foyer at the foot of a bunk I faced with a rough-sawn cedar herringbone pattern, she was mounted on an oak bike rack and remained poised there for adventure unless we were traveling.

Trek and I made memories together. When she captured my attention while at rest on her rack, in a magical way my mind became decorated with the recall of pink, purple, and white phlox, sprinkled with yellow daisies that grew in the fields along north Central Florida's country roads. I smiled when remembering the steady rhythm of pedaling Trek for miles and miles on cool spring days, shaded by pecan trees. And stopping to rest under them to eat nuts and visit with my adventuresome companions. Pure reverie overtook me when I thought of biking self-contained on her from Charleston to Enterprise with my friend Shana, camping on ground carpeted with russet-colored pine needles. And riding in the Carolina lowlands along bodies of sparkling water reflecting crystal-blue skies. Then grunting while peddling up the vertical Route 17 bridge spanning the Savannah River, at the top looking back with awe over what we'd just done. Best of all, I relished re-experiencing fist-raising triumph as Shana and I cruised down Main Street, side by side, wearing Charleston T-shirts, arriving home to be greeted by cheering friends standing in the front yard.

Kristina, a white-coated, blue-eyed cat, was the first of many who shared my space too. Only after I adopted nine others from shelters or from people desperate to find a home for one did I draw the line. As the number of felines dwelling with me escalated, I became curious about why I felt such empathy for their innocence. And I wondered why I experienced a sense of urgency to protect them—but I didn't discover the answers while living on Main Street.

Even with all the cats and the comings and goings of others who lived with me, The Little House served me well for nine years. The rhythmic sound of whirling fans cooling the air in summer or a crackling fire in winter, the scent of rough-sawn cedar, the sight of an inside window box with bright-green asparagus fern draping over the side, and off-white muslin, draw-back, ball-fringed curtains gifted my home with an organic, cozy feeling.

Even so, I began to feel a need to be more a part of the out-of-doors than the number of small windows allowed. I didn't know how I'd manage that until after I attended a personal growth seminar one Saturday morning.

When the facilitator instructed each of us to close our eyes and imagine manifesting a dream—disregarding fear and finances—I fantasized about building an urban tree house with a large deck fronting a street, privacy afforded by potted, flowering vines entwining themselves in latticework . . .

———

Branches of two giant live oak trees adorned with leathery, dark-green, cupped leaves drape over the deck in front of my tree house. Cool November breezes filtered by screening the only separation between me and the elements, tingle the air. Kristina, my constant companion of many years, warms my lap. Nicholas and Rishi, the only other cats of the original ten still living, are curled on my bed in the loft warmed by the sun heating the metal roof. Forest lies at my feet. Sipping coffee while crocheting a cream-colored market bag, I ease my way into the weekend day, knowing I'll be leaving here soon.

I've lived in this open-air space for nine years. Long, wide-bladed, dark-brown ceiling fans, suspended from the two-by-twelve-inch wood beams of the A-frame ceiling, have kept my place cool during warm weather, stirring moist, subtropical air. And, to make for comfortable sleeping, the temperature dropped to the low seventies every summer night, no matter how hot the days had been. On the few ice-cold winter mornings when the opening of the school's squeaky gate woke me, I'd turn off the heater that had warmed me while I slept in the loft, don a heavy robe, and then make haste while brushing my teeth at the only sink, situated in the kitchen island. And then, I'd fill a kettle with water and turn on a one-burner appliance that served as my stove. While my coffee water heated, I wasted no time dressing, a simple accommodation in exchange for the freedom of living interconnected with unbuffered climate.

Winds were seldom strong enough to drive rain sideways under the eaves overhanging the boardwalk that surrounded three sides of the tree house. And my sparse furnishings were nothing to be concerned about the few times during each year they did get wet.

Besides my original ten cats, and my dog Forest, more than one hundred and fifty others found refuge in my tree house. A few were rescued by someone else and then adopted by me, like Murphy, a loveable, slobbery, short-haired St. Bernard who was found chained to a stake, forty pounds underweight, with a metal-linked collar she'd outgrown embedded into her neck. After she was rehabilitated, I took her in and enjoyed four years of her docile, dedicated company until she died of pancreatic cancer.

Many stories, both magical and tragic, manifested in the midst of my work with animals. For now, the ones that filled me with sadness will go without the telling.

Perhaps the most remarkable story, and my favorite, began evolving one Saturday morning while I was driving to my office to spend a few hours working to ease the pressure of an upcoming busy week. While sipping hot coffee and munching on some crisp peanut-butter crackers, in the pre-dawn mist I spotted a doglike silhouette while passing an abandoned strip mall. Knowing there were no homes nearby, I couldn't make sense of the image. After turning around to investigate, I drove into the parking lot. My headlights revealed a dog with matted gray hair weighing about fifteen pounds.

When I called to her, offering some canned wet cat food I kept in my car, she darted into a row of shrubs near the highway. Thinking she might need water, I walked across the street to get some from a restaurant. One of the cooks told me the scruffy little thing I later named Muppet had somehow survived more than a year of crossing four busy lanes of traffic to beg for food. She'd outsmarted all who'd tried to catch her, and she later outsmarted my attempts to capture her with a humane trap.

In the end, one Friday after work while acting as if there were nothing strange going on as gawking drivers passed, I pounded green-coated steel garden stakes two feet apart around the shrubs where she lived. Early next morning, after I confirmed that Muppet was hiding in the plants, two friends helped me surround her refuge with orange plastic garden fencing. And then I stepped into the far end of her hiding place and began walking forward, forcing her toward the other side of the enclosure. When trapped, she began chewing the fencing, sure to escape if we didn't intervene. Even though we could visualize her bolting into traffic and getting killed, we froze from the fear of the flesh-ripping teeth we saw at work.

Only a scant bit of plastic fencing remained to hold Muppet captive when Jack, one of my neighbors, drove into the parking lot and stopped beside us. Realizing something awful was about to happen, he bolted from his car, and just when I thought all was lost, he reached into the surround and wrapped his hand around Muppet's midsection. She whipped her head around, teeth bared, but she didn't bite him.

From that moment on Muppet greeted me and those who

cared for her with licks and wags. Once she was spayed, I placed her with someone who was seeking a companion for another little dog grieving the loss of one. I would sometimes detour from my usual way home just to view Muppet and her new canine friend sitting on a carpeted platform built just for them, peering out a bay window.

And then there was Katie, the name I gave to a brown, short-haired tabby with white boots who was seen begging for food at the doorway from the cafeteria at the life-care village where my mother lived. I was known there as the "cat lady," probably because I provided older, affectionate felines and their support services as part of a program I developed for residents who wanted their companionship. So, no surprise when a resident called me for help with a stray cat. Turns out she was domesticated and easy to get into a crate and home. When examining her after we got there, I noticed her mammary glands were swollen, the area around her nipples bald—sure signs that she was nursing kittens.

After quickly returning to the place where I'd coaxed her to come to me, with one hand holding a leash attached to a pink harness I'd put on her and the other toting a carrier, I began an adventure I wasn't sure would end well.

"Katie, take me to your kittens," I urged. At first, she rolled on the ground, acting coy. When that didn't serve to get me off track, she strolled to a puddle of water, where she paused to sip some, and then sat, unconcerned about the harness but stirring impatience in me. "Katie, I need you to show me where your kittens are. I'm trying to help you and them. Come on now, show me where they are." At that, she stood, and began striding toward the back of some cottages, the leash taut as she quickened her pace. She halted when we came to a narrow, dark space between two of them. After securing her in the carrier, I removed stored lawn chairs and then squeezed myself to the end of the narrow passage. The sight of Katie's tiny babies, a calico, two brown tabbies, and a tuxedo, all with eyes still closed, made me smile.

When placed in the carrier, each one got a thorough licking

before Katie offered her engorged nipples. With the family reunited we headed toward home again, where mother and young stayed in my ten-by-fifteen-foot bathroom until the kittens were eight weeks old. In a synchronistic way that spoke of a mystical and Divine intervention, I found storybook homes for all of them, even Katie.

Word got around about my concern for animals. "Can you help me with Tessie, a collie?" a realtor pleaded, acting on behalf of a homeowner who had been forced to enter a nursing home and leave her dog behind. Tessie stayed with me until a breed rescue organization took her.

Another time a policeman called me while I was at work. At first, I was scared, thinking I'd done something wrong or something was off at home. Instead, he'd called me to ask for help with two cats who'd belonged to a woman just found dead by her mailbox. The officer explained that he had found my contact information in her address book under the label "Cat Care" and was hoping I could take in her pets so they wouldn't have to go to the county shelter. In truth, I was irritated by the request because I was busy beyond belief. Yet I didn't feel right not helping. So, with permission from my supervisor, I left in a huff to go retrieve the cats. As soon as I got to them and witnessed their distress, my feelings softened. Soon after I took them home, a veterinarian specializing in the treatment of cats agreed to foster-care and place them.

At times, when I had the emotional and financial resources, I'd free a dog from a kill shelter, provide veterinary care, and then place him or her in a home or get help from a breed rescue agency for those who were "purebred."

Star, a Siberian husky, was one of those, eyes haunting me from where she was caged. The posted information signaled her certain death: "This dog shredded an apartment." I figured she had been damned by someone not understanding that she was a working dog, bred to run, and had become destructive because she'd needed more exercise than she got.

Carolyn Martin Graham

Star had lots of exercise running in my big, fenced-in backyard, and up and down stairs to investigate what was happening in the neighborhood. She soon settled and became ready for the next step: a married couple from Florida's west coast who bred and rescued Siberian huskies agreed to take her into their care when they were in Orlando for a dog show.

More than once I found abandoned dogs when bicycling or running, and one evening a cat even showed up at my front door, meowing. Another time, a mother cat appeared in my path and led me to her kittens when I was merely walking home from a nearby bagel shop. For some unknown reason, over and over, creatures needing help appeared on a regular basis. Although I was sometimes irritated that my fun was interrupted by them, I felt called by a force that seemed way beyond the ordinary to ignore, and maybe I couldn't have ignored them anyway. I wish I could have taken all of them home, but I had neither the space, nor money, nor emotional energy to do that. So, with sadness I took some to a nearby Humane Society shelter with a low kill rate. And some I rescued weren't even that fortunate—with the best veterinary care, they were unable to recover from the horrors of human abuse. When I had them euthanized, always remaining with them while they died, releasing them from their suffering seemed too little in the way of compensation for what they had endured. And, even though the results of their abuse were hard to bear, their torture became an inspiration to keep caring for those I could.

Besides cats and dogs, a goat and lovebird spent time at 311 Main Street too.

How so?

One Sunday morning after Katie and her kittens were placed, I walked to the back of the house on the boardwalk to investigate a cacophony of barking and chirping. At once I saw the source of the commotion perched among the bright-pink blossoms of a crepe myrtle tree: a small bird with a neon-green body and rose-colored head. In an instant, he flew toward me and then landed on the walkway's railing. Vibrating with intensity, he peered into my eyes, prompting me to speak: "Well, hello there. Where did you come from? I'll bet you're thirsty. Wait here, I'll be right back." I don't know why I sensed the small creature was male, nor why I named him Korbi while he drank water from a saucer.

From then on, he lived in my screened-on-three-sides bathroom in a big cage that was hung from a wood rafter supporting the loft's floor. In the evenings, he joined me for bathing, sitting on my index finger, and then splashing in my bathwater. When he finished his ablutions, he'd fly back to his cage, enter, and perch on the swing, waiting for me to close the door and say good night.

Anticipating my move into quarters that didn't have space for keeping Korbi safe from my cats, I found him a home with someone who had an aviary and other birds like him.

What about the goat?

One evening I heard bleating coming from the yard of the only neighbors I had on my side of the street. Investigating from my perch in the trees, I was horrified at what I saw: a small white goat was being held by four of the five children living next door while the youngest, a small redheaded boy with a lisp, was trying to force his penis into the vagina of the struggling creature. Confusion and shock tore me up. I couldn't think straight and I spent a sleepless night feeling anxious and unsure of what I should do.

At first, I did nothing, then in a few days the redheaded boy greeted me in my yard when I arrived home from work to tell me a dog had attacked his goat. "I'm sorry that happened. Where is she now?"

"In the laundry room."

Because the six-foot-high fence surrounding my backyard was two feet higher than my neighbor's, I figured I had a valid reason to offer to buy the tortured animal that would disguise my real concerns.

Negotiating with the boy's father for the goat's purchase went with ease. I even had the sense he was relieved I wanted her. And so began my relationship with Alberta, named in honor of Albert Schweitzer. She was eventually adopted by a large family with a small goat farm for producing goat's milk and cheese for their own sustenance. She lived out her life there after birthing twin kids.

Me, cats, dogs, a goat, and a bird all managed to live in the metal-roofed, wood-sided tree house in harmony. Having no need to finish out the interior, open studs served as the crème de la crème of scratching posts. A screened "cat" door, shortened to allow enough space between the bottom and the floor for easy escape into the large room that served as a pantry and closet, kept the dogs from following my cats into their dining place and the stairs that went down to their litter boxes.

Homecomings were a wondrous affair, especially while the bird and goat were still with me. As soon as I turned the corner at the stoplight a couple blocks away, Alberta stuck her head over the deck's railing and bleated. Korbi's chirping made me feel happy as I closed the car door. "Hello, my friend," I often called as I walked to the chain-link fence surrounding the tree house. At the gate, Forest and fostered dogs awaited my entry. I was rubbed, bumped, and nuzzled while closing the gate behind me. And that's not the end of things. All cats were at the ground-floor, peach-colored double wood doors, ready to escort me upstairs the minute I stepped over the threshold.

My neighbors didn't mind my menagerie. Mother did. Although she never said so, I think she believed I was cracked because I lived with so many animals, especially cats. She came to visit one day to watch me bottle-feed orphaned kittens. While she bent over the kitchen counter observing the process, a long-nosed Russian wolfhound goosed her. That ended the visit, and her memory of the encounter snuffed any desire to come again.

Besides caring for the creatures who lived with me, I did what I could for those I found on highways, flattened and squished into steaming asphalt, sometimes rotting, mostly mammals like me who were simply trying to get to water, food, or a mate, or to care for their young. Their dead bodies tugged at my heart so much that I often stopped to bury one of them using a shovel I carried in my car. If I wasn't able to dig a hole, I at least found a shaded place under a bush or tree to put their remains, covering them with leaves or brush. After I finished doing what I could to be respectful and provide surcease for myself, I would bow at the risk of appearing crazy, and then say "Namaste" to acknowledge the bodies that once had been complex biological systems supporting a life that sought to fulfill needs not unlike my own.

———

As I prepare to leave 311 Main Street, my home base for eighteen years of robust living, I feel deep gratitude for the memories of happenings here that I know will go with me as immeasurable gifts to savor.

Here I've peered into my flower garden, contemplating my failure at sustaining sexual relationships, committing to celibacy. Here I fell in love with long-distance, self-sustained bicycle touring. Here I fulfilled a dream of living in a tree house. And, soon after I moved into my tree house, my father died, prompting the beginning of ten years of spending time with my mother on Sundays. And here I began my enchantment with Utah's Green River. A place to grow myself that has called me back more than once and will beckon my return in the future.

So, with all that in my heart and much more, I position three gray plastic cat carriers on end. One by one I lift Kristina, Rishi, and Nicholas by the scruffs of their necks and lower their limp bodies, feet first, into a space they're not one bit happy about.

After they're secured in my station wagon, I look at Forest, poised for action, standing by with his liver-colored nose pressed against the gate.

"Forest, go for a ride. Come on, let's go for a ride," I call, walking toward him.

He's all wags and wiggles as he bounds to the station wagon.

When he's settled in his dignified pose, sitting upright in the passenger seat, taking in his surroundings, I close the passenger side's car door.

Carolyn Martin Graham

One more thing is left to do before I leave: Saying goodbye to my across-the-street neighbor, Loretta, isn't going to be easy. We've developed a strong and unlikely friendship. Me with a graduate degree, Loretta with a fourth-grade education. Me with a management position at a community college, Loretta with a job as a maid at a nearby motel. Yet none of those and the rest of our vast differences managed to keep us from finding love for each other. Over the years, we've shared with each other the common ground of humanity, our feelings that have bound us together by heartfelt concern. And we found the capacity to respect each other no matter our external trappings.

When I wrap Loretta in my arms, I feel a deep sense of loss. Mine and her own. Although I'm on my way to a new adventure, I know I'll miss her kind presence, her ferocious protectiveness, her kindness. And I fear loneliness will overwhelm her, for I believe I'm her only friend. Although I promise her I'll call and visit, I feel guilty when I put my hands on her bony shoulders, kiss her on each cheek, and say the words that feel like they're going to break open my heart: "Goodbye, my friend."

After returning to my station wagon, I sit in the driver's seat, taking a prolonged look at 311 Main Street, The Little House now painted taupe. The silver, metal roof of the tree house gleams in the sun, a beacon of remembered happiness. The rusty red of the second story and the peach color of the ground-floor board-and-batten make me smile as I acknowledge my independent, creative spirit, and the opportunity I had to freely express myself. The oak and palmetto trees wave in the breeze, seeming to wish me well. And the sight of the elementary school reminds me that the district that bought my property to expand parking options will soon demolish all that I've cherished, yet I feel that things are as they should be.

Feeling closure, I fasten my seat belt, ignite the engine, roll down the window on my side of the car, and slowly, ever so slowly, move forward, waving to Loretta. And then, I direct my expectant eyes on the road ahead—my future at Sunny Hill Farm.

ABIDING
WITH NATURE

Sunny Hill Farm.

That's my home in the Central Florida woods.

A small cabin with a rust-red roof, off-white trim, and moss-green siding perches atop a cleared white sandy patch of land that's drenched most days with sunshine. All metal, my dwelling is maintenance free.

Dark-chocolate stain coats the framework of the back porch. A large bark-covered twig I mounted on the right side of the screen door, using screws inserted through washers for spacers before boring into the frame, serves as a handle. French doors open onto an eight-foot-wide deck spanning the entire front, facing a mixture of low scrub and sky-lining pines. The deck continues halfway along the southeast side, serving as a floor to an outside shower stall constructed of six-foot privacy fence.

In little more than a year of Saturdays, beginning in the early spring of 2000, while still living in my tree house, I helped build my cabin with my own hands, often wondering if I was insane to start something like that at age fifty-seven.

My questioning evaporated with one whiff of pine-scented air.

For expert direction and dedicated back-breaking labor, I employed a couple who'd constructed two homes of their own.

We knocked ourselves out erecting my speck of a shelter. Most days, when we were finished working, we were filthy, soaked with sweat, and done in, barely able to stumble to our cars for the drive to our homes.

Even so, I loved being in the open air hammering, sawing,

digging, painting, and climbing scaffolding. To me, there's not much better than being physically tired from hard, productive work, especially so when seeing my home materialize out of a stack of raw materials. Besides, building my own modest dwelling made so much sense to me. While being intimately involved with the process, I felt natural, in touch with the simple. And congruent with the short amount of time I have to spend on this earth. Creating a soft footprint felt right.

I wanted the smallest combination of screened and walled-in space Lake County's building code allowed: eight hundred and eighty square feet; five hundred and fifty square feet enclosed, three hundred and thirty square feet for a screened porch.

Why so small?

I knew the outdoors were to become my real home.

For a long time before I moved to Sunny Hill Farm, I yearned to be close to nature. To be near deer, Florida black bears, wildflowers, butterflies—all that was missing from my life as a city dweller.

When I drove to see the five acres that are now mine, I parked my car in the scrub along the side of a white sand trail called Red Oak Drive fronting the property. After opening the door and preparing to get out, I looked down before placing my feet on the ground. Etched in the sand was a fresh bear paw print.

A sign!

A sign showing up like so many other times in my life when I've felt the synchronicity of circumstances seeming, in retrospect, to have signaled "meant-to-be" events too related to be accidental.

The prevalence of that kind of phenomenon has sculpted my unquestioning belief that there's a mysterious, beneficent Divine intervention sometimes seeming to direct events of my life. Sometimes showing me the way.

Upon seeing that bear paw print so clear and fresh embossed in the sand, I knew the property I'd come to see was destined to be mine.

The southern border of my land shares a boundary with the Lower Wekiva River Preserve. Located in an area with a year-round temperate climate, eighteen thousand acres of protected land and miles of trails are my playground.

So I need little inside space.

What I do have isn't defined much by walls. Only a closet and bathroom are enclosed. My twin-bed sleeping area is situated across from them and separated from the living room by a narrow pinewood bookshelf and a three-section room divider made from oak and muslin.

When temperatures rise, my house temperature remains comfortable. I positioned my house on the acre I cleared to take advantage of the location of the sun changing during the day. The kitchen, where I spend early mornings, faces an unshaded pasture to the southeast. During the hottest part of the day, when the sun reaches the west side of my house, trees provide shade. The porch at the back never gets direct sunlight. Ceiling fans and extra insulation help keep my place comfortable when the sun cooks the earth. In fact, on the hottest of days my place feels as if cooled by an air conditioner.

Although I'm not home much, there's no place I'd rather be than at Sunny Hill Farm or exploring the nearby area. A full-time job, volunteer projects, and devoting my Sundays to spending time with my mother keep me running full tilt with little time to spare. When I'm with Mom, I'm restless, discontent, and wishing I could be home instead.

On occasion, she senses my feelings—feelings I think I'm disguising: "Carolyn, you don't have to come here. Don't feel like you have to visit me."

"I don't feel obligated, Mom. I want to be here."

I'd rather lie than hurt her.

When I get home, I often pause at the entrance to my drive, roll down the windows of my car to sniff the pine-scented air, and gaze at my surroundings. On my left, with a backdrop of dense foliage, waxy, jade-colored leaves sparkle in the sun, their surfaces cupping a matte-gray underside. Patches of saw palmetto, their muted green fronds spiking the air, add great contrast to the tapestry of greenery. A nearby stand of long-leaf pines carpets the ground with their russet-brown needles, creating an open space with no undergrowth where I imagine fairies gathering to dance.

To my right, Florida blazing stars sometimes bloom on stalks, their spires covered with deep-lavender flowerets, capturing my attention where the destruction of my land once enraged me. When I first purchased the property, I hired a man to clear only a winding drive just to the top of the highest point. I wasn't there while he worked. When I inspected what he'd done on a Sunday morning, envisioning ahead of time a gently winding access path as I'd requested, I was shocked. On the east and west boundaries, from the back to the front, a three-hundred-foot swath the width of a bulldozer blade had been decimated. Trees were lying criss-crossed on the ground, dead shrubs heaped in piles of disrespect.

What happened?

That I'll never understand, for I'd handed the man a drawing picturing the exact location I wanted cleared.

In daylight, I proceed up my winding, white-sand drive woven with pine needles and lined with tall slash pines leaning this way and that, sunbeams through their boughs, dappling the ground with golden light, welcoming me to Sunny Hill Farm.

There's more than a glorious sight greeting me at homecoming when I top the driveway.

Buttercup and Sweet Pea, my two inseparable donkeys, bray to announce my arrival to the entire neighborhood, their heads hanging over the pasture gate.

Forest and Nacomi, my two dogs, stand inside the backyard fence, fiercely wagging their tails, eager for me to join them.

After I pat each one on the head, they follow me into the porch through the open doorway, left that way so they can lounge in the shade out of the sun's scorching rays.

One day, after the dogs and I were on the porch, I plopped

down the forest-green backpack I carry to work on the round, green porch table, noticing that a pair of blue jeans I'd thrown over a chair the day before lay crumpled on the floor.

Mindless, I bent over and picked them up.

Peering at me was a four-foot yellow rat snake, curled into striking position, flicking his tongue.

Startled and unable to think at first, I gulped down a wad of fear—and my knee-jerk urge to kill. Barely able to think, I remained focused on making certain my first impression of the uninvited reptile's head wasn't triangular—the distinct shape of a pit viper.

Reason prevailed. I calmed enough to verify my original identification.

After sighing with relief, I wondered how the snake got by the dogs.

"Never mind, you have to go."

I opened the door to my inside living space, scooted my cats out of the way, and ushered my dogs off the porch.

Then, grabbing a broom, I gently nudged the snake with the straw end, directing him outdoors and under the fence on the west side of the backyard, away from the pasture.

Afterward, I continued my homecoming by greeting my cats who always wait at the door when they know I've arrived home. Only three of my original ten are still alive. Kristina, Nicholas, and Rishi—sixteen-year-old geriatric felines; for the first time in their lives, they are treated now and then with the opportunity to explore the outdoors. Sometimes one will nap on the deck; Nicholas once scampered to the woods then rushed back to the front door; Kristina likes to go under the deck. None of them stay outside for long before seeking the security of being inside.

The rat snake wasn't the last reminder that I'm living close to nature.

Often, white-footed mice show up dead in my living space, free cat toys.

One of my close neighbors told me he once left chocolate-crème cookies on the front seat of his truck only to find a bear sitting there, eating them one by one. Although I've not seen one myself, I frequently see bear scat when walking around my property, recognizable by size and content.

Several times I've spotted pigmy rattlesnakes, their twig-sized, dark-brown bodies stretched out, contrasting with the white sand road fronting my property. Although they're a threat, I fear more the Eastern diamondback rattlers. One afternoon when close to home, I stopped my car to watch a four-foot diamondback, as big around as my forearm, slither into a woodpile on the side of the road.

Shivering, I reminded myself to watch where I put my hands.

There's another menace showing up at times, reminding me of childhood when scorpions were frequently found in dark corners of our kitchen cabinets or closets: One evening, I disturbed a pile of tree branches with a stick before reaching to get wood for a bonfire. A three-inch Florida bark scorpion stomped out of seclusion, irritated at being disturbed. When I saw the dark-brown critter charging me, tail curved ready to sting, I jumped back, heart in my throat. As he turned and retreated into the woodpile, I spent a moment acknowledging to myself that I did, indeed, still want to live in the real Florida.

Ticks also flourish.

To keep their numbers under control, I bought a dozen guinea fowl and one bantam rooster. Within weeks, the guinea hens and cocks had been decimated by fox, bobcats, and great horned owls. I should have built a coop for them for roosting at night, but I didn't know that. My rooster, Hank, survived a little longer, then disappeared too. I missed his early-morning crowing and the way he shuffled through the woods at dusk each evening to perch on a limb near my porch.

More enjoyable than snakes, scorpions, ticks, and mice are the white-tailed deer that grace my surroundings with their lithe, tan bodies. They're abundant, grazing in herds on the grasslands of the preserve until hunting season opens. They evaporate when the killing begins.

Gopher tortoises can sometimes be seen plodding along the ground. Buttercup threw me once when I failed to steer her clear of a tortoise's burrow. I'd seen the opening to my far right, yet I didn't know the tunneling could extend underground as far as four feet. When her front legs plummeted into the tortoise's home, she began frantically kicking her hind legs to free herself. With lightning speed, she propelled me over her head, slamming me face first into a patch of sand spurs.

Every time I pulled a stinging spur out of a cheek, I glared at Buttercup, standing nonplussed nearby, peering at me as if to say, "What the hell just happened?"

Although I've never been one to bear arms, I did buy a 20-gauge shotgun before I moved into the woods. Mostly, I wanted protection for me and my pets against rabid animals or venomous snakes.

The day I got my gun out of layaway, the shop owner gave me instructions on loading and shooting, then let me fire a few rounds into an open-ended metal Quonset hut butted up against a dirt mound at one end.

Even though I was continually warned about living in the backwoods with a bunch of "rabid rednecks," I didn't pay much attention, figuring we could make our way with each other, to find common ground to exist together peacefully. So, I didn't think about using my shotgun to defend myself against people. Also, I was certain my ninety-pound guardian-trained mastiff mix, Forest, would protect me if necessary.

———

One day I was bored, so I strolled down Red Oak Drive looking for someone to shoot the breeze with. When I saw my neighbor Coleen sitting in an aluminum beach chair on the stoop in front of her trailer, I joined her, plunking myself down in a nearby rocking chair, thrumming the runners on the warped plywood floor.

Somehow the topic of Larry, her live-in boyfriend, came up.

She confides that he'd fondled her granddaughter, so she couldn't leave her alone with him. Nodding, I remember that my dog, Nacomi, never stopped barking the whole time he was installing fencing around the pasture and the backyard of my cabin. Larry creeps me out the same as my dog, although I don't say so to Coleen.

The next thing I know, Larry shows up in his truck, swaggers onto the stoop, and sits on a cinder block.

For reasons I'll never understand, out of the blue Coleen looks straight into my eyes and blurts, "What's someone like you living in a place like this?"

"Why not? I like being in the woods—same as you."

"Aren't you afraid someone will hurt you?"

I'm keenly aware that Larry is paying attention to what's happening, so my internal response is rapid-fire.

Although I want to say plenty, I remain silent, slowly rocking back and forth in the chair, feigning deliberation. Feigning calm.

Thrum. Thrum.

Thrum. Thrum.

Thrum. Thrum.

Adopting the vernacular of the neighborhood as best I can, I glare into the eyes of Coleen's boyfriend, "Well, I guess I'd just have tah sic my ninety-pound dog Forest on 'em. If he didn't shred 'em to pieces, well then, I guess I'd just have tah get my shotgun and shoot his balls off. I'd sure hate makin' a mess, though."

The target of my warning jumps up from the cinder block, Adam's apple bobbing, and scurries into the trailer.

Truth is, I didn't even remember where I'd stored my bullets, nor how to load the gun's chamber.

———

All that sounds like Pine Lakes is riddled with vermin, human and otherwise.

Not so.

There are just enough wild creatures reminding me to watch where I put my hands and feet. And, from personal experience, I know sexual predators and other criminals can live in any neighborhood. Their numbers are in the minority. Pine Lakes is no different.

And there's more to be grateful for than to be concerned about.

Wildflowers abound in this secluded wooded area, decorating a landscape that's free of herbicides. Their shades of lavender, red, yellow, pink, and purple delight me. Their intricacies captivate my attention when peering into my magnifying jeweler's loupe, viewing their breathtaking beauty. In fact, experiencing their minute majesty excites me as much as snow-capped mountains soaring into a crystal-clear blue sky, rising from a terra-cotta desert floor in Utah; as much as tall, dark-green balsam trees clustered amid giant gray boulders declaring the edge of a pebbled salt-scented seashore in Maine or a golden sunray sparkling in a morning dew drop adorning a rose petal.

When I was running on the winding dirt roads of the Pine Lakes neighborhood one evening, a patch of ground sprinkled with petite white star-shaped flowers stopped me in my tracks to gaze in wonder at their delicate splendor.

Another time, I felt the energy of a stare coming from above my head. Stopping and looking up, I saw a barred owl perched on an electrical wire, peering at me. We seemed to connect, bridging the vast difference between our species. I remained mesmerized for a time by what seemed to be an uncanny silent conversation speaking of mutual respect; when I thought we were done with our encounter, I bowed and extended a farewell, "Namaste."

After running a few steps, I turned, reluctant to leave. The owl had swiveled his head one hundred and eighty degrees to observe my departure, prompting me to marvel at his agility and the feeling that tendrils of our bond were still touching me.

Butterflies abound in Pine Lakes.

I've even seen orange-and-black monarchs swarming around light-pink milkweed blossoms, seeking nectar, a gift to my senses hungry for such encounters.

Experiencing the beauty of wildflowers and butterflies all around me also has a way of saddening me. I don't understand why we humans have destroyed so much of nature's wild beauty. Why mowed lawns, trimmed hedges, herbicides, and pesticides are preferable to meadows and wooded land. Why breezes carrying death fumes are sought, rather than air alive with flittering color. Why we have disrespected the intricate synchronicity and interconnectedness of all that exists on earth.

Despite my encounter with a pervert, the humans who live in my neighborhood have proven to be kind and helpful, belying their reputation.

My first experience with their eagerness to be neighborly came when the framing of my cabin was soon to start. The company supplying the metal siding and roofing also provided the two-by-six pine framing materials and trusses. Because the long-bed truck delivering them couldn't navigate my winding driveway, they were left in a stack on a cleared patch of land at the bottom of the hill.

On a Saturday morning, three female friends and I arrived at my property expecting to carry the trusses up the hill to my building site.

First, after gathering around the heap, we pried one of the trusses off the ground then positioned ourselves evenly along the forty-foot length.

When all of us seemed ready, I nodded and began a count:

"One.

"Two.

"Three.

"Lift!"

Grunting, we exerted every ounce of force we could, attempting to hoist the massive roof support.

Nothing happened.

After trying three more times, we let the truss fall sideways back to the ground.

Realizing further efforts would be fruitless, I headed toward the road. "Wait here. I'm going to get help. There's a couple living nearby I've only met once, but I bet they'll be willing to give us a hand. I'll be right back."

I knocked on their door.

After telling them my dilemma, I asked if they'd be willing to help. Without hesitation they agreed and beckoned other recruits from all over Pine Lakes using a CB radio. After donning ball caps, they followed me.

Before long other neighbors were swarming around the trusses. Ant-like, they carried all the framing lumber up my hill, depositing everything by the foundation slab of my cottage.

My neighbors, by and large, continue to be generous with their support.

I'm grateful to be included in potluck dinners, s'more-toasting bonfires, and other community gatherings. When I'm running, one or another pulls off to the side of the road and stops to chat. An elderly man with a small farm often beckons me to his gate when I'm riding Buttercup, offering her an apple.

Many living in Pine Lakes are poor. For some, near starvation is a reality. Unmarketable food, picked up from grocery stores to allegedly feed only livestock, is also used for human consumption. For some, feed stores are the source for their pharmaceutical care. When an antibiotic is necessary, they buy penicillin labeled for cattle, swine, sheep, and horses for self-injection. Horse liniment is used for pain relief. Emergency room visits aren't an economic option they even think about—no matter how severe the condition.

Veterinary care is an out-of-reach expense for many. Pine Lakes' pets and farm animals often suffer the plight of being cared for by those with lean wallets.

Seeing them suffer hurts.

On a cold winter's day when walking in my neighborhood, I

came upon two calves huddled together for warmth, peering at me from behind a fence, their eyes hollow with hunger. Bones protruding from draped hide spoke of a barren, sandy pasture and no money to buy hay.

For a time, when going to and from work, I passed a cow with a large, ugly tumor growing out of her forehead. Day after day I winced at the sight of her shriveling, dying a slow death. Seeing her finally lying dead in the pasture was a relief.

I'm pained knowing I don't have the resources to right all I see. Yet there's a part of me that appreciates living where I experience a broad spectrum of reality. Although sometimes uncomfortable to witness, there's authenticity here.

The Civil War is still being fought in my backcountry neighborhood. Abundant Confederate flags display thriving racism and hatred for Yankees like me.

I'm as careful where I tread in those matters as I am where I put my hands and feet.

Mother fears for my safety here, even though I've tried to convince her that my neighbors are no more threatening than those anywhere else I've lived.

That said, I admit the road to my land doesn't present a promising picture. Depending on one's outlook, ripped window screens hanging down the sides of oxidized trailers, sand yards strewn with plastic toys, and road trash have a way of speaking danger to some.

My mother came with me to see my property before any clearing had been done. I was excited about my purchase and eager to share my find.

When we pulled into a clear patch of land near where my drive would be one day, she froze in her seat, refusing to get out.

After that incident, she would only come to my country cottage accompanied by a male—a cousin's husband or my brother-in-law.

I wish she'd be more willing to be a part of my life here.

That's like me. Always wishing for my relationship with my

mother to be different. Always wishing she would try to understand me. We seldom find a way to connect on a deep level. We haven't found our way to friendship. And I haven't stopped wishing that we will.

Even though my mother can't identify with my feelings about living in the wild, all in all, I'm in love with my land, my small home, and the real Florida. I relish the adventure of wandering on the preserve and exploring an unfamiliar way of life. Best of all, I cherish the opportunity to grow while living on the fringes of cultural norms.

———

When I first moved to Sunny Hill Farm in November of 2001, the inside shower stall hadn't been installed. I showered outside or sponge-bathed inside with water heated on the stove and poured into a bucket.

In truth, even after I could wash myself inside, I never did.

The outside shower head is mounted on the southeast side of my cabin. Six-by-eight pressure-treated fence panels make for privacy on two sides. A third panel, the one closest to the front of my cabin, is only six by six, leaving an open doorway to the stall. On the inside of that one, there's a bench for my clothing and a basket of shower supplies.

There's something magical about bathing outside when stars twinkle overhead. When there's a full moon lighting my enclosure, that's the limit of wonder. Even when the temperature is freezing, hot shower water keeps me comfortable while cleansing myself and heats my body so as to remain warm while I towel-dry and don a bathrobe.

On June 2, 2002, the sun leisurely sets in the west, calming a hot summer's day.

While I'm bathing, glorying at gold-rimmed cumulus clouds gliding across the sky, embraced by the pink and blue shades of dusk, I wonder if anything could be better.

I scrub myself leisurely with an exfoliating bath mitt in no hurry to end my revelry.

While cleansing my stomach, I notice a black spot located about three fingers' width above my navel.

A mole?

When I investigate with a fingernail, eight legs appear, protesting the interruption to a gourmet meal.

A tick.

Ick.

Oh well, no big deal.

I put down the bath mitt, pinch the embedded tick between the thumb and forefinger of my right hand, and jerk at the embedded pest; my skin pulls up, the tick still attached, reluctant to let go. Annoyed, I give a no-mercy yank.

Success.

I flick the pesky arachnid over the privacy fence.

Good riddance!

Before continuing my bath, I investigate the tick bite site: In the middle of a patch of pasty white flesh, there's a speck of blood. A perfect red circle surrounds the area.

Must be a little infection from the tick bite.

No worry.

My body usually heals well.

I scrub the wound with plenty of soap for good measure . . .

WHEN JOY
WRITHES IN TORMENT

Sunny Hill Farm will go on the real estate market soon. I'm packing and removing my things a few hours on Saturdays.

That's all I can manage.

Gravity-sucking fatigue from a diseased body weights me into a struggling mass of flesh and bones, easy bait for despair.

I'm too sick to feel much, though. Or too afraid.

So, I plod my way through the process of saying goodbye to my beloved home in the woods.

Every time I come here to pack, a neighbor of my friend Rebecca comes too. He scrubs the cement floor and otherwise cleans while I put my things in boxes.

Because my body and mind have been void of energy and ambition, I haven't done housework in months. Litter tracked by my cats and sand the dogs carried inside on their paws coat the floor. Dust is everywhere, blown in from the pasture on windy days. The bathroom and kitchen are crusted with filth.

Most of the time I leave before my thoughtful helper, who doesn't seem to mind cleaning even when I can no longer work.

I feel guilty about that, yet I haven't the energy to be considerate.

All I can offer are apologies before I drag myself, slumped-shouldered, to my car to return to Rebecca's house, where I've been living since April 2003—a mere eighteen months after I moved to Sunny Hill Farm.

———

JUNE 2002

A few days after yanking the tick off my stomach, I feel a little nauseated and dizzy after getting out of bed in the morning.

At first I'm puzzled, trying to remember if I've been around anyone who's sick.

No one comes to mind.

Shrugging, I go on with my day, preparing to spend time with my mother even though I don't feel quite right, figuring I'm merely suffering from the twenty-four-hour flu.

No big deal.

Within a few days I feel fine, returning to running in the neighborhood after work, riding my donkey on weekends, and doing chores while continuing to be captivated by my life in the Central Florida woods.

JULY 2002

At the community college where I work, when climbing upstairs to my office, something I've done many times a day for years, appreciating the exercise, crippling discomfort in my hips drives me to the elevator.

Hmm. Old age setting in?

Seems like I'm a little young for that.

Maybe this will pass.

We'll see.

After a couple of weeks?

No more hip pain.

SEPTEMBER 2002

I sit down at my kitchen table to eat a spinach salad with raspberry vinaigrette, relishing my home and the view of my donkeys nuzzling each other in the pasture.

I take a mouthful of doused greens.

Before they're even off the fork, I spew them all over the table and floor.

My mouth is on fire!

Jeez. What's that about?

Rushing to the bathroom mirror, I examine my tongue and gums.

There's no sign of inflammation. No canker sores.

Feeling unsettled, I return to the kitchen and dump the salad into the compost bowl then prepare a piece of toast with peanut butter to ease my hunger.

Something else strange has been happening.

At times, when I'm at work, an urgent need to sleep slumps me over in my chair in bondage to inertia. Some days I hide my dire need from my boss and colleagues, pretending I'm going to see someone on campus. Instead I collapse, curling in desperation around a pillow I've secreted in a hidden space under the stairs by the back door to my office building. Although my boss is compassionate and encourages me to close my office door to rest when necessary, I feel guilty doing so. Scared, too, fearing that if I do sleep as often as I need to now, I'll lose my job, my income.

I struggle to make sense of what's happening.

Nights are torturous, sweaty affairs; I wrestle with feelings I don't understand. Feelings suppressed during the day.

Why don't I see a doctor?

I'm frightened. Hopelessness haunts me, grabs me, and holds me fast. Freezes me into the persona of a victim about to go down.

NOVEMBER 2002

Early one morning I peer into the toilet bowl, preparing to flush my bowel movement.

Oh my God!

Undigested food in my stool—whole pieces of masticated chicken and lettuce from lunch the day before—sounds an alarm.

I tremble.

Soon afterward, bananas, apples, raw vegetables—staples in my diet—double me over with stomach pain. My intake becomes restricted to cottage cheese, yoghurt, nut butters, sweet potatoes, meat, and bread.

Diarrhea begins an unrelenting, taunting rule over my pace when seeking a place to relieve myself.

One weekend after lunch, I rush to the bathroom, landing on the toilet just in time to keep from soiling my pants.

Fear shakes my body.

Then, a haunting memory of a sign I noticed recently at nearby trail head, warning of ticks and Lyme disease, flashes before me.

Terror strikes, opening the floodgates of horror—and truth: *flu symptoms, hip pain, fatigue, mouth on fire, digestive problems.*

A tick bite.

Hardly able to bring my eyes to my laptop screen, my heart pounds with dread as I open the internet browser.

———

Just before Thanksgiving, I sit on an examination table, my heart pounding at one hundred and twenty-five beats per minute as I wait for Lyme disease test results.

I'm quaking. Terrified. Expecting a confirmation of my own diagnosis of Lyme disease. Spooked by dread. According to what I read on the internet, if someone with Lyme isn't treated within a few weeks after the onset of infection, chronic illness often manifests into unspeakable horrors. Horrors like dementia, disability, dependence, and other torments.

When the doctor enters the examining room, she's holding a manila folder. Impatience hardens her voice. "Why are you so upset?"

"I'm scared. I'm scared I have Lyme disease."

"Calm down. Your test results are negative."

I should feel relieved. Instead, I'm confused and even more unsettled.

My screechy, fret-tightened voice begs for answers. "What's happening to me then? What about the bull's-eye? Fatigue? All the other symptoms? I've read that Lyme tests can be unreliable. What if mine are like that? And even though my test results are negative, may I have a prescription for doxycycline just in case?"

"No. I'm not comfortable with that."

"Please. Please. What if that's the solution? What if my test results are a false negative and a simple antibiotic could prevent chronic illness?"

Lifting her eyes above her glasses, looking at me as though my symptoms are phantoms of mental illness, she reaches for a prescription pad in her coat pocket.

Before she begins writing, my sense of urgency erupts, irritating the doctor further and compromising what could be the door to recovery. I plead, "I've been sick a long time. May I have enough of the antibiotic to last a month?"

"I'll give you orders for two weeks. That's all."

Before she tears my script off the pad, she scribbles lines below her writing to the end of the page, insinuating that I'm likely to forge changes to her orders.

———

Thanksgiving Day is amazing. Hope-filled.

Early in the morning, I move a huge pile of sand away from the bottom of my driveway, relieved to get that long outstanding chore done. I'm thrilled I have the energy to push wheelbarrows of dirt to the far side of my property.

The doxycycline is working, allaying my fears. I believe my own diagnosis of Lyme has been confirmed — that I've found what I need to get well.

Later, I help my mother prepare food to take to my cousin's nearby home.

Best of all, when we sit down at the table for dinner, I shovel dark turkey meat, dressing, green beans, and cranberry sauce onto my plate, knowing I can eat anything I want with no stomach pain. While eating the tasty meal, I believe that wellness is at hand.

When I return to Sunny Hill Farm later in the afternoon, under a cloudless blue sky I saddle Buttercup and ride her to the preserve, stopping on the way for her to be given an apple by a neighbor standing at his pasture gate.

———

MARCH 2003

I'm sitting on my friend Rebecca's couch in her living room, bent over, head in my hands, wailing and reeling from the remarks of an internal medicine specialist she'd recommended I see for help.

My well-being at Thanksgiving was short-lived.

Soon afterward, fatigue again weighted my days. Heart arrhythmia frightened me. Stomach cramps and diarrhea spoke of something inflaming my gastrointestinal system. I still couldn't eat fruits or vegetables.

Determined to get to the bottom of what was wrong, I sought help on Rebecca's referral of an internal medicine doctor who enjoyed a stellar reputation for his diagnostic skill.

With a list of symptoms in hand, including the red-ringed white flesh, continuing to signal the tick bite on my stomach, I went to my first appointment with him, feeling in control and determined to get to the bottom of my problems.

All tests he ordered returned negative results: Blood work to check for inflammation, and Lyme disease. A nuclear stress test. Endoscopy and colonoscopy, although the endoscopy did reveal slight inflammation in the lining of my stomach. (When reporting that, the attending gastroenterologist peered at me over his glasses and said, "Go home and take some milk of magnesia," face dripping with scorn, flipping his hand in dismissal.)

After the internal medicine doctor ordering the tests reviewed their outcomes, he blew me off too:

"Carolyn, there's nothing wrong with you. Nothing! Go home and ride your donkey. Be happy."

Crying, I drove to Rebecca's house, seeking the solace of a friend.

Despite what doctors say, I know something is wrong. I'm confused, distraught.

I'm suffering mentally because I know there is something physically wrong. The bull's-eye on my stomach haunts me. Based on what I've read on the internet, I've come to believe that the pasty white flesh surrounded by the angry red circle is a certain sign of Lyme disease—no matter what anyone says.

I'm failing and desperate, weighing seventeen pounds less than a year before.

Working has become a burden. I worry that I'm a millstone for my colleagues, doubting that I'm pulling my weight.

Anxiety tortures me.

Twenty years ago I began taking a drug prescribed by a psychiatrist for anxiety disorder. I've visited him every six months since then for prescription renewals. That steadfast drug, a friend of sorts, is no longer effective. Others my psychiatrist has tried recently haven't worked either. So, now I'm finding relief taking benzos, short for benzodiazepines, a highly addictive sedative prescribed to quell the symptoms of anxiety. At night I add another drug to induce sleeping. I'm hoarding them both now, contemplating suicide. I'm unable to face that fact, so I fool myself by thinking I'd merely be using a form of euthanasia, ending my misery in the same compassionate way I'd dealt with suffering pets.

Rebecca doesn't know about my suicidal ideation.

She does know I feel wretched.

When I stop wailing, she surprises me. "Carolyn, go get your things. You're coming to live with me."

"I can't, Rebecca. I've got my farm. My animals to take care of."

"Go get your things! You can bring your cats and dogs with you."

Sighing, I give in, knowing she's right. I simply can't go on by myself.

———

EARLY APRIL 2003

I haven't moved to Rebecca's yet. That's coming, doom marching to the persistent cadence of my dull moods.

I can't escape what's happening. To obscure my pain, I've hammered my feelings into numb, flat places.

One afternoon, the preserve beckons while I sit at the table on my porch.

Anticipating a walk on the preserve is one of the only things that can stir my emotions these days. I yearn to go to the vast expanse of trails, if even for a short walk.

I can't.

Fatigue anchors me to the chair.

Nacomi is lying by my feet, never wanting to be too far from me.

I found her after hiking in a park beside a lake; she was scavenging for food, digging and licking the soil around a picnic table. I offered her treats from the supply I kept in my car for luring cats and dogs needing to be rescued, taking note as she gobbled them that she appeared to be starving. Because I didn't know if her owners were on the lake or nearby, I left without trying to get her into my car, promising I'd return the next day to check on her.

She was still there, digging and pawing, searching for something to eat.

Coaxing her to get into my station wagon was easy, the smelly treats on the back seat irresistible.

She's been a close companion ever since.

On her left side, a fist-sized tumor, made bloody and raw with Nacomi's gnawing, needs to be removed.

Looking at her snuggled close to my feet, fear and sadness erupt despite my efforts to choke them down.

My head drops onto my folded arms resting on the table.

My body shakes. I sob, grieving with abandon for the first time since becoming sick.

Blubbering, I cup Nacomi's head with my hands. "I'm going to be saying goodbye to Sunny Hill Farm and you too. I don't want to be sick. What's wrong with me?"

Empathetic, Nacomi whimpers and howls.

I bend over and kiss her forehead. She nuzzles my wet cheek with her nose.

She doesn't know she will be euthanized in the morning. I'm too afraid to spend money on her needs for fear I won't have enough for my own if my health keeps deteriorating. I'm haunted by the possibility that I could get too sick to work.

I've already said goodbye to Buttercup and Sweet Pea, their braying echoing my agony as they disappeared in a trailer down my driveway.

My cats, companions for sixteen years, will go down the day after Nacomi.

Even though Rebecca offered to give them shelter, she lives in a tiny home; the room where I'll be staying has barely enough space for twin bunk beds, a bookshelf, me, and Forest. Besides, Kristina pees in my bed a lot and could ruin Rebecca's furniture. The sad truth is, I don't believe I'll be able to care for them much longer anyway, and I'm too sick to try to find homes for them.

The day after Nacomi is euthanized, I put my three old cats in carriers. From then on they cry. They cry for twenty-five interminable miles while we travel to a veterinarian's office near work. They cry when they're placed on a shelf behind the receptionist.

Kristina is especially loud. Insistent. Her high-pitched wailing tortures me as I turn my back, head bowed by the weight of unbearable pain, and leave her and the rest to die alone.

After work, I pick up their bodies, each one wrapped in a white, cotton towel and placed inside a crate, prepared for burial in graves I'd managed to dig the day before.

Acid tears I can't shed pour into wounds made raw with the

agony of their loss as I tenderly lay each one into graves lined with hay.

———

AUGUST 2003

I'm sitting at the closing for Sunny Hill Farm, barely able to hold my head erect.

Within a month after listing, my property sold to investors for cash.

When the closing agent asks if there's anything I'd like to say, I tell the buyers where I bought the metal siding in case they want to construct additions, and hand them the instruction manuals for the water-treatment equipment and pump.

A dumb sort of sadness, an aching for my land to be loved, seduces me into describing a delicate, rare pink wildflower blooming in the front yard.

My description fades into the bored eyes of the buyers eager to be done with the closing.

IDENTITY RAVAGED, SANITY RAPED

LATE OCTOBER 2003

I expected to be dead by now.

Instead, here I am, sitting on a driftwood log, mist from ocean waves splashing against the beach, hiding me from view. I'm feeling buzzed and frustrated.

Before I left Rebecca's house this morning, I pulverized hundreds of milligrams of the medication I use for sleep in a mortar, thinking that if a few induce slumber, hundreds will euthanize me, end my misery.

On the way here, I bought a vanilla milkshake and stirred my stash of powered pills into the ice cream mixture.

When I got near where I'm now sitting, I drank the spiked shake, thinking I'd pass out within a half hour or less after walking into the sea.

With waves surging, lifting me off the ocean's bottom, I waited to die, thinking of those who care about me. First, my mother and sister came to my demented mind: "They'll feel sad when I'm gone—sad until they've cried themselves out talking with each other. Then they'll go on with their lives, my memory a mere blip in the scheme of things."

My friends?

I didn't think they'd miss me too much.

While I was pondering all that, my suicide attempt wasn't going well.

First, high winds started blowing the waves and me toward shore.

I struggled to remain in control of my position—toes touching the sandy bottom enough to hold my place. Although I intended for the undertow to carry my body out to sea, the last thing I wanted was to experience the sensations of sucking in water and drowning before I was unconscious.

Time after time I used my tippy-toes to creep back into deep water, hoping to pass out.

Instead, my heart started racing, pounding in my ears.

After repositioning myself in the water over and over again, waiting and waiting to get sleepy, but only becoming more agitated, I finally gave up hope of dying and plodded out of the sea.

So here I am, head bowed, my body trembling with panic, sitting on a log wishing I were dead.

Facing tomorrow's abyss is unavoidable.

———

Fear stalks my sanity as I sign my official retirement forms. At age sixty, I'm forced by illness to stand down from a huge part of my identity, forced by illness to relinquish my income and $250,000 of benefits accruing in merely the beginning stages of a state pension fund. My boss encouraged me to reconsider when I called to tell him the time had come for this, but his goodness and my feelings for my colleagues inspired me to be fair, to persist, for I could no longer pull my weight.

Sometime in late September, I had begun taking sick leave.

During the previous summer, still seeking help, I had made an appointment to see an infectious disease doctor. He readily diagnosed me with Lyme disease, using only clinical symptoms, noting especially the bull's-eye on my stomach. Yet, he puzzled me by what he said: "I know how to start treatment, but not the protocol to continue."

In the brief moment while I was trying to decide if I wanted to take the risk of working with him, the doctor glanced at my intake information.

Without preamble, he closed my folder, shocking me with his abruptness: "I can't treat you. You're taking psychotropic medications."

With that, he rose, motioning me to the door of the examining room, then escorted me to the exit of his office.

Mired in clouds of confusion, I found my way to my car, feeling ashamed that I was taking drugs for sleep and anxiety, yet feeling certain I needed them. I couldn't fathom why the doctor didn't know that too—why he didn't feel I was worthy of his treatment, his trust.

Instead of feeling supported, I felt like a criminal.

After recovering from that insult, I kept searching for answers. On lymenet.org, an online information resource, someone pointed me to a Lyme-literate doctor in Tarpon Springs, Florida. During my first appointment with him, I knew he was different: He asked me about symptoms before I could go through my own list. Best of all, he didn't insult my sanity. Even though he diagnosed me on the spot based on clinical symptoms, he sent blood samples to the specialty lab IGeneX. Although the overall test result was negative, there were enough positive indicators on facets of the test, combined with my symptoms, for him to feel certain Lyme disease was at the root of my suffering. And he convinced my insurance company of that certainty, prompting payment for my treatment with an antibiotic.

Within days after the antibiotic began coursing through my body via an intravenous catheter, a PIC line, I felt fantastic, announcing at work more than once, "I'm back to myself. I'm getting well. Finally, I'm getting well!"

Four weeks into treatment, canker sores erupted in my mouth. White thrush coated my tongue. Treatment was halted temporarily, or so I thought.

A few days later, I looked into the bathroom mirror after taking a hot shower. My chest was mapped with blue, bulging veins, signaling a thrombosis at the end of the PIC line terminating in the superior vena cava, a vein emptying directly into the heart.

What caused the thrombosis?

No one knows, except to say that, judging from the condition of the removed PIC line, my body was rejecting and disintegrating the very channel that was delivering potential relief, debris perhaps clogging the end.

After the PIC was removed, I was prescribed an oral, new-on-the-market antibiotic in hopes of killing the rampaging Lyme bacteria.

Instead of halting the disease process, my condition deteriorated.

My tongue fired up, feeling like red-hot pins were jabbing the sensitive, tender flesh, although there was no sign of inflammation.

My brain was often stoved into fog. Words wouldn't materialize to express ideas. Sentences beckoned, taunting me with their hidden forms.

Many times I couldn't find my way to Rebecca's house after work.

Traffic signals confused me.

I couldn't remember how to perform my job at the community college where I was employed. I couldn't recall how to perform tasks that had evolved over a period of sixteen years: data submissions to the Florida Division of Community Colleges, aggregating funding projections, writing funding proposals.

Worse, I couldn't sit up at my desk long enough to even try.

Taking sick leave became my only recourse until I had to face the inevitable.

So, this morning, Rebecca drove me here to execute my good-bye to my job and my colleagues, many of whom are like family.

I appear stoic as I sign form after form, thinking I'll never finish. Wishing I didn't have to.

When I get in Rebecca's car after the formal and tragic ending of my career, I bend over and vomit dry groans of angst that can't be shackled by numbness.

———

NOVEMBER 2003

Thanksgiving Day is nothing like last year.

My sister, Janet, and her husband drove down from Georgia to be here with Mother and me. Mom is in a rehabilitation center, recuperating from surgery to install a pacemaker.

When dinner is served in the small dining area, I poke at my food, too sick to eat.

Within minutes of sitting down at the table, I excuse myself, bowing my head, feeling guilty that I can't stay upright long enough to be with my family—especially my ninety-two-year-old mother. I barely make my way to her room in time to collapse on her bed instead of the hallway floor.

—————

FEBRUARY 2004

My gallbladder is removed after tests determined the organ to be nonfunctioning, rendered useless by sludge deposited as a side effect of the high doses of the antibiotic used to treat me for Lyme.

—————

MARCH 2004

Forest is sitting in the car beside me, like he always did when I was well.

I called to him, after I opened the door to Rebecca's porch to let him out, remembering the times we used to go to the beach together: "Forest, go for a ride? Come on boy, go for a ride."

He's always loved riding in the car, sitting in the front seat just like a person, facing forward, never one to hang his head out the window. People in other cars often looked over at us and laughed at the irony of him acting just as important as any human.

In my mind he is that important. A brother and companion. A guardian.

Forest is *in the moment*. He's good at that.

When we're both in my car, I reach over to stroke his back and give him a kiss on the forehead. He's never been much of a kisser, but today he gently leans toward me and licks my cheek.

I wonder if he knows we're soon to be separated—forever.

I can't take care of him now. All I can do is give him food and water or let him out the door to relieve himself. He deserves more.

I'm feeling sick and distraught over having to say goodbye. No matter how bad I feel, I'm determined to be the one to take him to his new home, where he'll be living with my friends Jeff and Dan.

Before leaving Rebecca's house, I called Jeff to let him and Dan know I was coming. When we arrive in their driveway, they're standing outside their front door waiting.

I'm mute with pain as I walk Forest toward them, a smile pasted over my anguish.

While handing Jeff his leash, I thank him and Dan for their compassion, then bend over and rub Forest's body, wanting to remember the feel of his muscular warmth, his friendship.

When I turn to leave, he steps forward to follow. Jeff and Dan hold him still, reassuring him with soft words of acceptance.

With my back turned on my big, russet-colored boy, I trudge to my car.

I start the engine, glancing at his empty seat while sucking my tears into a dark void, unable to summon the courage to feel the deep loss of his presence.

———

APRIL 2004

My symptoms persist.

During the day, I suck ice to soothe my fiery tongue. Anxiety gorges on my terror, fed by my fears of being penniless and homeless. I'm neither of those, yet their threats taunt me. Every six hours a benzo tempers my restless twitching. When that's not enough, I take an antihistamine.

Explosive diarrhea propels feces from my body, often within moments after I eat.

My stomach is still irritated; to avoid crippling pain, fruits and vegetables continue to remain off limits. Meat, sweet potatoes, bland soups, and nut-butter sandwiches are mainstays of my diet.

My brain is fogged, lost in confusion.

I'm no longer able to drive.

At night, I'm taken from my misery by pills.

One evening my sister calls to encourage me to move to Georgia to stay with her and her husband.

Flesh sags over my hip bones. I'm continuing to fail.

I'm beginning to need help merely to exist.

Rebecca is retired and often traveling.

I know the time has come for me to leave Florida, my mother, and my friends who have sustained me for decades.

I accept my sister's gracious invitation.

———

I'm standing behind Mother, arms draped over her shoulders as she sits in her motorized wheelchair. Her right hand reaches up, crossing her heart, grasping my left hand, holding me dear while we pose for a picture.

Both of us paste smiles over our unspeakable pain, holding back grief for the sake of each other.

Rebecca drove me here because I'm too sick and upset to drive myself.

Even if I could have driven myself, I didn't want to be alone to say goodbye.

I love my mother. We're close in a certain way, us two. Even though I've never understood why I don't like her much or why we can't be friends, now there's no mistake that I'm protective and otherwise care about her.

She lives in a continuing-care retirement community, so her

physical needs are taken care of. Although some of her many friends provide emotional support, I'm the main deal.

Since my father died twelve years ago, we've spent every Sunday together, shopping and dining out or running errands. Before ending our time together, we've paid bills and I've gone to the ATM located in the lobby to her apartment building to get her the cash she wants for a coming week.

For a long time now, all I've been able to do during our time together is eat lunch in the deli located down the hallway from her apartment and help her with finances; I've been done in after that, collapsing in her bed to sleep. She's invariably motored her wheelchair to the bedside and tucked me under the covers, always my mother.

Now we're being torn apart.

Sick with Lyme and grief, I can hardly stay standing to finish saying goodbye.

Mom and I have never been ones to engage in small talk, so we both know what we have to do when our pictures have been taken.

I nod to Rebecca; she begins our procession to the outside by opening the door to Mom's apartment.

Mom motors herself into the hallway. I walk behind her, shoulders bent with sorrow.

When we're all positioned on the sidewalk near the parking lot, Rebecca leaves to get her car.

After she arrives by the curb, I lean down and hug my mother, then slide into the car and lower the window, knowing there's always a head-out-the-window-looking-backward wave goodbye.

As we slowly pull away, I look back to wave at Mom, feeling desperate, forlorn, hoping she knows I never intended to leave her like this.

Momma, Momma, I cry inside. *I so want to be with you to the end. I so want to be by your side, holding your hand when you die.*

I never see my mother again.

One year later, on April 26, 2005, she dies suddenly from heart failure.

In a strange quirk of fate, my mother's death occurs at the juncture when my immune system fails as a result of antibiotic treatment, and when insurance-paid, standard medical treatment for Lyme disease ends.

All therapies henceforth are paid for from my inherited resources from my mother's estate.

―――

JUNE 2005

"That's all we can do for you. I'm so sorry."

Dreadful words no patient wants to hear, no doctor wants to speak.

After moving to Jasper, a North Georgia mountain community, to live with Janet and her husband, I was seen by their trusted, respected physician, hoping he could help me. Although I formed a lasting bond with him, the test results and exams by specialists he referred me to were a dead end. In fact, the infectious disease doctor confided to me that he didn't know much about Lyme disease.

During an internet search for answers, my sister discovered a clinic in Charlotte specializing in Lyme disease treatment.

There, I was again diagnosed with Lyme. For eight months I was infused with megadoses of antibiotics administered through a port.

Once a month, or more often if necessary, Janet or a friend drove me the two hundred and fifty miles to Charlotte for monitoring until I heard the words that terminated my treatment there.

Why was my treatment ended?

As a reaction to massive doses of antibiotics, I stopped producing neutrophils, the white blood cells that are the body's primary defense against foreign bacteria.

―――

Carolyn Martin Graham

JULY 2005–JUNE 2006

Before the disappointment of another failed treatment has a chance to settle into despair, I reach for hope, asking the doctor at the Charlotte clinic to refer me for hyperbaric oxygen therapy: I read that Lyme bacteria can't survive in an oxygen-rich environment, that blood infused with oxygen enhances immune-system function, and that some Lyme patients have recovered using that form of treatment.

So I am referred to a neurologist in Naples, Florida, who's experienced some success reversing Lyme disease by using hyperbaric oxygen therapy in his specialized clinic.

When discussing my plans to stay in Naples for at least a month, Janet offers to fly there with me for my initial evaluation with the neurologist and to help me find a place to stay.

Just before our mother died, my sister was experiencing the dissolution of her marriage: her husband announced he was leaving Janet to reunite with his high school sweetheart.

On the morning of the day we're scheduled to fly to Florida, Janet and I stand together arm in arm, waving goodbye to her husband of twenty-seven years. Janet's arm tightens around my waist as he drives away. I, too, experience a sense of enormous loss — the loss of someone who'd become a brother.

———

I spend two months in Naples, Florida, living in a long-term-stay hotel. Every weekday morning, a taxi takes me to the hyperbaric clinic, where I strip in a dressing room. After donning a cotton gown, I lie down on the mattress slide-out of a half-cylinder enclosure with a clear plastic lid.

Then comes the hard part.

The mattress is slid into the cylinder. The lid is lowered — and bolted closed.

For over an hour, I fight claustrophobia while the atmospheric pressure inside the chamber is adjusted, first up to infuse my body with increased oxygen, and back down again to normal, sea-level conditions.

While receiving oxygen therapy is challenging, the loneliness is tormenting. My need for connection causes me to blab to anyone for company. The taxi drivers taking me to and from treatment listen to the mindless chatter used to fill my woebegone emptiness. The hotel clerks listen too. So do the maids.

When nearing the end of my treatment, I develop blurred vision and severe nausea, the effects of oxygen toxicity. After returning to Jasper, those symptoms leave; I feel less sick and less anxious too. For a while. I begin driving again, although I can only manage to get myself to and from appointments or the grocery store.

Not long afterward, I crumple into illness once more, yet I'm still able to drive sometimes.

Persisting in my search for help, I begin treatments with Reiki, a technique using universal energy emanating from the hands of the practitioner.

Although Reiki heals some, I'm unaffected.

While the treatments are in progress, someone tells me about a Native American healer. After relating my story to him during my first appointment, he tells me he'll have to see me naked to help; I'm not bothered by his request because I feel like a piece of fetid, worthless garbage. And I'm desperate, so I strip. With piercing eyes, he scrutinizes my body, then remarks that I could be attractive if didn't hide under drab gray sweats. He goes on to tell me my thoughts are my only problem.

As things turn out, he's partially right, yet he doesn't know how to lead me out of disease and darkness. So, I move on to try acupuncture. Colonics too.

Nothing changes.

I keep searching for answers, seeing a chiropractor I saw advertised on a billboard. He diagnoses me with low levels of testosterone, announcing that to be at the root of my problems, especially anxiety. I agree to allow a colleague of his, a gynecologist, to insert a testosterone chip in my right hip, figuring anything is worth a try.

The result?

More challenges: my increased libido arouses sexual desire at inappropriate times and places.

Another chiropractor is next.

I arrive at his office by mistake, or so I think at the time. I was actually looking for a doctor with the same last name as his and picked the wrong listing for directions on my GPS. Looking around at the office I walked into arouses my curiosity, so I ask for more information. After speaking with the chiropractor himself, I opt for treatment using his protocol that includes a combination of alternative diagnostic techniques and healing therapies.

During the ensuing eight weeks of expensive treatment, I have the opportunity to speak with a few of his patients who've experienced reversals of grave conditions.

I don't respond in kind.

Nothing can break through the barriers, stonewalling my healing. My symptoms remain dire.

The end of June 2006 arrives—endless, hopeless days, strung together by one discouraging sigh after another. Anxiety stalks. I'm no longer an employee. I can't see myself as much of anything anymore. All that was dear has been ripped from me: my job, my home in the woods, my pets, my friends, my mother. My very purpose in life has been despoiled by a ravaging disease, my sanity raped.

THE LAND
OF DARK PEACE

EARLY JULY 2006

Everything I attempt is a terror-ridden chore.

Making a simple phone call fills me with fear. When I walk into a grocery store, I feel disaster lurking in every aisle. Wherever I go, I tremble with suspicion, as if a six-foot, agitated rattler is coiled at my feet, flicking his tongue, waving his head back and forth, beady eyes calculating a strike.

I feel worthless, broken.

I'm living from one benzo to the next, unknowingly developing tolerance and dependence.

My heart never stops racing.

I want to run.

I dwell on euthanizing myself and traveling to The Land of Dark Peace.

When I hear cement trucks thundering downhill by my sister Janet's house, I yearn for the courage to hide in a nearby hedge so I can throw myself in front of one.

I consider tying myself underneath a floating dock in a nearby chilly lake to die of hypothermia; when I imagine feeling the cold and shivering, I discard that idea, knowing I'm not brave enough to experience that kind of end.

Although I'm clearly contemplating suicide, I'm still wedded to the mistaken idea that I'd be euthanizing myself. I feel enshrouded by hopelessness, living in a fear-shadowed counterfeit of the truth, a world that obscures my many blessings.

Desperation reaches for the extended hand of madness.

More ideas for dying come to mind: I think of starving myself, but figure Janet won't allow that under her watch. She'd get law enforcement involved.

I consider slicing my wrists and bleeding out in a tub, holding my arm near the drain, or buying a gun and shooting myself. I decide against those methods. Too messy.

A grim solution emerges from the deep shadows of my crazed mind.

Although a prescription drug didn't work the first time I tried to kill myself, I decide to try with the benzos I've hoarded for four years, believing I've enough to take me out—enough to stop anxiety's torture.

I begin planning, determined to be dead blue by the time my body is found.

Sick with happiness, I set my suicide date for two weeks before Janet's wedding to her fiancé, Mike, whom she's been dating for several months.

By the time they marry I intend to be gone, freeing them from the responsibility of my care, though they've never even hinted at concern about that. My disquiet is purely my own sense of worthlessness projected onto them.

After Janet and Mike leave to go hiking one day, I execute my plan. I muster the energy to drive to Dahlonega, a charming small town located about forty miles from Janet's house. When I arrive, I seek a hotel with a parking lot out of sight of traffic, so my car can't be easily found by the authorities who will surely search for me.

I find the perfect one: parking is completely hidden from the highway by a cement wall. Leaving the engine and air conditioner running, I inquire in the office about the cost of rooms.

They're cheap.

Perfect.

Yes!

After arriving home that day, Janet and Mike ask where I've been. "Amicalola Falls State Park," I lie, deliberately planting a false clue, thinking they will probably look for me there after I've gone missing. (The park is in the opposite direction of the hotel where I plan to end my suffering.)

The day of my premeditated death arrives none too soon. I wake up pumped, full of purpose, eager to be rid of anxiety— forever.

After eating a light breakfast, I dress in shorts, a T-shirt, and brown leather sandals, and grab a red plaid bill cap and my old forest-green backpack. And then I and sit on my bed to tear the labels off the hoarded benzo prescription bottles, fearing a doctor might be blamed for my death. Once my stash is stowed, I plop my backpack and cap on a chair near the front door, knowing Janet and Mike will also be leaving soon for a day's outing.

Pacing, I wait for them to come to the door, poised to execute the next part of my plan.

Janet and Mike fill water bottles in the nearby kitchen and grab their own packs, then move toward me. They notice my stuff in the chair and ask where I'm going.

"To Amicalola Falls State Park again. I really like that place."

After they're out of sight, I drive to an ATM to get a wad of cash to pay for my hotel room without leaving a trace to my debit account, of which Janet is an authorized user. Then I go to a drugstore and buy a pack of adult diapers, for I don't want to mess up the bed with feces and urine when I die.

My distorted and frayed sanity feels seamed tight with sound reasoning.

I pull out of the drugstore parking lot and turn my car toward Dahlonega, excited and eager to drive through the North Georgia mountains on this sunny day shadowed with dark plans.

When I arrive in Dahlonega, I find a place to park on the town square, feeling smug. Wanting to enjoy myself for a while before I die, I take one more benzo than my current prescription allows. In minutes I'm entirely free of anxiety!

Enjoying myself, I walk around for a while, sitting on a bench under a shade tree, watching people come and go.

But soon I rise, knowing I have a job to do.

After moseying to my car, I drive to the hotel I identified the week before.

I pay cash for a five-night stay, thinking I'll die that night so there's plenty of time to be good and dead before I'm found.

The room I select is on the back side of the hotel on the second floor at the end of a hallway—as far away from the front and center as I can get. Once my car is parked, I grab a pair of diapers and put them in my backpack, sling that over my shoulder, and walk upstairs. After opening the door to my room, I walk around inspecting my accommodations, as if I'm here on holiday.

While taking things out of my car, I realize I'm hungry. I figure there's no need to rush, so I walk next door to a fast food restaurant.

Although I don't eat that kind of food much, there's no reason now to care what or how much I eat. So I buy a double hamburger with cheese, a large order of fries, and a large chocolate milkshake. I take my food back to my hotel room, where I gorge.

The food tastes as delicious as only a guilt-free last supper can.

My skin tingles with fear when I finish eating. With the help of the benzos I'd taken earlier still coursing in my veins, I squelch the drive to survive.

After throwing the crumpled food packaging in the trash, I pick up my backpack to retrieve my horde of pills.

I combine all that will fit into three bottles, filling each one to the brim. As I do, I feel fleeting empathy for the maid who will find my decomposed, stinking body.

My sister and others who love me come to mind too. I shrug. *Oh well, they'll get over me easily enough. There's not much about me worth grieving about.* The vivid and constant expressions of love and concern extended to me by my sister and others who care about me are dulled by the vision I have of myself: worthless, a mere sack of sick and decaying flesh and bone, lower than a pus-eating maggot.

I'm existing in a reality that defies understanding by the sane.

My impoverished self-worth discounts the momentary awareness that what I'm doing will sadden others.

Continuing the task at hand, I decide for some reason that
throwing the prescription bottles in the dumpster behind
McDonald's after I've taken the pills is critical.

Planning ahead, knowing I'll only have twenty minutes to get
to the dumpster and back before I pass out, I take off my capris
and don a pair of adult diapers. They crinkle insults when I move.

I sit down on the edge of the bed, eyeing the pills.

Fear erupts again. I wonder about my afterlife.

Will I be forgiven? Will I burn in hell?

I don't care.

I'm done.

With that, I gulp down hundreds of milligrams of benzos—
until I'm full. So full I can't take one more pill.

Grabbing what's left along with the empty bottles, I hasten to
the dark-green dumpster at the back of McDonald's and heave the
remains into the trash.

After rushing back to my room, I put the Do Not Disturb sign
on the outside of my door, turn down the air conditioner, and
snuggle under the covers, sighing with contentment.

———

Three days later I wake up after dark, soaked in urine.

Only partially conscious, I bolt out of bed, open the door to my
room, and walk toward the stairs to get the package of diapers
from my car.

The rest of this story is fragmented.

Why?

Because I was in and out of consciousness. A drug-induced
haze left only segments of memories . . .

Bright-red lights flash on the back of an ambulance. EMTs are
bending over me where I lie on cement at the bottom of stairs. I
feel what must be blood oozing down my forehead.

I'm in a hospital emergency room, adamantly refusing treatment.

I sign papers releasing the hospital of responsibility for my outcome, then stumble out of the emergency room doors into the darkness.

I can't get into my room; I pound on the office door. No one is in the office to give me a key.

I see a large hotel in the distance.

Tripping on stones and brush while staggering there, I approach glass doors to the lobby, grimacing at my reflection of snarled hair framing my wild-eyed face marred with blood.

The clerk at the counter appears alarmed as I approach the counter.

Will he let me have a room?

Although he looks puzzled, he does allow me to register.

Acknowledging to myself that my attempt to euthanize myself has failed, I pay cash for one night, planning to return to Janet's house in the morning.

After riding the elevator to my room on the fourth floor, I open my door with a card key and collapse on the bed. Later in the night, I awake, feeling urine soaking my buttocks. Stumbling out of bed, I jerk off my wet garments and then open the door to my room and walk into the hallway, intending to get more diapers from my car.

The door slams.

Jolted by the realization that my car isn't nearby, I turn to go back into my room.

I can't. The card key is inside the locked room.

I'm stunned that I can't open the door.

I'm left standing in the hallway naked from the waist down. A wide-eyed couple appears and stares at me while I cross my hand over my pubic hairs and implore, "Tell someone at the desk to come up here to open the door to my room."

The couple scurries onto the elevator.

A clerk exits the elevator, glances at me, glances away, then glances at me again, unbelieving eyes bulging. He opens the door to my room and rushes back to the elevator.

In my car I reach into my backpack, finding my cell phone, intending to call Janet to tell her I'm on the way home. My phone's battery is dead.

My car is in a ditch. A sheriff's deputy is questioning me. "Who is the president of the United States?"

Summoning every scrap of consciousness I can gather, I answer: "George Bush."

"What is today?"

"Thursday."

"What is the date?"

"July 6, 2006."

I sign an accident report. The officer writes the incident number on a card that he hands to me.

A tow truck arrives and pulls my car out of the ditch.

I'm aware that the sheriff's deputy is observing my interactions with the truck driver.

My effort to act normal is convincing. I'm released to be on my way.

I'm startled awake. I jerk my car off the shoulder onto the road, noticing in the rearview mirror a road sign I'd flattened.

My windshield is shattered.

Peeking through a small hole in the broken glass, I continue driving.

Finally, a foggy consciousness informs me that I've been passing out; I dredge up the determination to stay awake so I can get home.

At the gate to the community where I live, I give identifying information to the goggle-eyed guards.

After swerving into Janet's driveway, I park haphazardly, get out of the car, and go to the front door.

"Janet, I'm home . . ."

REALLY?
REALLY!

Janet flings open the door, urgency spilling from her mouth as she hugs me. "Where have you been?"

"I stayed in a hotel for a few days."

"You did *what*?"

"I needed a break."

She allows my sorry explanation to pass for the time being, stepping back to look me over.

"What happened to your head?"

"I hit the windshield when my car went into a ditch." Waving my hand in a swerving motion, I continue lying. "To keep from being hit by an oncoming car."

"You need to go to an emergency room."

"No! I *need* to sleep."

Janet persists until I relent.

After I'm settled into an emergency room cubicle, a doctor asks questions about my head wound and then orders bloodwork and a CAT scan of my brain.

I'm not bothered by the idea of a brain scan. I expected that.

Having my blood tested is another matter, for I'm certain the overdose of drugs I took will show up and bust me.

When the doctor returns to share the results, I hold my breath.

I listen with disbelief as he declares, "All test results are normal."

Phew. I'm off the hook!

The next morning I see Janet walking toward the kitchen, where I'm filling a glass of water at the refrigerator.

I tense, noticing the concern wrinkling her brow and the piece of yellow paper she holds: my copy of the Dahlonega hospital's emergency room discharge form I forgot about and left on the floor of my car.

"What's up?" I croak with a lump in my throat when she's close.

Janet hands me the form, pointing to a handwritten note. "What does this mean?"

I read the note I didn't know was there: "Drug overdose suspected."

When I look up, my sister's piercing hazel eyes insist on the truth.

I tell her everything, freezing my feelings into stone-cold, flat responses.

Janet's reaction to my story is impassioned.

She shares the anguish she felt when she realized I was missing. She tells me how afraid she was that I'd been abducted and murdered. About filing a missing-person report. About driving with Mike to Amicalola Falls State Park to search for me and my car. About hearing my voice calling at the front door, sounding happy and well, late on the very night I overdosed: "Janet, I'm home!" About the dogs frantically barking while she and Mike rushed to embrace me, only to be overwhelmed by a dark, empty night.

Although I apologize to my sister and later to Mike, I'm devoid of empathy. I can't understand their anguish nor their feelings of love and concern for me.

How can I?

For I am unable to relate to anyone who considers me precious and worth saving.

————

During the summer of 2006, soon after my attempted suicide in Dahlonega, Janet marries Mike—with the condition that he accept me, her two dogs, and a cat into the marriage. With gracious kindness, he agrees. Soon afterward Janet and the rest of us settle into Mike's home in Canton, a community north of Atlanta, and my journey with chronic illness continues.

Soon after Lyme struck in 2002, my brain became inflamed, creating havoc with my capacity to reason and my memory. My second brain, my gastrointestinal tract, evidenced profound disruption with explosive diarrhea and the passing of undigested food. Those complications and others signaled systemic dysfunctions, rendering useless the antidepressant that had been a powerful antidote for anxiety's torture.

For four years, different psychiatrists both in Florida and Georgia attempted to help, prescribing one antidepressant after another, moving through the entire suite of available psychotropic remedies. Most I couldn't tolerate for one reason or another. Those few that I could were effective for a scant two weeks or less.

That grim scenario changes in late summer of 2006 when Dr. Lahasky, my internal medicine specialist, finds a solution: he combines an antidepressant with a drug used for medicating epileptic seizures and bipolar disorder while continuing to prescribe a benzo and the sleep-inducing drug I've been taking.

Feelings that had seamed themselves to the belief that danger lurked everywhere, even in a mere cup of tea, finally recede. Anxiety is quelled—for a time.

Relief slows my heartbeat. My skin ceases to prickle.

Lyme symptoms persist, though. My tongue still burns when I try to vary my diet by eating fruits and vegetables; excruciating pain in my stomach continues to hold me captive to sweet potatoes, meat, and gluten-free bread. Besides having become gluten-intolerant, I'm now lactose-intolerant too. Unpredictable, violent diarrhea keeps me wearing diapers when I leave the house. And fatigue steals my daytime hours by forcing me down into the depths of weighted afternoon sleep.

Even so, I find enough energy, now that I'm not sparring with fear, to volunteer and make friends, even spending nights with some.

Reclaiming a portion of my life, I revel in the feeling of freedom for three months, although heavily drugged.

Then, without warning, anxiety erupts again.

Why?

I don't know.

When I plead for help from my internal medicine doctor, he engages his ever-active, creative mind and, once again, finds a solution: He decides to rotate different antidepressants, changing every third month or sooner if one becomes ineffective. And he increases the daily number of benzos.

Gripping on to that tentative regimen, I continue, once again, to reclaim a margin of my life. For the next three years, I'm able to craft meaning and purpose, sometimes even feeling a hint of joy whispering in my heart.

Within that period of time, along with volunteering to help an animal rescue agency and being an assistant for therapists using horses for treating children with certain disabilities, I teach knitting and crocheting to female inmates in a detention center.

There I meet two individuals who will touch me deeply: Marilyn Goff, the project coordinator, and Crystal, an inmate.

I like Marilyn from the minute we meet. I become blood-sister close with her, and every time I'm with her I feel mystified by something bonding us even beyond our intention to serve others. Until more tragedy plays out in my life, I won't understand the full measure of our connection.

My relationship with Crystal begins taking shape in a window-less, cold, cement-block room in the detention center where she awaits her fate.

After she's released because there's not enough evidence to convict her for theft, she calls me every day. Every day for months. I speak to her in a rote, inattentive manner without understanding that I matter, yet at some level knowing there's a reason we're staying connected.

In the fall of 2006 I also begin my long-standing relationships with Dr. Milton, board certified in family and homeopathic medicine, and Brenda Stockdale, a soon-to-be-published author and health psychologist.

Dr. Milton, focusing on integrative medicine and systemic balance, recommends I take a homeopathic antimicrobial and a suite of supplements. I make appointments to see him several months apart, yet I often see him more than that if necessary.

Brenda, a behavioral medicine specialist, is another story. Because my emotions are volatile and difficult to handle, I seek her counsel once a week, spilling my pain. Her compassion is profound.

Besides helping me deal with mental and physical illness, she begins teaching me strategies to prompt my immune system to function at its peak and about the research supporting their efficacy.

Although Dr. Milton and Brenda provide masterful and groundbreaking care, I'm unable to fully respond.

What's in the way?

Hopelessness continues to anchor me in despair. Anxiety stalks in the nexus where darkness meets light, stalling my progress. I skim the surface of reality in a drug-induced calm, continuing to create wisps of meaning and purpose in my life until the spring of 2009.

———

One night in May, anxiety explodes in my chest. Fear stalks again, prickling my skin. My heart pounds.

All the psychotropic drugs I take are failing to be effective. When I attempt to ingest merely a single dose of one of them, my face flushes. My heart races, pounding in my ears.

Lyme has somehow twisted my neurological system, creating a heinous rejection of pharmaceutical help. My body will no longer tolerate the drugs that have given me back a portion of my life.

I'm forced to stop taking them.

For two months I pace, fidget, and tangle my sheets, thrashing during sleepless nights.

As I attempt to harness a body that's seeking escape from phantom threats, the raw edge of fear becomes intolerable.

By early July, I'm desperate, realizing I need inpatient psychiatric intervention if I am to avoid another suicide attempt.

I fantasize for a short time about being in a hospital under the care of my therapist.

Knowing that's impossible, sighing and bowing my head in defeat, I face up to a long overdue decision. Shoulders drooping, I trudge to the back of Janet's house.

When I enter her bedroom where she's working on her computer, she looks up with deep concern in her eyes. "What's wrong?"

"Anxiety is eating me alive! I need to admit myself for treatment in a psychiatric hospital. Will you please take me?"

"Sure. Where do you want to go?"

"I don't know."

———

As we drive beside the beautifully appointed landscaping of the driveway to the psychiatric hospital my sister and I chose together, we're greeted by a reassuring billboard boasting, "Voted Top Ten Psychiatric Hospitals in the Nation."

"Look at that, Janet. That's reassuring!"

"I know."

The pastel hues of a late summer's day paint the sky while we park. After Janet opens the trunk, I take out my suitcase. We then walk to the hospital's entrance, me towing my luggage.

Once inside the reception area, decorated with the fine touch of an interior decorator, my sister takes a seat.

I make my way to an off-white counter with a gleaming granite surface where a receptionist greets me.

"What can I do for you?"

Pushing through shame and fear begging me to flee, I squeak, "I need to be admitted for help with anxiety."

"All right. All right then. Let's get you started on the process."

Picking up keys and stepping out from behind the counter, she motions for Janet and me to follow her.

We're escorted through a doorway, down a dingy hall, and ushered into a small room. As we're taking our seats, the receptionist announces, "An intake counselor will be with you soon."

I nod.

She turns, and leaves.

Behind her, the door closes—automatically—with a too-loud click.

"Janet, that sounded creepy. I think we just got locked in."

To be certain, I peer at the crack between the frame and door—a deadbolt holds us captive.

Terror and confusion erupt. I turn to my sister, eyes wild with fear. "I hope we made the right decision to come here."

"I know what you mean."

While we wait for more than an hour for someone to speak with us, I notice unsettling details about our prison: The thread-picked royal-blue upholstery on the chairs we're sitting on is stained in places where body holes leak fear and disease. Paint on the surrounding walls, the color of baby-shit yellow-beige, repulses me. There are no windows to allow for even mind-wandering escape.

Finally, someone comes to evaluate my condition, which has been made worse by confinement.

I plead for help for anxiety, explaining that I think I'm having so much trouble because I recently—abruptly—withdrew from a benzo, a drug I'd taken for seven years. To justify my opinion, I hand the intake counselor a copy of an article: "Benzodiazepines: How They Work and How to Withdraw," posted online by Dr. Heather Ashton, renowned British psychiatrist and authority on benzodiazepine withdrawal.

While the intake counselor slips the article into a manila folder I assume is my file, she rises from her chair, explaining that she needs to confer with a psychiatrist regarding my admittance.

———

After signing consent for treatment and saying goodbye to Janet, I'm escorted down hallways sheathed with linoleum, an attendant insistent on wheeling my suitcase.

Feeling awkward empty-handed, puzzled and uncomfortable about someone else handling my luggage, I appeal to the attendant. "I'd like to take care of my suitcase."

"No. No, I don't mind doing this."

We pass through two sets of steel double doors that close hard.

Click.

Click.

Raw fear signals incarceration I don't understand. My urge to run knows I can't.

I'm haunted.

Another click.

After entering a twenty-bed female ward, I'm taken to the far end of a hallway, rooms on either side.

My suitcase is handed over to two black women sitting behind a counter.

They tell me to sit down in one of the spindly, chromed, metal-framed chairs facing them, their blue, plastic seats iced with a freezing temperature.

Shivering from fear and the cold, I hug my chest with my arms, barely able to keep from rocking.

Without speaking, the attendants open my suitcase and rifle through my neatly packed clothing, saying nothing. Their icy, silent treatment makes me long to be free. I wonder if they treat everyone with such hardened distance or if they're giving me a taste of racial prejudice.

Feeling disrespected, I wait for them to finish, still and silent as a stone frozen in a winter's storm, wondering why they're inspecting—and messing up—my belongings.

Exhausted, I ache to lie down.

After midnight, the attendants finish inspecting my belongings; one steps from behind the counter, wheeling my suitcase, motioning me to follow her.

She leads me into a room with two twin beds. I'm assigned to the one near the far wall.

"May I have a pillow?"

"There aren't any."

"What about an extra blanket?"

"None extra."

When I collapse onto my bed, only one thin, cotton blanket is at hand to insulate me from the icy temperature and the blood running cold through my veins.

Throughout the sleepless night, rustling plastic taunts my fear-laden body every time I turn, attempting to find solace.

The next morning, I stumble my way through the daily check-in process because I'm given only incidental directions by other patients who notice my befuddled expressions.

To find out about the breakfast drill, I mimic those I see writing their names on a list on a counter, then stand where they do, leaning against a wall, frightened and silent as a trapped rabbit.

Two female attendants arrive. One barks, "Stop talking. Stand single file in the order you signed in."

The other one picks up the sign-in list and begins a roll call. By the time she gets to my name, I know what's expected.

"Carolyn Graham?"

"Here."

After everyone on the list answers, we're counted by both women.

After their counts match the number of patients on the list, one of them moves to the head of the line, the other to the rear.

We're escorted—through two sets of locked steel doors—into the cafeteria.

I have no appetite, yet I ask for scrambled eggs and bacon, knowing I should eat something.

When seated at a table, picking at my food, I listen as some of the patients reveal their circumstances. All five sitting nearby were given a choice—by a judge—to come here or spend time in jail.

Hearing that information, plus the inspection of the things in my suitcase, should have given me a clue about what's happened to me, yet I still don't understand.

————

As soon as the other patients and I enter our ward after breakfast, one of the escorting attendants orders us to report to a certain meeting room in a half hour.

The room is already crowded when I show up. Men from an adjacent wing have joined us in a crammed circle. A facilitator sits in our midst.

She begins speaking, addressing the challenges of withdrawing from drugs and alcohol.

I want to bolt.

Knowing better, I grip the sides of the chair to keep myself anchored in place, for I now get the picture.

I'm jailed.

Held captive in a locked-down travesty of excellence.

No help for anxiety here.

How could this have happened? I pled for help with anxiety. Pled.

Now what?

If I say I've been misdiagnosed, no one will believe me.

Even if I could somehow convince someone, I don't want to stay in this place.

Who knows, my treatment could get even worse!

With a mask of emotional balance superglued over my terror, I adopt the persona of a recovering, remorseful drug addict, securing my release after a week of incarceration.

Carolyn Martin Graham

Once I've written a $1,000 check for my Medicare co-pay for psychiatric hospitalization—a condition for liberation—I'm escorted through the reception area to a portico where Janet is waiting for me in her car.

I open the front passenger-side door, sit down, bend over, and retch dry, groaning primeval terror, suppressed during my stay in one of the top ten psychiatric hospitals in the nation.

THE THRESHOLD
OF A DREAM

I'm reclining in a hospital bed in a geriatric psychiatric hospital, waiting to see a psychiatrist.

One week after my experience in the drug-addiction treatment program, still tortured by anxiety, I've once again admitted myself for inpatient treatment.

This time I chose a treatment center affiliated with a well-known, respected university, that specializes in treating late-life depression.

Because anxiety and depression are closely linked, and psychiatrists have expertise in both conditions, I'm convinced I'll get help here.

When the psychiatrist arrives, he pulls up a chair and sits beside my bed, prickling with ill will.

I'm not in the best of mental states, so I'm not certain how to work with him. With care, I think. He strikes me as a crocodile with swollen hemorrhoids.

On the other hand, his female physician's assistant standing beside him smiles, conveying much-needed warmth.

"Why are you here?" the psychiatrist asks, scooting his chair closer to my bed.

With a slab-flat voice, I tell him about my infection with neurological Lyme disease and my related intolerance of medications. Most critical, I describe in the best way I know how the severity of my anxiety and my abrupt withdrawal from a benzo, which I believe has exacerbated my symptoms.

"I've tried everything," I blurt.

"Are you willing to try ECT, electroconvulsive shock therapy?"

"At this point, yes. I'll try anything."

Nodding, the psychiatrist explains that I may experience memory loss—*usually* temporary—and other dangerous side effects that I let slide into the nowhere land of the anguished.

Without reading the details on the consent form he hands me, I sign. Overwhelming sadness makes further conversation difficult. Wishing to retreat, I pull myself inside out to continue speaking with the psychiatrist.

After agreeing to his notion of including pharmaceutical support for anxiety and depression in my treatment plan along with the ECT, our dialogue centers on antidepressants, benzodiazepines, and my recent systemic rejection of drugs. With that, our conversation trails into an unexpected shared moment of silent answer-seeking—common ground.

An idea somehow surfaces from the murk of my roiled mind: I remember an antidepressant I took early on in my illness—one I couldn't tolerate then, because with the combination of other drugs I was taking at the time, I was forced to sleep most of every day. Since I'm not taking any prescriptions, and I'm in need of sleep, I suggest trying that one.

While rising from the chair, the psychiatrist agrees.

Peering at me over his readers, he suggests that I watch a video of someone receiving electroconvulsive shock treatment that's available by asking one of the attendants. Then, nodding in the direction of his assistant, he tells me she'll check on me daily and report my progress to him.

———

For two weeks, every other weekday morning, beginning on Mondays, I'm awakened early and given an antacid. Although I'm curious about the need for one, I don't ask questions.

No breakfast is allowed to prevent choking during treatment, when I'll be anesthetized, convulsing, and unable to breathe on my own.

Each time the ECT lab is ready for me, I'm wheelchaired to the reception area and positioned at a table where I complete the Beck Depression Inventory, composed of scaled questions related to symptoms, yielding a final score indicative of severity.

When space is available in the lab's preparation room, I'm taken into an area partitioned by white curtains, where a nurse assists me in scooching myself onto a hospital stretcher and lying down.

I so look forward to what always comes next.

"Would you like a warmed blanket?"

"Ahhh, yes. Yes. That would feel wonderful."

Compassion speaks again when the nurse tucks one end of a soft, toasty cotton blanket around my feet, making certain they're completely covered.

Tears of loneliness spill from my eyes.

As I rub them with a fist, trying to hide my feelings, another nurse offers solace, asking questions of genuine interest and concern while she preps an arm, a hand, or a foot—anywhere a good vein can be found for the insertion of an IV catheter.

I don't look forward to the ECT, yet I do welcome the time I have with the nurses who prepare me for treatment in the lab. They're the only ones extending humane warmth and kindness at this center for late-life depression—the only ones I feel connected to.

When fluid drips into my body from a bag hung at the head of my stretcher, the nurses clean up the gauze and packaging lying on my blanket.

Knowing my shock treatment is merely moments away, my stomach roils with fear and dread.

Too soon, the double doors to the ECT treatment room swing open.

Two other nurses exit, striding in my direction.

My heart pounds. My muscles tense.

———

No time is wasted on even a pretense of warmth. The goal is shock treatment.

With goal-driven deliberation, the nurses push my stretcher through gray metal doors with black rubber buffers on their edges.

Once inside the treatment room, I'm spun around so my head is close to the oxygen supply, monitoring equipment and electrodes that will be placed behind both ears.

To my left, I see only the chest and head of a psychiatrist in a white coat, standing behind an ominous, black console. Sometimes the reptilian one I saw on my first day in the hospital is there, preparing to administer ECT. Sometimes there's another psychiatrist on duty.

I nod a greeting to the doctor who will induce a grand mal seizure, convulsing my body.

At once, a blood-pressure cuff is placed around my ankle.

What's that used for? To stop a paralytic, which will soon be administered, from entering the veins in my foot and halting muscular activity. Free from paralysis, my foot will shake; seizure activity can be monitored in that way to regulate the level of electricity shocking me.

Electrodes are glued to my head. An oxygen mask is placed over my nose and mouth.

Soon I'll be given anesthesia and the paralytic that will prevent me from breaking bones or cracking teeth during treatment. (Because the paralytic will inhibit breathing, a nurse standing by my head will have to use artificial means to breathe for me.)

"Ready?" the anesthesiologist asks.

I nod.

In a split second, I'm gone.

Gone.

———

Dazed, I awaken in a recovery room.

Shaking my head, I try orienting myself.

After I manage to figure out where I am and what's just happened, I'm wheeled back to my room, where I sleep off the anesthesia and the brain-stunning effects of the ECT.

Other than that, the days in the hospital are boring. Although my short-term memory *is* affected by treatment, I don't forget the interminable boredom weighting my days.

There are no facilitated groups to connect me with the rest of the patients. No one to help us understand we are not alone. No one to foster compassion for ourselves and each other. No one to teach cognitive behavior therapies or other mechanisms that have the potential to change thoughts and emotions. And no one to talk with about the emotional pain of shock treatment. Or the burden of shame I carry about being in a psychiatric hospital.

There is, however, a horticultural therapist who comes a few times to educate us patients about plants. Although I can't figure how learning about plants will help me work with anxiety and chronic illness, I do welcome the relief from monotony, feigning keen interest when I attend botanical sessions while sitting around a table with other patients.

A few times a week, an occupational therapist leads armchair yoga, I think with the intention of fostering mental health through exercise. Yet I'm unable to get therapeutic relief by merely moving around while sitting in an armchair or standing behind one holding on to the back for balance.

The occupational therapist does mention the critical relationship of diaphragmatic breathing to healthy emotions, encouraging us to breathe deeply. However, she doesn't assess individual breathing patterns. (Mine is, and has been for decades, rapid and shallow, although I don't discover that until months later.)

When I try to use my diaphragm to breathe like the occupational therapist suggests, I can't. So I give up trying.

Recreational therapy is also part of my treatment protocol. Along with other patients, I'm treated once in a while to the pleasure of viewing photographs, paintings, and plaques on hallway walls, or taken on a grand tour of the hospital.

That's recreational?

Yes indeed, when framed by intense boredom. That's the only way they could be.

Musical therapy is provided too.

Boxes of drums and baskets of tambourines, castanets, blocks, and other percussion instruments are brought into the same area where armchair yoga is led.

We shake and rattle what feel like second-childhood toys for the demented.

I feel patronized, troubled that I can't jump into a high.

———

When I'm dismissed from the hospital after two weeks, I have in hand a potted plant and a prescription.

I leave behind nothing of my story about disease and suicide.

No one asked why I wanted to die. And I had been too riddled with anxiety and depression to direct my own treatment. To ask for what I needed.

Each morning, when I reported my status to the physician's assistant I met the day I admitted myself, her responses were knotted to the manipulation of medications. No other concerns mattered to her.

The imprint I left behind as I walked out the door of the hospital at the center for late-life depression was nothing more than a shadow.

———

As an outpatient, I receive two more ECT treatments and go for a few twenty-minute consultations with the psychiatrist who'd recommended the procedure.

Again, my condition deteriorates. Anxiety escalates despite ECT and medication. Nights are sleepless.

Now I know for certain there's no relief for my emotional

turmoil in psychiatric hospitals, what I'd thought of as the ultimate answer to relieve my emotional suffering.

Hopelessness blinds me to the spectrum of other options, blinds me to my own personal power. To the possibility of stepping out of the victim's role to engage with my therapist as a person believing I can heal.

Instead, I focus on desperation, becoming frantic.

Again, I will attempt suicide. And this time I'm more determined than ever to kill myself.

With my debit card linked to a checking account my sister can access, I buy rum at a liquor store to make the drugs I plan on taking more lethal. Using the same card, I buy adult diapers at a drugstore. At a nearby building supply retailer I purchase two box cutters—an extra in case one fails to be sharp enough to slit my wrists if the drugs and alcohol fail to take me out.

Afterward, I withdraw cash from the same account, planning to pay for a motel room without leaving a trail.

One Sunday morning at the beginning of October after the early church service, and knowing my sister is going to Sunday school as usual, I say goodbye to her like always. Only this time, calculated deceit taints my farewell: "I'll see you when you get home."

Not far from the church, I stop at a convenience store to get a cup of ice and purchase a few bottles of a diet soda. Before continuing, I make myself a drink with rum, thinking I'll enjoy being high while driving to Blue Ridge, a small town in the Georgia mountains where I'm planning to seclude myself.

When I get to Blue Ridge, I settle on a small motel facing the highway, and pull into the parking lot.

Standing at the counter in the office, I fumble with the stuff in my backpack, feeling for my cash. With my hands on the bills, a strange thing happens: a senseless fear of running short—or something else at work—prompts me to pay for a five-night stay with a debit card for a cash account no one can access except myself.

With the receipt for my room in hand, I return to my car, start the engine, turn the car around, and back into the parking space in front of my room to hide the license tag.

———

I put one box cutter on the bedside table, ready at hand, then take off my long, loose gray cotton pants and underwear, and I pull on crinkling diapers that remind me of Dahlonega.

As an afterthought, I decide to use the plastic shopping bag that had held them to cover my head, thinking I'll suffocate without struggling once the drugs have rendered me unconscious.

I'm ready to die. Eager.

No second thoughts this time.

After leisurely swallowing hundreds of benzos with the help of another robust rum and Coke, I crawl into bed, positioning the plastic bag over my head and tying the handles around my neck.

I crash into the pillows, passing out.

———

I'm thrashing, struggling to breath. Suffocating.

Frantic and barely able to stay conscious, I rip open the plastic bag, acknowledging that I'm too much of a sissy to take that route into The Land of Dark Peace, then I collapse again.

Three days later, I'm awakened by incessant pounding on the door to my room, a familiar voice calling me.

"Carolyn. Carolyn, open the door. Let me in. Carolyn, open up. This is Jan!"

Dread at facing more misery sucks at my consciousness, miring me further into a drug-weighted fog.

"Carolyn, open the door."

While I roll out of bed, sluggish with a hangover, shame and despair weighting me, I wonder how I've been found.

Staggering, I make my way to the door.

After that, I don't remember much.

I do recall our pastor sitting beside me on the edge of the bed and putting the box cutter into her handbag. "Do you have anything else for hurting yourself?"

I lean over the side of the bed, reach into my backpack. While handing her the second box cutter, I proclaim, "That's everything."

"Are you sure?"

"Yes."

My friend Marilyn crawls in bed beside me and wraps me in her arms. Holding me close, she whispers in my ear, "God has more for you to do."

I turn my head away from her in disgrace.

In my muddled state, I somehow understand there's a bed waiting for me at the psychiatric hospital where I last admitted myself.

I'm told there are EMTs outside, insisting I urinate to rule out kidney damage before they will release me to the care of my sister and friends to transport me there.

Someone helps me to the toilet.

I pee.

The next thing I remember, I'm crawling into the back of my sister's red station wagon, where I escape into a deep sleep.

————

This time at the geriatric psychiatric hospital, a different psychiatrist supervises my case. Each morning he wheels a podium-mounted computer into my room and angles his equipment perpendicular to my bed, his face remaining invisible and tethered to distance.

His focus when asking me how I feel?

The computer screen and keyboard, used to record my response.

My medications are different: Drugs for sleep and lithium are added to the antidepressant I've taken since my first stay. A benzo becomes part of my regimen, too.

Although my system rejected medications during the previous spring, for some unknown reason they now tolerate them well.

Some things haven't changed. Three times a week, I'm treated with electroconvulsive therapy. I pot a plant, walk the hallways for recreation, feigning interest in plaques and pictures, and sit on chairs, stretching during guided armchair yoga. And, sitting on those same chairs, I play rhythm instruments once a week to upbeat music that irritates me.

I leave the hospital with appointments for more ECT treatments and one to see the reptilian psychiatrist I was assigned to for outpatient treatment as well prescriptions.

And another potted plant.

———

As the end of 2009 approaches, I'm wondering why I'm beginning to feel better.

I believe the new drug regimen is responsible for my improvement rather than ECT. So, believing no one could know if I'm right without testing my theory, I ask my outpatient psychiatrist if he'll sanction my withdrawal from ECT and supervise the process.

He refuses.

Scared, yet believing in my own judgment, I terminate treatments myself, taking charge for the first time since Lyme disease struck. A part of me is reaching for tendrils of lost personal power and confidence in myself.

The next time I see my outpatient psychiatrist, after we're seated in his office facing each other across a dark wood desk, I announce without preamble, "I stopped ECT. And, I'm feeling well!"

"Why didn't you ask me first?"

"I did.

"You refused to work with me."

We don't talk much more.

While I watch him write a prescription, the awkward silence makes my skin prickle.

When he's finished, he stands, reaching his hand across the desk. With a cordial look, masking my distaste, I take the prescription, seeking the psychiatrist's face while preparing to say a rote thank-you.

I don't expect what I see.

Peering over the rim of his glasses, his piercing eyes overflow with concern.

"These pills could hurt you," he warns, waving the prescription back and forth.

———

On a winter day, I'm sitting in my car at a railroad track, black-and-white gates blocking my progress, lithium flattening me into a dull mood. I'm feeling as dense as the clouds hiding the blue sky.

Ding. Ding. Ding.

The warning is hypnotic.

A train chugs forward and then stops. Metal clangs. Freight cars jerk. Squealing, rusted wheels slowly turn, moving the train backward. More clanging. More spasms of metal forced to connect.

I glance to the passenger seat, where I placed an orange plastic container just filled to the brim by a pharmacist with the antidepressant that, according to the outpatient psychiatrist I've been seeing, could "hurt me."

I pick up the bottle with my right hand, bringing the lethal drug before my eyes, considering suicide.

Twirling the bottle with my thumb and forefinger, I muse:

I could use these to attempt suicide again.

Drugs haven't worked out for me, though.

Now that's an understatement!

Humm.

Maybe, just maybe, I could find other ways to cope with anxiety and disease.

I reach my hand over to the passenger seat, open my fist, and release my grip on the pills. I release my grip on suicide as an ultimate answer to escape misery.

Why at this particular moment?

I'm not certain.

Could be because I signed another agreement with Brenda, my therapist, to contact her if thoughts of suicide arose. I'd done that when I first began working with her, yet I did so without making a commitment. This time was different. There was a real promise at work. And merely the signing spoke of hope, too.

Or, perhaps, because I've been reading her book. Just partway through, I've already read stories of individuals who stood up and took charge of their lives, and despite all odds, healed themselves.

Maybe my change in direction happened because, until just now, I'd only sought fixes outside myself. And when taking charge of ECT treatment, I experienced a trace of my own power to influence an outcome, enough to believe I have inner resources I can trust.

Who knows?

What's important is that the moment I let go of the pills, I begin accepting life. Accepting life as my go-to alternative, no matter the challenges.

A speck of hope glimmers in the dark, brightened by the contrast of tragedy and despair, that has ruled my life for so long.

Ripened, made ready to receive the gift of health, one foot inches forward, tiptoeing out of darkness, the other seeking the light of infinite possibilities. Remnants of my past hang in the balance, preparing to nurture the future.

I'm standing on the threshold of my dream to be well.

PART II
THE GIFT
OF THE CIRCLE

*Hope emerging in the midst of tragedy kindles new beginnings and
sparks the soul to manifest the improbable.*

THE WATCHER

During the eight-year period of time when Carolyn was physically and emotionally ill from the catastrophic effects of Lyme disease, she continued avoiding stillness and cultivating a relationship with me. Her therapist recommended that she practice mindfulness meditation daily to enhance her immune system's functioning; however, for a time, she chose not to follow that advice.

That said, she was vaguely aware of my presence simply because she'd meditated years before. She could still hear my "whisper voice" now and then, as I'm hard to forget once someone becomes aware of me.

One day, Carolyn began meditating again. And when she did, she was still highly agitated; staying quiet even for a brief amount of time was a huge challenge for her. But she hung in there, and I'm glad she did.

Even though the time she spent meditating each day wasn't long, I began to build up a "head of steam" while she kept searching for answers to help herself heal.

Besides being physically ill for so long, she was emotionally fragile. Her thinking was fraught with habitual, unnecessary fear. Without emotional health, she was bereft of the ability to guide herself toward wellness.

For eight long, tedious years she'd spent much time and money searching for a solution for healing both Lyme and anxiety. She had no idea her solution was so close at hand.

I was instrumental in helping her discover her pathway to freedom. Once that happened, she started to walk free of both Lyme disease and emotional imbalance.

What happened?

Calling on my relationship with The Divine and a stroke of my own genius, I prompted a revelation: Thoughts affect feelings. And they're never permanent. As Carolyn began to awaken to those truths, she was able to experience the sensations of feelings arising, and then receding from the shore of awareness.

Soon, she began to trust the process of change. To expect anxiety to subside—when she remained present in the moment.

That was a monumental breakthrough! Being aware that she didn't have to stay stuck in anxiety, where she'd been shackled for eight torturous years, was the beginning of her journey toward wholeness.

Before I step aside to let Carolyn tell more of her story, I want to mention one more lesson I can take credit for teaching her as a result of the time she dedicated to cultivating a relationship with me: Nothing has innate value. Nothing has value except for the importance we assign to a living being or nonliving entity.

To capture the essence of my teaching, Carolyn coined the word "isness," meaning that emotional sway is established by perceptions. The dimensions of value for every person, place, and thing is solely a matter of individual conditioning.

She'll soon show you how that concept played out for her as she resurrected herself from a living hell.

I won't be with her forever. As she grows, she'll realize one day that "I" am not what she thinks now, and I'll disappear. That prospect is years away, though, so I'll be around until the end of this journey.

For now, I've said enough.

I'm going to do my thing again—be still and watch . . .

THE WARRIOR
TAKES FLIGHT

Come to the edge.
We might fall.
Come to the edge.
It's too high!
COME TO THE EDGE!
And they came,
and he pushed,
and they flew.[1]

—Christopher Logue

Imagine sitting in a cozy room tucked into a comfortable armchair, holding a book in your hands. Thoughtful, you've paused from reading to gaze out a nearby window. Bright, clear sunlight streaming into your space silhouettes trees standing barren in the bitter cold. Your wandering mind wishes you could find a way to brighten your mood to match the radiance that seems to be calling to you.

Then, you drift further, remembering someone who died— someone you loved. Someone whose death left you feeling empty.

Remaining pensive, you bring your attention back to the book still in your hands. You're somehow prompted to think about the dear loved one you miss more than anyone you've ever lost—and the past you shared together with reckless abandon.

With a mourning heart and eyes overflowing with sorrow, you

wish that person, who was so full of life, would come back to be with you once again.

Then, the hairs on your neck stand up. Goose bumps tingle on your arms.

A sensation urges you to look toward the doorway.

Standing there, looking right at you, is your loved one—the one you thought was dead.

At first, you can't believe what you're seeing.

Then you don't care.

Leaping from your chair, you rush to embrace the one you've missed so much. The one you thought you'd never see again.

Vibrant energy fills you with joy. The air ripples with your laughter. Your eyes, once full of sorrow, spill over with gratitude.

The emptiness you've felt for so long begins to fill with the warmth of life and wonder.

———

In my bedroom, in Janet and Mike's house on a cold winter's morning, I sit tucked in my mother's armchair, gazing out the window beside me, awestruck at the enormity of all I've read in *You Can Beat the Odds*, a book published just a few months ago and written by my therapist, Brenda.[2]

Holding the book in my hands, I think about the concepts she wrote about. Then I notice something remarkable: I'm calm, which is unusual, since I've suffered from roiling, gut-wrenching anxiety for eight long years.

Even though I don't feel anxious, depression still enshrouds me with a gloom darker than the maw of a tomb. I miss my vibrant, even-tempered, courageous self more than anyone knows, except for maybe my sister and my therapist. The combination of fragile emotions and Lyme disease has crippled me, vesting me with a self-appointed membership in the cadre of the living dead.

Even so, this morning I continue searching for a way to heal, somehow believing there must be a way.

Still holding *You Can Beat the Odds*, what I've read swirls in my head, coalescing into meaning. Energy builds. Gloominess begins to evaporate. I feel expectant.

In seconds, I'm prompted by something subconscious to search my memory, to go on a quest for the common thread in circumstances when my anxiety suddenly subsided—like just a few moments ago.

First, I think back to 1983, when I calmed down soon after being admitted to a hospital to determine the origin of terror I felt. I'd been frantic, trying to figure out what was wrong with me. Once I thought I was safe in the hands of those who could tell me, I stopped worrying.

Then I remember I didn't feel anxious just a few years ago while intently focused on passages from Eckhart Tolle's *The Power of Now*. Being in the moment, engrossed in what I was reading, had halted my incessant thoughts about my dire circumstances.

Then, my probing mind arrives at the memory of what happened soon after rereading *The Feeling Good Handbook* at my therapist's suggestion.[3] At the beginning, the author, Dr. David Burns, identifies troublemaking thoughts as a major anxiety-provoking culprit. And then he directs the reader to notice what one is thinking when anxiety surfaces.

After I began revisiting Dr. Burns' work, I remembered jotting down my thoughts once when I couldn't stop feeling anxious. When my mind was intently focused on discovery, I felt tranquil.

Just like I feel now, I think, as I sit still captivated by what I've just read in *You Can Beat the Odds*.

Without realizing what's happened, I've inched my way to the edge of a significant discovery.

A miracle beckons.

Then, an explosion of scintillating insight startles me.

I'm instantly alive—wide awake—vibrant with energy, brimming with insightfulness.

I see now! I get it! I have to change my thinking—my mind's focus. My thoughts have been everywhere except the present. I've been mourning my losses so much, I've forgotten to see how well I'm loved and being taken care of by my sister. My thoughts have kept me agitated: forecasting a hopeless future, perpetually planning suicide, believing I'm a hopeless, helpless, useless bother. No wonder I've been anxious for so long.

I pause, allowing revelation to weigh anchor.

Then my eyes leap to Brenda's book, and another exciting realization bursts forth:

I can heal myself. I've found the way! Mind-body medicine. Why not! You Can Beat the Odds *is a handbook—a handbook for healing! This very book holds the key to enhancing my immune system. And the key to stabilizing my wild-eyed emotions. Right here, right now, I hold the pathway to my recovery.*

I've believed all along that if I could stop anxiety's rampage, I might be able to reclaim my physical health. With a sick body—and a disabled mind—I've thought of myself as a helpless victim of circumstances.

Until just this moment.

The female warrior I can sometimes become knows that, in mere seconds, I've transformed myself from being powerless to becoming my former self—a conqueror. To being the woman who could build her own house and ride her bicycle from Charleston to Central Florida, the one who canoed solo—more than once—fifty miles through Utah's Green River wilderness: the woman who will now heal herself!

In a split second, I've come full circle—returned from the dead.

Warm joy splashes my heart; tears of gratitude spill from my eyes.

My skin tingles, my legs can't stay still.

The promise of life propels me out of my mother's chair, across the house, and into my sister's bedroom where she's sitting at her computer. I burst into her space, spilling the news that I know how to heal. After hurriedly answering questions while hugging her, I rush back to my own bedroom.

There, to etch the date in my memory, I write, "January 4, 2010: I returned from the dead after receiving The Gift of the Circle."

ON EAGLE'S WINGS

After noting the date I was bequeathed the gift of life—my pathway home to the woman I am meant to be—I take a few moments to reread the last few pages of *You Can Beat the Odds*.

Once again, I'm awed by the author's eloquent ending: "We can apply the principles of healing to every aspect of our lives . . . and experience a more congruent way of living, a more harmonious way of being in our own body. In doing so, we will make room for miracles in our lives."[1]

Yes!

Promise for my future washes over me. More gratitude for what's just happened makes my heart feel warm and full. I'm spellbound by wonder. I play "On Eagle's Wings" over and over, soaring with the song's message of hope.

Reverence for my circumstances emerges in my thoughts: an incomprehensible number of choices executed by me and others has brought me to this moment in time.

My therapist finished her book soon after my tragic experiences in psychiatric hospitals, and after I'd spent thousands of dollars to pay for antidotes for Lyme disease that came to naught.

I put aside the bottle of pills while waiting for a train to pass, thinking maybe I could find a better way to deal with my misery than suicide.

And what about all the events leading to my living in Georgia with my sister, locating me near Brenda, who could teach me how to heal myself?

Have I been led from birth to the moment of resurrection from the living dead, to be right here, right now?

I feel like that.

Choice after choice, made by me and countless others, appear to have influenced my arrival at each moment in time. I sense connectedness to others in a way I've never realized.

The import of that concept resonates with me. A mysterious sense of order manifests that feels somehow orchestrated by Divine Timing, Grace . . . and Love.

While swaddled in self-nurturing, I come to believe I've been ripened. Opened by adversity.

Although I don't believe I was meant to be sick, my experiences with sorrow and disability seem to have prepared me to be receptive.

Open to The Light.

I've never felt like this, ethereal, rebirthed through the passage of pain and misery.

Joy splashes all over my future now, which seems kaleidoscopic, shimmering with a jewel-toned vibrancy. I feel borne on eagle's wings, eager to create meaning and purpose. Eager to make my face shine like the sun. Even though I'm far from well, I know with certainty that I soon will be.

I'm puzzled, though. Why me?

While living with my sister, I have returned to the Methodist religion of my childhood, seeking comfort in the known. When all that seemed to matter unraveled and left me feeling as though an abyss of loneliness would swallow me whole, I found comfort in holding on to something familiar. Although I no longer relate to an anthropomorphic God, I so resonate with the concept of a Divine force orchestrating certain aspects of my life. Even so, figuring out the manner in which goodness is meted out by an omniscient entity is beyond me.

Why am I on my way to freedom while others dream of rising and can't find a way? Yes, I've done my share of seeking and searching. After each time I tried to kill myself and wasn't successful, I got right back to the task of searching for help. Even so, that can't explain everything.

I'm humbled by my newfound promise. I feel honored, too. Yet there's a big part of me that doesn't feel deserving of The Gift.

———

My mind continues to explore my feelings. Thoughts weaving their way to a consciousness arrive at the understanding that, through my own suffering, I've become aware of those who are struggling to heal and can't.

I'll never forget about them. They will be a part of my heart forever.

And I know that, for myself and for them, I must learn how to heal myself.

Then, maybe, just maybe, I can return the blessing of my wellness, showing at least some of them how to get well.

I stop reveling in my emotions and the future, knowing I've gotten ahead of myself. I've got some work to do. I've got to get well now that I know how.

Even so, for a few moments longer, I bathe in the glorious feelings that have sent anxiety and depression elsewhere—for the time being. Then, I reach for a yellow legal pad and a ruler, both resting on a nearby bookshelf.

I'm certain the mind-body medicine strategies I've just read about in *You Can Beat the Odds* will rouse my immune system into peak performance. The supporting research and the stories of those who've used them to recover from even the most dire diseases is convincing enough. And the endorsements of the book by Dr. Bernie Siegel and Joan Borysenko, two renowned proponents of the mind-body's healing efficacy, have grabbed my attention!

What isn't certain is my capacity to stay on track with a healing plan.

True to my nature, I prepare a checklist to seal my commitment to a daily routine for getting well. First I draw a grid on the legal pad: a wide column on the left for each healing strategy, fourteen narrow columns on the right for each day of the coming two weeks.

Then I start at the beginning of *You Can Beat the Odds*, turning the pages until I find every immune system–enhancing strategy I intend to employ for my physical and emotional benefit.

Excitement builds each time I find one and read again the related research.

Although I'm itching to get started, I stay put until I'm done with my list: imagery, stream-of-consciousness journaling, affirmations, vibrations in the form of music or autogenics, exercise, and mindfulness meditation.

For years I've believed my body knows how to heal. Although I've read a lot about it, I couldn't find comprehensive directions for facilitating that process until now. While marveling at the simplicity of the methods I'll be using, I acknowledge that the simple can be powerful, like a deep, slow-moving river caressing rocks, carving a majestic canyon in the wilderness.

Before I finish making my list, I add a few of my own reminders that I sense will be important to keep myself on track: Devotions. Supplements. Reading.

Reading?

I figure I'll need to keep my beliefs grounded in sound theory supported by contemporary research, so I plan to read material that reinforces the concept that my mind and body hold powerful healing resources. And that I'm innately capable of changing both.

———

While reflecting on my daily plan that's now in the form of a checklist, I recall reading about a workshop facilitator who stood behind a table at the front of a classroom; on the table she had a flask filled with beach sand along with two large, glass, wide-mouthed jars beside small piles of different-sized gray rocks and pebbles.

When the facilitator began, she put as many large rocks as she could into one of the jars. Then, she placed small pebbles amongst the rocks. Finally, she poured beach sand into the jar, every now and then shaking the container to make room for more.

When the first jar was tightly packed, she picked up the second jar, reversing the process.

First, she filled the jar with sand.

After glancing back and forth at the rocks and pebbles, then the jar, a puzzled look wrinkled her brow.

Then she threw up her hands, feigning frustration.

I figure I'll have good reason to remember that lesson in the months to come. Disciplining myself, making certain I first occupy my time with the big rocks—the daily mind-body healing routine I've planned for myself—will bring challenges. Because I've experienced temptations to avoid disciplining myself in the past when training for physical adventures, I suspect I'll sometimes be enticed to fill up my time with pebbles and sand. And, I figure I'll feel oppressed, too, when holding myself accountable for my own healing.

When, not if, that happens, I want to be ready with a reality check, so at the top of my first to-do list I write: "A life free of Lyme and despair *is* worth any effort. Eagle's wings won't take me anywhere if I don't do my part."

I look at what I've written for a few moments, puzzled by the juxtaposition of discipline and freedom: curbing impulses to yield liberation?

Quite a paradox!

———

When I finally finish creating my to-do list, I'm more than ready to take my first steps toward wholeness. Donning a flannel-lined windbreaker, boots, a cheery, bright-orange fleece hat, and scarf, then grabbing my media player and earbuds, I bolt out the front door, rush down the steps, and bounce onto the pavement in front of the house.

Walking at first, then twirling, I dance to the rhythms of bluegrass, mariachi music, and an oh-so-happy happy heart!

Even though I'm not capable of going far, I begin a journey like no other.

I don't have a clue in those high-flying moments that my passage ahead will be strewn with obstacles. That my feelings will soon plummet, and that sometimes I'll feel raw, fragile, too transparent. And that memories of the past eight years will terrorize me day and night.

I don't know in those first exhilarating moments that I still have much to learn about the nature of my anxiety and quelling irrational thoughts. Nor that I'll be compelled to learn how to celebrate the beginning of my new life while facing up to the tragic events wrought by disease—and childhood trauma.

When Lyme exploded my life into broken dreams, piercing my soul with shards of torture, I didn't have the emotional strength, nor the courage, to work with my feelings; the fetid pain I rammed down my throat rotted in my guts. And, even if I'd found a therapist to help me process my feelings—someone like Brenda—I don't think I would have been receptive to the idea that mind-body medicine could heal me, despite my beliefs. In fact, during the three years I'd worked with her before her book was published, I hadn't fully committed to following her directions.

During the ensuing months, I'll come to believe even more that I've been ripened by adversity for transformation. All the grief-stricken disappointments over failed treatments, the misguided therapies in psychiatric hospitals, and the out-of-pocket medical expenses at times threatening to bankrupt me, created an opening for Light, adversity's crucible, to enter my doom-darkened soul.

When the long road ahead presents me with more challenges than I think I can overcome, and discouragement threatens to cripple me again, I'm led to pause just long enough to notice how far I've come. Joy baptizes me again, and for a while I'll dance anew in the sparkling rain of hope.

And persevere.

At the journey's end, I'll come to know that if existing as a member of the living dead, writhing with Lyme and my broken emotions, hadn't been so rugged and shadowed, I might not have arrived at the pinnacle of healing to dance with the stunning spectacle of Light celebrating my homecoming—my wholeness.

I've a long way to go before that happens.

I began my healing journey by setting down my intention to heal in the form of a to-do list, then I danced and twirled to the music on my iPod, celebrating my resurrection. Now I'm ready to be taught an essential lesson.

My teacher?

Crystal. The unassuming former inmate, comely and young. A messenger bearing a lesson rippling from the epicenter of The Gift of the Circle.

THE CRYSTAL
EPIPHANY

When hearts reach across boundaries
to share unadorned love,
miracles of humanity unfold.

Three days after receiving The Gift, I have a morning appointment with my pastor, Rene Watson. Snow covers the ground; black ice slicking our driveway a day ago has melted, so I figure I'll be able drive safely to see her.

I scheduled the appointment in December when the weight of depression felt like a demon's heavy boot was pinning me facedown into a murky swamp. Finding the energy for the slightest movement was a struggle. I'd experienced depression before, yet never like that—not during the past eight years of illness, nor any other time. Although I wasn't certain why this depression was so oppressive, I thought perhaps my brain was rebounding because I suddenly halted shock treatments, or that I was suffering side effects from the prescription drugs I still took to temper my emotions.

Who knows.

My feelings scared me, especially because I knew my therapist was traveling and unavailable. Reaching out to the psychiatrist I'd been seeing as an outpatient for prescription refills would most likely result in medication changes or a recommendation for more shock treatments. I was done with his scant choices for helping me with my emotional challenges.

So I called my pastor, Rene, believing that merely talking with her about my feelings would help. And I was deliberately strengthening my tentative resolve to seek another way out of misery besides suicide.

When I called Rene, there wasn't room in her schedule to see me right away; even though I felt desperate, I didn't push her to squeeze me in. We found time for an appointment a few weeks out. Merely knowing I would soon be able to open up about the way I was feeling gave me the courage to hang on.

When the time comes for me to meet with Rene, the urgency to get to her office weights my foot to the gas pedal.

———

I get to Rene's office ready to burst!

After a receptionist announces my arrival, Rene comes to greet me.

Smiling, she silently ushers me to her office, where we sit facing each other in burgundy-print, wing-backed chairs with no desk blocking connection.

Seconds after we're seated, feelings overwhelm me. I feel a need to hold Rene's hands—to feel a concrete, supporting presence. When I reach out, yearning for solace, she takes my hands in her own. Compassion fills her gentle brown eyes, telling me of her concern.

When I see her response, tears erupt. Weeping, I bend over, laying my head on our clasped hands. My emotions choke back the words begging to be spoken.

"What's wrong?" she asks, handing me a tissue.

"There's nothing wrong. Everything's right!"

She's mystified, of course. "What do you mean?"

With speech made ragged by nose-blowing, I tell her about The Gift, the promise of healing. I tell her I know Lyme is backing off: "I can eat fruits and vegetables without burning my stomach. Brain fog that has muddled my thinking is finally clearing. My energy is returning too."

In the background of this otherwise poignant scene, a hint of humor plays. Only six months ago, I met Rene for the first time when she came to visit me at my bedside in a psychiatric hospital. Just a few months later, she was part of a group rescuing me in a distant motel where I was sequestered, poised to cut my veins with box cutters if a drug overdose didn't kill me first.

In less than three months since, I'm sitting in her office, avowing The Gift of the Circle's blessings, weeping all the while.

To her credit, she doesn't doubt I'm on the way to recovery. After all, she *is* in the business of miracles.

The gut-wrenching weeping continues, and I'm awash with awareness of my suffering over the past eight years; at the same time, I'm thrilled in every cell of my body by the hope dancing inside me.

Seeing the razor-sharp contrast between the destruction in my past and the promise of wellness in the future, I keep speaking of my immeasurable blessing—a chance to live a robust, adventurous life again.

Then, more puzzling feelings surface from this emotional cauldron: "I feel lower than a pus-eating maggot. I'm unworthy of The Gift I've been given."

The truth is, I'd never been aware of my intrinsic value.

I mistakenly believed I mattered to myself and others only when I got gold stars on my report card, earned college degrees, landed jobs with good salaries, achieved superb performance evaluations; when I had extraordinary friends, volunteer projects going on; and when robust health allowed for incredible stamina.

When Lyme disease shredded my life, and my superficial—and tenuous—definition of my self-worth disintegrated, my leavings seemed valueless—worth less than a heap of stinking garbage. Despair yelling of worthlessness taunted me over and over again: when I mattered so little to myself, how could I possibly have imagined mattering to anyone else?

Although my sister, friends, and someone who thought of me

as her mother expressed their compassion for me with tender care during my illness, I didn't understand why they loved me . . .

———

After my internal medicine doctor finds a unique pharmaceutical cocktail to quell my anxiety, I'm able to muster enough energy to volunteer at a detention center. This makes me feel like I'm worth something again.

Eager to feel purposeful, I'm sitting in a cold, hard, dark-blue plastic and metal chair. Along with my friend Marilyn and another woman, we're locked inside a windowless room painted a glossy, agitating yellow. We await the arrival of female inmates soon to be escorted here by guards to learn how to knit or crochet. We're hoping to establish influential relationships with the women while we teach.

Each week, the usual array of females comes to be with us, sometimes as many as ten. They are mostly white, ranging in ages from early twenties to late fifties, jailed mainly due to charges directly or indirectly related to alcohol and drug abuse. More than half are repeat offenders.

The women wear either solid-colored orange or green uniforms—orange on those awaiting trial, green when they've been found not guilty and are awaiting the paperwork for release. Or when they've been sentenced and will soon be transported during the night at an unannounced date to a Georgia State penitentiary. Many of the women have gap-toothed smiles, missing front teeth primarily as a result of both using harsh drugs and eating what's available for those with meager limited financial resources.

While we're with the inmates, crochet hooks and knitting needles move in rhythmic motion, belying the turmoil represented by their histories. One by one, as they get comfortable with us, they tell horrifying stories of chaotic, destructive family lives, rife with sexual abuse, leaving little doubt about their underlying emotional turmoil.

When I'm with them their tales of arrests and criminal charges remind me of my own youth, when I, too, could have been jailed for illegal, unwise behavior: shoplifting, or driving after drinking enough alcohol to make my eyes bounce around. Although I never sold my body like some of them, I used sex indiscriminately, and sometimes for ulterior motives.

I'm sometimes tempted to feel superior to the inmates we visit; usually, though, I can't. My heart pesters me with reminders of my own past until I acknowledge that I'm no better than they are. I'm just more fortunate.

One day, when a guard opens the locked door to let inmates come inside the room, one of the women slips by us unnoticed until the group settles down. When my eyes scan the room, they're drawn to someone we haven't met before who's sitting near the far corner against the back wall. She's in her middle twenties, markedly pretty with long, curly, dark-brown hair framing her oval face.

Her large, brown eyes jerk in their sockets, unable to return my gaze. Darting from side to side, they seem to scream out gut-roiling terror. Leaning her chair against the wall, she appears to be getting as far away from us as possible. As much as an escape to safety as she can manage.

Soon, I notice the other inmates tormenting her with derogatory remarks they think I don't understand. They seek to disguise their intentions with laughter. Wringing hands and a trembling body tell of the pain they've inflicted on Crystal.

When we ask her to tell us her name, her head lowers. She whispers, "Crystal."

The few times Crystal comes to be with us, she sits in the same defensive location, saying little no matter how much we try to engage with her.

All that changes one day.

Before anyone else sits, she plops down in a chair next to me and announces that she's going to be released—without a trial. She slaps a scrap of paper on the nearby table, commanding Marilyn and me to write down our phone numbers.

I'm rattled. Unsure of what I should do—until I remember why I came here in the first place.

Even so, when I give Crystal my phone number I forget about any common ground we might share. I don't realize that feelings of superiority have leaked from my hidden arrogance:

Talking with Crystal will be a real trip.

I'm not sure I want to listen to mindless chatter.

What if she finds out where I live? Then steals from me? Hurts me?

Struggling to uphold my desire to be helpful, I push my fears aside and write down my cell phone number, even though I believe I'm entering into a one-way arrangement.

———

For two years after Crystal leaves the detention center in 2008, she calls me every day except for the rare instances when she's too blitzed on drugs to talk or when she can't pay for cell phone minutes.

Frequently she invites me to visit where she's living. I've been too sick to drive the forty miles to be with her. But over our months of chatting on the phone, I've learned of her tragic, mind-twisting background.

When Crystal was only thirteen, her drug-addicted mother pimped Crystal's body, selling time slots with her daughter as if she were an inflatable doll.

When Crystal was fourteen, her mother forced her to quit school to care for her younger brothers.

More torture continued when her father demanded: "Take your brothers into your bedroom, Crystal. Teach them what sex is all about."

Like her mother, Crystal eventually started abusing drugs—meth, coke, and anything else she could buy with the money she made by selling her own body.

At fifteen, she gave birth to a son. Before his first birthday, he was taken from her after she was convicted of a felony. While serving time in prison, she was diagnosed with schizophrenia and bipolar disorder, then drugged with a ton of mind-dulling prescription medications. As crippling as anything else twisting her, she was told by authorities, in and out of prison, that she would be forever emotionally disabled. That she could never work again.

I don't believe any of that. Never have. Crystal isn't compromised beyond rehabilitation.

She's savvy enough to convince healthcare providers to prescribe sedatives and pain-killing drugs when she only needs them to feed her addiction. She knows how to negotiate profitable deals selling drugs on the street. She has completed and filed the paperwork necessary to qualify for Social Security disability benefits. And she fools her probation officer into thinking she's drug free by abstaining long enough to pass urine tests. Or to take drugs that aren't screened for.

Although I talk with Crystal often, I'm not able to inspire her to attend Narcotics Anonymous meetings. I've tried to reverse her self-deprecating thinking, sometimes telling her that she's smart, pretty. That she's got the brains to earn her GED.

Although she calls me daily, I don't feel like I'm important to her, or anyone else, for that matter. So, I'm bewildered by her response to one of my encouraging remarks: "You're the only one who's ever believed in me. I know more about dying than I do about living."

Breathless, she then asks if she can call me *Mother*.

Even so, I still fail to grasp how much I matter to her.

———

I've returned from my time with Rene. Sitting in my bedroom, I reflect on our visit.

My cell phone interrupts my musing. Rushing, I rummage in my daypack, answering before the call goes to voicemail.

"Hello."

"Hi."

Crystal always expects me to know she's the one calling.

For a long time, I've wanted to pick her up at her home in the North Georgia mountains and then go together to a nearby town for lunch. I've been thinking about how I'll get to Crystal's home, knowing I'll be forced to drive more than a mile on a rutted dirt road with steep drop-offs and switchbacks in dense woods. But, because ice and snow have melted where I live, I assume they're gone near her, too, making for safe passage.

In a split second I learn the fallacy of my thinking: Without preliminaries, Crystal blurts, "Don't come tomorrow!"

"What are you talking about?"

"Ice. The road to my house is dangerous. I don't want you to go off a cliff and get yourself killed. I don't want to lose my best friend."

With the light touch of an angel, Crystal's remark penetrates deep into my soul where no one else can reach, filling me with emotion.

I'm able to remain calm until we finish talking.

Then her message becomes Light-borne:

Crystal cherishes me. She cherishes me even though all I've given her are broken pieces of a wounded heart.

She loves me anyway.

She loves me.

I sob.

What if I'd killed myself? My death would have tortured Crystal— another tragedy in her short life. I didn't know. I didn't know I mattered so much to her.

How could I?

Cradled in the lingering Light of Crystal's message, I see there's more to understand:

Rene. The Gift of the Circle. Feeling unworthy to receive such a blessing.

I've believed so many cankerous, mood-darkening lies about myself. Am I really worthless? Useless? A bother? Can I turn that around? Can I find the same kind of love for myself that Crystal has for me?

I'm drawn further into The Light with my questioning. Crystal's unadorned love has, indeed, touched my soul, warming my heart, opening me to the possibility of a renaissance.

Then, a shimmering epiphany bursts into view, inviting me to learn what I must one day know if I am to heal. What I must learn if I am to come home to myself:

No matter what I've done, no matter what I can and can't do, no matter what I believe or what I've been told, I am a treasure greater than gold.

I am precious merely because I breathe.

I am priceless merely because I exist.

TENDER MESSAGES

On our skin, as on a screen, the gamut of life's
experiences is projected: emotions surge, sorrows
penetrate, and beauty finds its depth.[1]

Where touching begins, there love and humanity
also begin . . .[2]

                           —Ashley Montagu, 1905–1999

A few days after experiencing the epiphany evoked by Crystal's loving message, snow quilts the earth and snuggles me into the house for more than thirty-six hours straight.

Often I sit in my mother's armchair reflecting.

Thoughts about Divine Timing and Grace, so apparent recently, weave their way in and out of time.

I'm a spiritual person, but not by virtue of sitting many boring hours during childhood, squirming in hard-backed pews.

Rather, I found my connection to the Divine through witnessing the grandeur, order, and symbolism in nature. I bow to the power and mystery of a Divinity I feel, much like the Sioux, who called their Great Spirit Wakan Tanka, roughly translated as "great mystery." Avoiding dogmatic assumptions about a spiritual domain too vast for me to understand, I leave others to freely seek their own existential definitions.

I sometimes wonder if I've created my beliefs to comfort myself. Even so, I embrace them, continuing to honor a Divine presence I feel working in my life, especially now.

In the end, what matters most is how my spiritual beliefs play out in my thoughts, words, and actions. The rest seems inconsequential.

Besides thinking about my spiritual beliefs on these snowy winter days, I ponder the veils of false identity, the "gold stars" that obscured the tender reality of my self-worth. And I marvel at how the shattering of my life and the illusions I'd created to feel worthy somehow opened me to receive Crystal's message, a message that led me to the trailhead of the pathway to understanding that my self-worth is innate.

Gratitude for my humble friend and her love warms me. Gratitude bathes me in wonder at The Gift of the Circle too. Gratitude paints a deep appreciation for the world around me no longer colored in dark shadows. And gratitude spills from eyes that can now grasp the enormity of my blessings I couldn't perceive during my illness.

Many walked beside me, long and far, to save me from a rampaging disease and myself: Janet, my sister. Friends. Rene. Doctors. My therapist, Brenda Stockdale.

Although I felt desperate and alone during my struggle with Lyme, they were nearby, offering patient kindness. Because my mind was focused on nerve-jerking fears and self-deprecation, my heart was blinded to their loving, caring presences and to the bountiful circumstances existing throughout my illness.

The gratitude I feel for those who stayed with me until I found my way will find expression in the months to come. I will thank many. Each for a unique, intangible gift to my well-being. Each for a treasure of untold worth.

My sister, Janet, saved my life. I wouldn't be sitting in Mom's chair, enjoying the luxury of thinking and feeling, had she not persisted in searching for me when death beckoned in a distant motel room. Janet gave me a home when I was too ill to care for myself. She felt deep sorrow when I was critically ill and yet another treatment failed to halt Lyme's rampage. She was overwhelmed with anguish each time I tried to kill myself. And she endured heartache, watching me suffer the aftermath of each shock treatment.

When I thank those so generous with their time and concern, I don't thank Janet first. For reasons I will soon uncover, I thank her last.

Before I honor my sister in a simple, profound moment of new-found freedom, some memorable events circle my expressions of gratitude to others.

———

My therapist, Brenda, and Dr. Milton have been by my side for a long time, awaiting my healing from Lyme disease and emotional illness with abiding kindness and hope.

Their offices are side by side in the Advanced Medicine suite. They're married, yet I found each one separately under radically different circumstances.

Remembering how I discovered each of them softens me into an innocent sort of vulnerability, opening my soul to feel that I've been nurtured once again by Divine Love and the great mystery of Divine Timing and Grace.

One night, just as I was turning out my light to sleep, my right shoulder dislocated for the third time in just a few months. In agony from the pain and the emotional discomfort of having to inconvenience my sister with yet another emergency room visit, I trudged into the living room where she was enjoying a TV program.

As soon as she saw me holding my right arm close to my chest, she knew what was up. We were soon on the way to the hospital.

After a miserable wait, the emergency room triage nurse finally called for me. Once I was seated beside her in a cubicle, she asked me routine questions. My answer to one of them elicited a response from her that made the horrific pain in my shoulder seem inconsequential: "Do you have any diseases?"

"Yes. Yes I do. Lyme disease."

Because the nurse appeared to be completely healthy, she astounded me, remarking, "I had Lyme disease. This time last year I was in a wheelchair."

Scooting to the edge of my seat with an urgency I couldn't hide, I asked, "Where did you get help?"

"Dr. Michael Milton. His office isn't far from here. I've got his card. In a minute I'll make you a copy."

Even though I called his office the morning after my emergency room visit, I was unable to see him immediately. He was booked months ahead, so I took what I could get.

Before my shoulder dislocated, I'd already scheduled a session with Brenda.

How did I find her?

Although I didn't respond to the eight weeks of alternative medical treatment administered by the chiropractor I thought I'd found accidentally, something else turned up that was life-changing. During the introductory session with him, he briefly described his treatment protocol. Excited about what I'd heard, I asked if he'd helped anyone with Lyme disease.

That's when Brenda entered the picture.

The chiropractor told me his treatment protocol had been instrumental in healing Brenda Stockdale, a psychologist.

Full of excitement and a sense of promise, I asked the chiropractor to give my contact information to Brenda, and to request that she call me.

What a package deal I'd have if I someone who has healed from Lyme disease could encourage me to do the same thing and help me with my emotions, too!

My first appointment with Brenda was in October of 2006. During my time with her, she didn't mention Dr. Milton as a resource. She couldn't. Ethics prevailed.

Now, four years later, I sit reflecting on my experiences with both Brenda and Dr. Milton.

Before Dr. Milton started to treat me, using integrative, functional medicine, focusing on systemic balance, I could barely sit upright in an office chair long enough to see him.

I'm noticeably different now when I see him. Full of energy and beaming with happiness, I vibrate with a sense of expectancy.

And Brenda. She's been extraordinarily patient with my trauma-ridden, slow-moving healing process, made more sluggish by self-induced darkness. Despair that closed the door that has now been opened by Brenda's messages of research-based hope.

One poignant, vivid moment with Dr. Milton plays like a video recording in my memory: After my last suicide attempt, I called Brenda to find out if she'd continue to work with me. My heart pounded, fearing she'd say no.

Relief surged through my body when she agreed to schedule an appointment. I expected her to greet me as usual for that visit, standing in the open doorway to the waiting room. Instead, the receptionist told me Brenda was waiting for me in her office. I wished I had a shroud to cover the shame I felt as I plodded down the hallway toward her, shoulders drooping.

Dr. Milton glimpsed me from the open door of his office. He rose and walked toward me, arms opened wide.

I leaned into his chest, sensing his compassion.

His words soothed my shame. "I love you, Carolyn."

Tears well up in my eyes when I think about that moment with Dr. Milton. And whenever I think about Brenda, too. I feel like she rebirthed me with her enlightened therapy, even though I wasn't as responsive as I could have been at first. She did so by writing her informative book for people like me and extending hope. By never giving up on me.

Louis Cozolino, a clinical psychologist and therapist, makes a statement in *The Neuroscience of Human Relationships* that speaks to my relationship with Brenda: "The optimism of the healer parallels that of the encouraging parent who has dreams of her children's success and supports their well-being. The psychological reality of ongoing neuroplasticity and neurogenesis provides us with a solid foundation for ongoing optimism with any client at any time, regardless of his or her struggle."[3]

———

Still snuggling in Mom's chair, embraced by gratitude, I return my thoughts to the moment, thinking of the appointment I have with Brenda in a few days.

I'm sure she realizes I'll be there. She doesn't know, however, that I'll be walking into her office with a whopper of a story that might seem unbelievable—except to her.

When I imagine seeing her, I feel the urge to offer my thanks to her and Dr. Milton. I wonder how I can possibly do that. Then I know. I'll make something, give them something of myself—crocheted doilies, one for Dr. Milton, one for Brenda. (I'm certain Dr. Milton will appreciate the beauty in my gesture of thanks, rather than getting hung up on gender issues.)

Full of enthusiasm, I flip through pattern books stored in a crate on my left. I find just the right motifs, both coaster-sized: a square doily for Dr. Milton and a round one for Brenda. Then I rummage inside the red-print bag on my left containing balls of crochet thread, deciding on a fine-gauge cream color. After finding my crochet hooks, I pick out a metal one I think will work well.

Once settling myself, I begin to crochet, noticing the symbolism in the stitches, each loop a circle. Throughout the day, while the doilies take shape, I feel the love flowing through my hands, expressing gratitude to Dr. Milton and Brenda for their part in restoring my life, even though I'm not well yet.

When the doilies are finished, I handle them with care, washing them in warm water then laying them on a towel, right side down, to dry overnight.

The next day, I weave thin paper labels into the design, designating who is to be the recipient. Even though the doilies are uncomplicated and small, they seem precious, tender expressions of my heart.

The day before my appointment with Brenda, I carefully slip them inside one envelope on top of a card where I've written something, hoping my note and the doilies will adequately express my feelings.

The message on the card is simple, yet I couldn't find words to make the message grander. They're from my soul, yearning to be understood.

> *Dr. Milton and Brenda,*
> *Thank you*
> *for your understanding*
> *for your compassion*
> *for your care*
> *for your love.*
> *L'chaim — To Life!*

———

When the day of my appointment with Brenda comes, I put the envelope with my note and doilies inside my brown canvas messenger bag.

But I have something else in mind besides a thank-you.

Music: "On Eagle's Wings."

I want to share the song I've played over and over again since I received The Gift, so I take my computer with a one-song playlist set up.

Shortly after arriving at Advanced Medicine, Brenda opens the waiting room door, greeting me with welcoming words and her radiant smile.

After stepping into her office, I head straight for "my" large, squishy, leather recliner where I always sit. Brenda takes her seat, observing, while I place my computer between us on a round glass table.

She continues regarding me, holding her yellow legal pad and pen, waiting patiently for me to get settled.

I'm not finished "moving in" until I grab a soft, salmon-colored pillow that rests in "my" chair. Somehow hugging that pillow helps me hold my heart together—a heart that wants to explode with emotion.

I look up to see Brenda's eyes, beckoning me to speak.

I hold back.

The same thoughts and feelings that stirred me when I was telling my pastor, Rene, about The Gift of the Circle roil in my guts. I feel like a pauper who has unexpectedly received an inheritance of untold wealth. From that perspective I feel at once the full measure of my poverty—and my blessings.

Even though Crystal took me by the heart to begin my journey to wholeness, I'm feeling vulnerable and unsure of myself on this new adventure. Only a glimmer of my intrinsic value invites me to believe in my self-worth.

My pounding heart urges me to speak.

I don't. Like a small child, I want to hide. Until now, I hadn't known that Brenda had become my hero. I'm awestruck. Scared too. Finally, I get brave enough to express myself.

Touching is not a part of my sessions with Brenda, but my hands seem to be a metaphor for a heart that wants to touch this remarkable woman sitting beside me. I'm scared she won't extend her own hands when I ask for them, but I push through my fears to ask anyway.

I scoot to the edge of the chair and reach out to her.

Without hesitation she clasps my hands in hers, eyes questioning.

Although a tangle of joy and sorrow tries to strangle the words in my throat, I manage to tell Brenda about reading her book while sitting in Mom's chair. About the split second in time when I'd just finished her book. About the awareness that exploded, revealing the fact that my pathway for healing is the very one mapped out in *You Can Beat the Odds*. And how, in a burst of insight prompted by own wisdom and Divine Love, I was led to discover the root of my torturing anxiety.

I tell her I'm in flight—that I'm on my way to wholeness. On eagle's wings preparing to shine like the sun.

With my eyes wide and staring intently at hers, making certain she knows I'm about to say something significant, I thank her for my life.

Then, with a synchronicity born of intuitive grace, we part hands, both of us teary-eyed.

I go on a bit to reflect aloud about the information in her book, especially the science underpinning the methods I have on my to-do list. I mention how critical the research findings are for me as a baseline motivation for belief and action!

And how the stories she tells of her patients who defeat disease using her mind-body medicine protocol inspired me to believe I can heal too.

After pausing a moment, I tell her I'd like to share music that entrains me to the rhythms of healing.

She nods.

After I turn on the music, we spend a few minutes listening to the emotional words and soft rhythms. While we listen, I know she understands the majesty of the message, my recent revelations, and the profound hope I feel.

I've shared my life's stories with Brenda. She's aware of my talisman-like relationship with red-tailed hawks and raptors. She knows about my burgeoning faith in Divine Love. And her empathy with my profound need to feel meaning and purpose in my life is palpable.

Brenda is also intimately aware of the treacherous terrain of my disease-ridden insanity. Yet she doesn't doubt me when I tell her I've finally begun my journey home to wholeness. Somewhat like my pastor, Rene, but of a different sort, Brenda is in the business of miracles—the biology of miracles premised in research outcomes. She doesn't doubt my story. She doesn't doubt my power. She never has.

As my session with her comes to an end, awe mutes us both for a time.

She breaks the majesty of our silence by telling me she's thrilled to see me on this new path. And I *know* she is, this warrior and hero sitting beside me. She's worked hard for this moment.

After slowly fading the music, and turning off my computer, I prepare to leave her office. As I'm walking away, I hand her the envelope containing my note and the doilies I made for her and Dr. Milton.

While I'm still standing at the checkout counter, Dr. Milton comes up beside me and wraps an arm around my shoulders, hugging me while acknowledging the expressions of gratitude Brenda must have just shown him.

After saying goodbye to Dr. Milton, I go to my car.

When preparing to turn on the engine, I realize I've become tense from wondering if my card and doilies "spoke" enough of my appreciation for those two hearts of majesty I've just left.

Then a deep-running river of understanding settles me into comfort: *They'll know the full measure of my message even though the words are simple.*

The gratitude that courses through my heart will find the same level in theirs. For that's the way of things among those who have grown to understand and cherish each other.

NECTAR
IN THE SIMPLE

A month or so after thanking Dr. Milton and Brenda for my life, my friend Marilyn calls; excited, she tells me something astounding: A Georgia state prison inmate whom we met when volunteering, teaching knitting and crocheting to inmates, will soon be graduating from a tough residential substance abuse–treatment program. And, she's invited us to her graduation ceremony.

After we marvel at the accomplishment of this woman, who once jumped out of a second-story window when overdosing on drugs, breaking her back, Marilyn invites me to join her on an overnight road trip to attend.

I hesitate just long enough to assess my health. Ever since I made my to-do list, I've been religiously orchestrating my days around my mind-body medicine strategies; as a result, my stamina is becoming reliable. Feeling ready to extend myself, I say yes.

After Marilyn and I make travel plans our call ends, but I don't stop thinking about her. Marilyn nurtured me many times when I was sick. I never had the sense that I was diminished in her loving eyes because I wasn't well. And she had an uncanny sense of timing, knowing precisely when to offer a gesture of kindness. For holding me dear when I thought there was nothing to hold, and for her bright smile when my dullness grayed everything around me, and for holding on to me when I couldn't hold on to myself, I want to thank her.

Without knowing how or when, I plan to do just that while we're on our upcoming road trip.

And there's more on my mind about our soon-to-come time together: The last thing I remember after being found in the motel room in Blue Ridge, Georgia, where I lay full of drugs, longing to become an aura in the wind, is my friend Marilyn crawling in bed beside me. She snuggled close and reached her right hand around me to grasp my head, then cradled me against her shoulder. For a moment, I felt her strong, warm shoulders supporting my heart gone limp with sorrow and the burden of facing more tomorrows, as she held together the tattered remains of my raw, vulnerable soul. I was in and out of consciousness after I was found. I lost consciousness for the last time with Marilyn holding me in her arms. Although I know hearing the details of that poignant time will be challenging, I want to know what happened.

Talking with my sister, Janet, about all that is too painful. When I speak of my most recent attempt to kill myself, I see the haunting aftermath in her eyes. We'll talk one day because that's the way we work, but not now.

So, I decide to ask Marilyn to share her perspective while we're on our road trip—when the timing is right.

I have no idea that Marilyn will share a deeply personal story from her childhood. That she will remind me that treasures of untold worth are sometimes born from tragedy. Although I've known there's something unique about my friendship with her, I've no way of knowing that while she held my frail body in Blue Ridge, she was fulfilling a shared Divine destiny.

———

On our way home from the prison graduation ceremony, and while Marilyn and I are traveling along the highway in pensive silence, I muster the courage to ask her what happened in Blue Ridge.

After taking a deep breath, she begins telling me.

"Janet called me on the Sunday afternoon you disappeared, fearing that something was wrong when you didn't return home from church. After checking to make sure you weren't visiting me, she sounded an alarm: you'd disappeared once before, then attempted suicide. I didn't want to lose you. My worst fears tormented me. I felt helpless. The only thing I could offer Janet was my prayers. Before ending our conversation, I asked her to keep me posted. We spoke often after that, so I know she contacted Rene to ask for prayerful support. Because you were still missing on Monday morning, your brother-in-law, Mike, stayed home to be emotional ballast for your sister. With Mike nearby, Janet filed a missing-person report with the local police, saying she suspected you were on a mission to kill yourself and hoping the authorities would find you in time to save you.

"Desperate to find you, Janet then signed in to the bank account you use for cash expenditures, looking for a trace of your whereabouts."

I nod, remembering that I'd granted Janet access to my debit account for emergencies.

"In your online records, your sister saw three transactions occurring near the end of the week before you disappeared: a withdrawal of several hundred dollars in cash, a Home Depot purchase, and a liquor store purchase. Because you withdrew cash to keep from using your debit card before you disappeared the last time you attempted suicide, when Janet saw the identical pattern developing, she became convinced you were once again on a death mission, hiding your whereabouts. Still wanting to know more about what was going on in your mind, she contacted customer service at the Home Depot listed on your bank transactions. The customer service department willingly reviewed their videos of purchasing activity. What they found terrified your sister: you had bought two box cutters."

"Yes. I remember too well. They were for backup just in case overdosing on liquor and drugs didn't kill me. I'm sorry for interrupting, Marilyn. Keep going."

"After a sleepless night, Janet felt your time was running out. She knew instinctively that you were planning to use the box cutters for vein slicers; she figured the alcohol you bought was intended to intensify the effects of drugs she suspected you had with you."

Marilyn pauses a moment, taking in a deep breath.

Looking out the side window, I sigh.

Hearing the story hurts. Guilt and shame wash over me, making me wonder if I'll ever be able to forgive myself for traumatizing others I love. I bow my head, burdened, but I don't want to stop Marilyn. This is a part of my past. The part of my past that formed precious crucibles.

L'chaim!

I turn my head to look at Marilyn as she begins speaking again.

"After another tormenting night for Janet, on Tuesday morning she was driven by desperation. Using her astounding genius she discovered you were in Blue Ridge—in a motel."

"How did she figure that out?"

"I can't tell you except to say that someone gave her the information she needed to find you. I promised not to reveal the identity of that person. A career is at stake."

Figuring I'll try solving *that* mystery another time, I leave more inquiry alone. "I understand."

"Once Janet knew where to find you, she called your friend Jan who lives, as you know, close to Blue Ridge. Janet told her what was happening then gave her the address of your suspected location, urging her to get to you as quickly as possible. Jan drove at breakneck speed. When she arrived at the motel, she saw your car, confirming your presence. After begging the motel owner to give her your room number, she called 911 on her cell phone while rushing to your door."

"You know, Marilyn, I vaguely remember hearing a knock and a familiar voice calling my name. And feeling crestfallen that I'd been found."

My friend nods her head, then tells me Janet had made arrangements for Rene to meet her and follow her to Blue Ridge.

"Where were you, Marilyn, when all that was happening?"

"About eight miles from where you were discovered, eating lunch with family members. Janet called, telling me she'd found you. After hastily explaining the circumstances, I excused myself. After grabbing my purse, I rushed to my car then sped toward you, not knowing if I'd find you dead or alive. By the time I arrived at the motel, the police and paramedics were there."

My mind drifts, wondering if I'll ever understand that I matter. If I'll ever love myself like my friends and family do. Love myself enough to feel like the trouble to save me was worth the effort.

Pensive, I reenter Marilyn's story.

"Afraid of what I'd see, I opened the motel room to peer inside. There you were lying in the bed, disheveled. Nothing could have stopped me from going to you. Nothing. I snuggled lengthwise while holding your head against my shoulder."

"I remember. You moved your face close to my left ear, making certain I'd hear you. Then you said, 'God's not done with you!' That's the last thing I can recall."

"What about Jan changing your clothes, Carolyn?"

"What do you mean?"

"After your sister arrived at the motel, Jan left to buy you clean clothes. Yours were soaked in urine."

"So Janet and Jan must have cleaned me and changed my clothes."

"Probably. I wasn't there yet. I learned about all that later."

"Anyway, after holding you, I got up intending to go outside, where I heard Janet talking with the paramedics. While leaving, I saw Rene sitting beside you, nudging you into consciousness, insisting you give her anything you had with you for killing yourself. You reached into your backpack that was on the floor beside the bed, retrieving the box cutters.

"Outside, Janet was working hard to convince the paramedics to release you to her care. Even though she'd told them she'd arranged for your admittance to a psychiatric hospital in Atlanta, they were concerned about an immediate need for treatment of possible kidney failure. They finally agreed to allow your sister to transport you for hospitalization—if you could urinate; a couple of us helped you to the bathroom where you did what was needed."

"Marilyn, my sister is amazing. How did she manage to think clearly enough to make hospitalization arrangements—before she left for Blue Ridge, no less?"

"Your sister loves you, Carolyn. And yes, she's awesome! Besides arranging for a hospital bed for you, she'd put pillows and blankets in the back of her station wagon. Rene and I helped you crawl into her car with the paramedics watching. You passed out before we could cover you. Then Rene and I escorted you and your sister on the long ride to the hospital."

Marilyn pauses for a moment, then finishes her story, telling me she and Rene stayed at the hospital with my sister until the staff assured them I had, once again, survived an attempt to kill myself.

I'm stunned by her story's ending. My story.

I feel like Marilyn's just told me about a queen's entourage.

No pomp, though. Just the compassion of a sister and friends carrying me, broken hearted, on wings of love.

———

The energy in the car settles around us as I breathe in the effects of an account that moves this way and that inside my heart. I feel a sense of awe at the love that surrounded me on a bleak day in my life when all I had left of myself was a beating heart. And I'm certain a Divine purpose was operating that I couldn't feel at the time, but was there nonetheless.

Lub dub.

Lub dub.

Lub dub.

Looking back to Blue Ridge with different eyes than the ones that blinded me then, I see a vision of human beauty crafted by the tender concern of my sister and friends.

Even though hearing Marilyn's side of my suicide attempt was painful, I'm glad I went there with her on that look into the past.

The present seems even more blessed now. Merely sitting beside my friend on a simple road trip feels like I'm doing the most spectacular thing I could ever imagine.

I'm learning there's a certain fundamental integrity in the simplicity of a naked thank-you, and I know the time has come to offer my thanks to Marilyn for her love.

Eyes overflowing with tears of gratitude, I say, "Thank you, Marilyn. Thank you for loving me."

Unexpected silence baffles me until Marilyn speaks again.

"I was an only child. Do you remember that?"

"Yes, you've told me."

"I always wanted a brother or a sister—to hold in my arms. But that never happened. In 1945 I was the first of six children born to my parents. I'm the only one who lived. I set off Rh factor antigens in my mother that would later 'mysteriously' kill all of my siblings; little was known in those days about the Rh factor and how to treat affected women. All of my brothers and sisters were fully formed babies born between 1947 and 1955. All five were either stillborn or died a few days after birth.

"In 1949, my mother went into labor to deliver a baby she knew was dead in her womb. As she was preparing to leave for the hospital to give birth to that dead child, she intoned, 'I'm going to the hospital, but I'm not coming home with a baby for you to hold.'

"That sibling who never came home was a sister named Carolyn."

My mind leaps to grasp the majesty in Marilyn's story: *I'm the sister Marilyn never got to hold in her arms.*

So that's why I mean so much to her. That's why our friendship feels different than most.

Gifts are born of tragedy, grandeur born of contrasts. The promise of sisterhood was born from the womb of desperation and the pain of emptiness.

I reach across the space between us, the space which is pulsing with Divine mystery and secrets about the way things work sometimes.

I take Marilyn's hand, my sister's hand. Feelings pour from my eyes, revealing how blessed I feel to have her in my life and how thankful I am that I didn't kill myself. I feel honored, too. Honored to be the one who didn't die. The one who came back from the living dead for Marilyn to hold in her arms.

Lub dub.

Lub dub.

Lub dub . . .

———

Soon after my journey with Marilyn, a coda punctuates my story of dying and living. At the beginning of a Sunday-morning service, the pastor begins reading scripture, as usual; his following remarks mist into obscurity as my mind drifts out of the present and into an outside that beckons me to play in the sunshine.

I bring my attention back to the sanctuary, focusing on the pastor and a teenage girl now standing beside him at the podium. He introduces her, saying that she has an important message.

While he moves toward a seat, she walks to a nearby standing microphone.

She's pretty, with long, black, curly hair and a radiant face beaming with a smile. She begins speaking with an assurance that's unusual for someone her age, telling the congregation that her friends call her Ricky.

She wastes no time getting into her message, declaring that something catastrophic happened in her home. Something that turned her life into an ugly mess she didn't recognize and didn't want.

After that, depression and anxiety took hold; she couldn't shake free of their grip despite prescription drugs, psychotherapy, and a stay in a psychiatric hospital. She tried to kill herself many times.

Waves of understanding wash through me as I absorb the impact of this young woman telling her story with a courage belying her age.

Her honesty captivates me like nothing else.

Honesty powers healing in the message. For her. For us.

Ricky speaks a language understood only by those who've traveled to the place of emotional despair and hopelessness—like me.

My heart entrains with hers in the rhythmic cadence of sincere empathy.

Lub dub.

Lub dub.

Lub dub.

Ricky leans into the microphone, eyes connecting with some in the sanctuary, telling us what finally made her want to live again: the smiles of those who greeted her when she entered the church seeking hope, the arms embracing her that in a way said, "You matter to me; I'm glad you're here."

Then Ricky tells us about someone who became a mentor. Someone who took the time to listen to her when she struggled to understand why she was still here when she didn't want to be. She tells us her mentor directed her to lay a hand over her heart, to become quiet. To feel her heartbeat.

Now, Ricky lifts her right arm, placing her hand over her heart. She asks us to do the same thing. Except for her voice, the sanctuary is silent, spellbound. Next, she softly asks us to feel our hearts beating.

Lub dub.

Lub dub.

Lub dub.

"That's my purpose, and that's why I'm here. That's why all of us are here," she says.

I don't remember Ricky's comments after that. I'm stunned by another one of those explosions of awareness happening these days, taking me inward:

When I wanted to die, perhaps my heart—beating with the rhythm of Divine purpose, signaling a promise I couldn't feel—kept me alive in a mysterious sort of way.

Yes! I was born to be with my sister, Janet, until one of us dies a natural death.

Lub dub.

Yes! I am meant to be a sister for my friend Marilyn to hold in her arms.

Lub dub.

Yes! I am meant to heal myself and walk free of disease to offer hope to others.

Lub dub.

Yes! I was born to love and be loved.

Lub dub.

I am meant to live simply, give generously, and hold the hands of those around me.

I am meant to see the wisdom of the ancients, to soar on the up-drafted breaths of those who sustain me with their love and care.

And so I shall.

Lub dub.

Lub dub.

Lub dub.

NOBLE LESSONS

Someone risked a career to give my sister information essential to locating me where I'd secluded myself in a motel room, seeking death. That information and my sister's tenacity saved me from the dark side of myself. In order to protect an identity and a career, neither my sister, nor my friend Marilyn, would reveal the name of the individual who effected my rescue.

As a result of my own investigation, I discovered the name of the person they chose to protect. And I, in turn, intend to preserve anonymity. However, that individual's story is important to my own. To honor that extraordinary person and further my tale of lessons and gratitude, I've written an allegory.

In the allegory that follows, I become The Wee Tiny Sparrow. The Noble One represents the wise authority who responded to my sister's desperate call for critical information.

As in many allegories and fables, defining the moral is left to the reader.

Ancient Seekers tell of The Land of Ebbing and Flowing, where all life hangs in the balance. There, the Noble One is sovereign: a raptor with deep, golden eyes that spar with delusion. With soaring grace, his display of russet tail feathers is often seen painting the wind in the sky.

The Noble One is wisdom incarnate.

By honing attention to Luminous Awareness, he has earned the gift of omniscience.

His perch of distinction is the highest of all, where he roosts on a bold, sturdy branch of a tree, trimming the heavens.

There, he upholds The Law of the Land: knowledge borne of all-knowing is sacrosanct, to be held in guarded secrecy no matter the shades. Although that mandate is sometimes burdensome, The Noble One holds far-seeing secrets as tight to his breast as the sun that clings to a beam. As tight as the dark that bonds to the night.

Near the abode of The Noble One, The Wee Tiny Sparrow lives with her younger sister, Sings at Dawn, nesting in a low-lying bush. Their twig-woven home is pillowed with soft, downy feathers and small, fluffy clouds.

The Wee Tiny Sparrow is sick.

Her once perky tail feathers drag on the ground. Her eyes are as dull as the dust on a gray slab of stone. Her happy song, once sung at the break of dawn, is buried in grief.

Early one morning while moisture is still on the ground, Sings at Dawn coaxes The Wee Tiny Sparrow into flying with her a short distance to visit a rose-scented glade, hoping her sister might find a nurturing peace there.

When they arrive, Sings at Dawn breathes in the fragrance of blossoming flowers while regarding her small, sick sister. The Wee Tiny Sparrow appears to take pleasure in their surroundings, peering at dewdrops kissed by the rays of the sun.

But, she is sometimes a convincing trickster, feigning solace when she yearns to be taken to The Land of Dark Peace, where death claims the soul.

Pretending tranquility, The Wee Tiny Sparrow hops on top of a moss-covered log. While feigning interest in the green at her feet, she invokes the presence of The Velvet-Tongued Vulture, feared by all in The Land of Ebbing and Flowing.

Fooled by her sister's masterful charade, Sings at Dawn

leaves The Wee Tiny Sparrow, beckoned home by nest-cleaning chores.

While she's emptying the nest of debris, a foreboding sky boils in blacks, purples, and dark, angry greens. A mournful howl of wind shatters the illusion of calm.

Sings at Dawn shivers.

The truth unravels her: The Velvet-Tongued Vulture, beak dripping with gore, has taken The Wee Tiny Sparrow. With his soft-toned finesse, he's lured her once more with the promise of freedom from her sorrow and pain.

With a fluttering heart and wings beating fast, Sings at Dawn streaks across the dark, ominous sky to seek an audience with The Noble One.

When she lands on the ground of his sky-touching roost, the piercing eyes of The Noble One acknowledge her presence.

Before he has time to speak, Sings at Dawn, her feathers fluttering in panic, chirps and chirps, spilling her fears: "The Wee Tiny Sparrow was taken by The Velvet-Tongued Vulture. If I don't find her in time, he will rip her open and eat her wee heart. Only you can tell me where he has taken her."

She repeats her cry as if The Noble One were deaf.

Hopping and hopping, she utters a plea: "Please! Please, I beg you, tell me where my sister is abiding with death! Reveal the secret you're bound by your perch to hold to your breast."

At that, The Noble One blinks his all-knowing eyes and draws in a deep, stirring breath, summoning wisdom, and a Code of Ethics reigning outside the laws of The Land of Ebbing and Flowing.

For a split second, he considers his choices.

Then, for him, there is no other. A life is at stake!

Preparing to risk his high-in-the-sky perch in The Land of Ebbing and Flowing, he sighs. Raising his wings, then settling his regal, fine-feathered body, he speaks with assurance. "The Wee Tiny Sparrow has been taken to the Life-Sucking Cave in The Land of Dark Peace."

Without invitation, Sings at Dawn flies up to The Noble One's perch, where he makes room for her small trembling body, knowing she has need of comfort.

Then, bursting with terror, Sings at Dawn trumpets a call, heralding the great white wolf who roams The Land of Ebbing and Flowing. "Knows the Soul, come to my aid as fast as you can. The Velvet-Tongued Vulture has The Wee Tiny Sparrow in his ravaging grip."

The alarm freezes Knows the Soul in place. She shivers.

Then, spinning around, she answers the summons for help at top running speed, her coat glistening as white as fresh-fallen snow on a moonlit night.

When she arrives at The Noble One's perch where Sings at Dawn impatiently awaits, Knows the Soul commands her to speak and then grasps her fearsome task in a matter of seconds.

Without further ado, she commands the terrified sparrow to hop on her strong, sturdy back.

Once Sings at Dawn is gripping her thick white coat, Knows the Soul speeds to The Land of Dark Peace and the maw of the Life-Sucking Cave.

They arrive with no time to spare.

For The Velvet-Tongued Vulture has The Wee Tiny Sparrow pinned to ground.

His razor-sharp beak is poised at her throat, eager to rip open her wee tiny breast.

Knows the Soul steps into the black menace of the Life-Sucking Cave. Her eyes pierce the dark with daggers of radiance. The lightning-bright essence of her life-saving force streaks in the air, blazing a pathway as she treads toward The Velvet-Tongued Vulture and the scene of impending slaughter.

Sensing the presence of her pulsating power, The Velvet-Tongued Vulture cautiously lifts his ugly, bald head. He sees Knows the Soul, glaring with threat just a few feet away.

The Velvet-Tongued Vulture's eyes become turgid, bulging with hatred. He chokes on defeat.

Then, with caution-drenched terror, eyes riveted on Knows the

Soul, The Velvet-Tongued Vulture backs away from The Wee Tiny Sparrow and flattens himself against the wall of the Life-Sucking Cave.

Certain that The Velvet-Tongued Vulture is immobile with fear, Knows the Soul glides across the floor with maternal assurance. She leans down and nuzzles The Wee Tiny Sparrow's breast with her soft, warm nose. Then she scoops up the diminutive bundle of feathers and sorrow in her now gentle jaws.

Turning her massive white back on The Velvet-Tongued Vulture, Knows the Soul strides out of the cave, her giant white tail held high in the air.

Once outside, she nods with compassion when hearing Sings at Dawn sigh with relief. Then she motions Sings at Dawn to come close. Tenderly, she places The Wee Tiny Sparrow into the wings of her long-suffering sister, then points her nose toward the top of her back.

When Sings at Dawn is securely seated, Knows the Soul hastens toward their twig-woven nest.

After she safely delivers the two sparrow sisters, she sits on her haunches and bows, acknowledging the Divinity she sees in them both.

Certain The Wee Tiny Sparrow will find her way to Divine Healing Light, Knows the Soul heartens, "All will be well."

Then she pivots on her hind feet, departing to roam freely in The Land of Ebbing and Flowing, where her footprints will soon leave their unforgettable mark on other lives that hang in the balance.

Soon after Knows the Soul has gone on her way, Dances with Radiance appears, called to tend to The Wee Tiny Sparrow. Commencing her care without ado, she feeds the sick little bird sweet, mint-flavored nectar she gathers for mending disease-broken hearts.

With her nurturing support, The Wee Tiny Sparrow's feathers soon lift from the ground. Her eyes, once filled with sorrow and pain, begin to gleam with the promise of hope.

Before long, gratitude fills her wee tiny heart and spills from her kindhearted eyes.

Then, the most thrilling of sounds trills from her breast, although late in the morn. At first, The Wee Tiny Sparrow's whispering chirps can barely be heard. After just a short while, The Land of Ebbing and Flowing awakens with her song turned fortissimo, insistent and spirited, as soon as an ombre of gold opens each day.

One morning while singing, unfinished business wafts in the breeze: The Noble One enters the mind of The Wee Tiny Sparrow.

Summoned by her own sense of what's right, and after reviewing his part in the recent events of her past, she knows she must thank him for her life. But she wonders, "How can I thank The Noble One for a gift so great? Even if I'm not certain, I will try my wee tiny best, for I must."

Shimmering with purpose after singing her morning song one day, The Wee Tiny Sparrow arrives unannounced at the tree where The Noble One perches.

He acknowledges her presence with a dignified nod.

At first The Wee Tiny Sparrow avoids his golden, knowing eyes, shame bowing her head. Her heart flutters in fear of this awesome guardian of secrets.

Finally, a determined courage prods her to peer into The Noble One's all-knowing eyes. Sucking in her breath and wasting no words, she speaks from her small, humble heart, saying all she knows how to say. "Thank you for my life. You risked your perch high in the sky to save me, a mere speck of a bird. But why?"

The Noble One stretches and flutters his wings, then digs his talons into the bark of his perch, holding on to emotions threatening to burst from his chest. Unbridled tears moisten his fathomless eyes. Outstretching a great, splendid wing and leaning his head to one side, he directs The Wee Tiny Sparrow, "Come. Sit next to me."

Both mystified and awed by his gesture, she flies quickly to sit close by him.

Wrapping an enormous wing around The Wee Tiny Sparrow, The Noble One soothes her fear. And her shame. He speaks silently at first, peering into The Wee Tiny Sparrows eyes, connecting their souls with compassion. Then, in a slow, measured, straightforward voice he speaks, "The answer to your probing question is quite simple, one you must never forget.

"Listen carefully to my answer, and with your heart, for there's more than one meaning forthcoming."

With that, The Wee Tiny Sparrow nods her head and blinks her eyes, preparing to receive a gift of immeasurable value.

The Noble One removes his wing from The Wee Tiny Sparrow, composing himself.

Then he turns his great, regal head to face her. In a voice as deep and wise as any the universe knows, he intones, "I felt your pain when Sings at Dawn pleaded for my help. Saving you was an investment of immeasurable value. An investment that eased my heart, benefitting both of us. An investment I couldn't ignore.

"And, no matter how you felt then, no matter how you feel now, my life is no more important than yours. Compromising your life to protect my perch would have darkened the universe. What happens to one happens to all."

With a regal bow to The Wee Tiny Sparrow, The Noble One speaks a benediction to their encounter and to The Land of Ebbing and Flowing, where all life hangs in the balance:

"Remember this, Wee Tiny Sparrow: We share the same breath. We share the same breath!"

CEREMONIES
OF THE HEART

And the woman spoke, Tell us of pain.
And the Prophet said:
Your pain is the breaking of the shell that encloses
your understanding.[1]

—Kahlil Gibran

———

The unborn chick knows
shells are meant to be broken.
But only when the time is right.

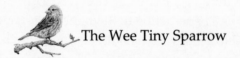

The Wee Tiny Sparrow

More than a month has passed since I thanked The Noble One for his part in my rescue from The Velvet-Tongued Vulture. Longer than that since I expressed gratitude for Marilyn's caring.

But I've yet to thank my sister.

I often reflect on the steadfast love and concern Janet expressed during the entire eight years of my illness. When I do, I feel my heart push against my chest while tears streak down my face. Even so, my gratitude for what she did for me remains immobilized inside a shell of silence and crusty emotions I don't understand. Knowing I'll figure out what's going on tempers at least some of my guilt about what seems like an illogical delay. And restrains me from cracking open a protective barrier that's not ready to be broken.

While weaving in and out of expressing gratitude to others, I've been tailoring the mind-body medicine strategies on my to-do list. By working with them daily, I'm crafting a unique fit and a different way to be in this world.

As a result of the strategies' powerful capacity to heal, I feel even better than I did when I agreed to take the recent road trip with Marilyn. As a result, I'm entertaining the idea of living alone again.

For more than seven years, beginning in the spring of 2003 when I began staying with my friend Rebecca, I've been living in someone else's home, too ill and financially compromised to live alone.

Now, I believe I'm well enough to fledge, and confident enough in my burgeoning health to trust that my out-of-pocket medical expenses will lessen.

I'm scared though. I would never have guessed that, at age sixty-seven, I'd be afraid to live by myself. Yet I am.

I'm as scared as I was just before pressing down on the pedal of my bicycle to start the long ride home from the Charleston airport to Florida. As frightened as the time I picked up my cell phone to call for the first building inspection of my home in the woods. As terrified as when I sat in my canoe, poised to paddle my first stroke in a turgid Green River on a fifty-mile solo wilderness adventure.

Those experiences speak to me now, reminding me that in the past I've deliberately challenged my fears. That I've sought experiences to teach me about liberating myself from the unnecessary shackles of contrived phantoms—when I felt ready.

Like now.

Although the effects of Lyme stifled my daring for a time, the warrior in me is, indeed, taking flight once again. Even though I'm frightened by the challenge of facing my fear of living alone,

I'm thrilled too. Thrilled because, until I received The Gift of the Circle, I'd given up on life and growing and thriving. Like a fledgling poised on the edge of a nest, I know I must let go of the security I've felt living with others if I'm going to discover a new threshold for growth.

When I make an appointment for a realtor to show me a house that speaks the language of another era, I begin reclaiming my life: an adventure like no other. And one that will guide me to a rugged trek through the mysterious, beautiful terrain of my inner world.

At the house, I pull into a yard overgrown with tangles of unruly weeds. While I turn off the ignition, raising my eyes over the dashboard, peeling, oxidized yellow hanging off the side of the house grabs my attention. Then, a sagging roof, frowning from neglect, alerts me to more serious problems.

When I step over the threshold into the living room, fear jolts me. Fear that has nothing to do with the house.

My prickling skin and racing heart signal anxiety, squeezing logic out of my brain. My thoughts taunt me:

What if I'm making a mistake. Am I really well enough to live alone?

What if I get sick and no one knows?

What if I can't pay my expenses and I go bankrupt?

Unable to keep silent, The Watcher makes her presence known for the first time in decades. Somehow the wise part of me wedges space into my fiendish fears. Thoughts that give no credit to my reasoning capacity and personal power.

I met The Watcher in the 1980s. Then, I called her my Whisper Voice when she made known my motivations—preceding action, offering me an opportunity to change direction.

She's bolder now. I'm not certain if her voice is louder or I'm listening better. At any rate, she's speaking in the insistent language of wisdom I yearn to embrace:

Look around you, Carolyn.

Stay in the present.

You aren't signing mortgage papers. You're merely looking at options.

Stepping over the threshold of this house triggered some thoughts that aren't helping you now.

Trust yourself.

You know how to maintain your health now.

Trust those who love you.

They'll be there if you stumble.

They've never left your side. And they're not going away any time soon.

Trust me, too, Carolyn.

There's nothing more trustworthy than your own wisdom.

The Watcher's counsel soothes my agitation. As I calm down, becoming contemplative, I realize the old house begging for attention isn't for me. My interest was prompted by an enthusiasm that didn't acknowledge I'm not able to shoulder the responsibilities of a renovation project right now. My energy is still compromised. And my focus needs to be on healing my body and my emotions.

Shortly after I realize I need an uncomplicated place to stretch my boundaries, I'm running an errand. While at a red light, I look around, noticing an entrance to an apartment complex I've driven by countless times, yet I didn't notice.

Acting on impulse, I turn in, heading straight to the office, where I speak to the manager. With a brochure in my day pack and an appointment to return to see a model apartment, I drive home intent on telling Janet what I've done.

She's surprised and hurt because I haven't said anything about moving, yet she understands my need to spread my wings and agrees to go with me to see a one-bedroom model. Just a few days after we do a walk-through, I sign a yearlong lease without ever seeing the actual apartment I'm renting.

I don't need to.

A profound confidence in Divine Orchestration is in operation: I know the perfect apartment has been selected for me, an offering of care, propelling me forward into life and the opportunity to experience a treasure-laden future.

While I pack my things, preparing to move into my one-bedroom apartment, I make a commitment to be careful about the way I populate the wide-open future of my new life with things and people. Especially people.

Judging from my experience with past relationships, figuring out if a relationship has the potential to be harmonious on the front end is much easier than struggling to exit one that doesn't fit well. Also I'm protective now, driven to foster my health.

To glue myself to a reality I can't afford to ignore as I prepare to move, I review a passage in *You Can Beat the Odds*: "Your brain is like a virtual pharmacy, influencing your body as it responds to your emotions and your thinking processes. In every moment of our lives, an ever-changing array of hormones and molecules interact, nudging us either toward health or disease."[2]

That's a statement I intend to remember, knowing that I've always had, and will continue to have, emotional reactions to people I allow to enter my life.

My new apartment is entry into my realm of a hard-won resurrection I won't compromise with loose boundaries.

With that in mind, I carefully plan the next sequence of events.

———

Light.

I feel an urge to clean my entire apartment with light before I move in. Although that seems like a strange idea at first, trusting my intuition, I buy candles and old-fashioned blue-tipped matches.

Alone, I go to my apartment, preparing for a thorough house-cleaning.

When I stand at the door for the first time, I feel crazy, fearing someone will think I really am if they see me light the candle before I enter.

Then I don't care, deciding that worrying about what others think is absurd. I've come too far to stop doing something I believe necessary—no matter what others think. After steadying myself to open the gateway to my future, lighted candle in hand, I turn the key and open the door of my apartment. Then I step over the threshold into the tiled foyer—and my new life.

Awe startles me at first, then hugs me tight, bringing me into the magic of this moment as I take in the vision of the space that is now mine, for a time.

I wonder why I'm so blessed.

Those who are shackled by their circumstances or their thoughts seem to be with me. I know some of them would give anything to be where I am now. I wish they could be.

Then, shimmering hues of autumn colors waft into this mystical moment. Tears release memories of my sixty-four-year-old, redheaded sister.

I wouldn't be standing here if Janet's love-borne determination hadn't protected me from myself.

A knowing floods me. *This is the place. This is where I will thank my sister for my life—for loving me when I didn't love myself.*

Shuddering, I weep, while the gratitude for my life opens me to what seems like a Divine message. "You know, at the heart of The Gift of the Circle, there's something waiting for you to unwrap: your purpose. You have a story to tell. A book to write."

Wonder surrounds me as I wait for what comes next. "The Gift of the Circle—the gift of life. Your purpose has been waiting until you were ready to receive the challenge. No obligation. No weight. An inextricable bond—a universal law of receiving and giving—a circle of Light. Your purpose in a heartbeat."

I leave the threshold where I've been spellbound.

As I move into the living room, reverence directs my steps. Slowly shining candlelight into every room, every cabinet, closet, and corner—a metaphor for a new way to be in this world—I offer a prayer of thanksgiving for my new purpose, borne in The Gift of the Circle. Next, I invite my pastor Rene to come there, asking her to bless where I'll be living. And to dedicate me and my surroundings to fulfilling my newfound destiny.

Rene doesn't question my request; her tacit agreement is a welcome validation.

When she arrives, I open the door to receive her, holy moments beckoning. Time seems to stand still while Rene moves through the rooms, anointing the doorways with oil and praying softly. She glows—an angel of light—whispering and moving in the spiritual language of ritual and prayer.

After she finishes blessing my apartment, she motions for me to stand before her. I'm humbled by my own presence. Humbled by knowing that because I've been loved and cared for, I'm alive for this moment of serene beauty.

Rene anoints me with oil, dedicating my life to the expression of wisdom, to the nurture of my well-being, and to the service of The Divine and others.

As we part with hugs, our eyes share a truth: what appears to be a simple step forward is a miracle wrought from tragedy!

Standing at the doorway to my apartment watching Rene depart, I feel beautiful. Decorated by a mosaic of broken parts seamed together by promise. Colored by the splendorous hues of mystery and wonder.

———

Sitting on the carpeted floor in the living room after Rene leaves, I muse, unraveling a tangle of emotions and thoughts.

Why haven't I thanked my sister? Why is that so hard for me? Maybe because I know being my caregiver, nurturing my ruptured sanity, watching me suffer from an unrelenting disease, was tough for her.

Janet has a fine-tuned sense for shifts in my energy. She knows when things aren't right—like when I was beckoning The Velvet-Tongued Vulture to take me to The Land of Dark Peace.

Hmm.

I suspect her sensors that notice my subtle behaviors were honed in childhood—by a need to survive. To escape before my father's unpredictable wrath erupted in violence. That keen awareness contributed to saving my life.

Gently, an insight begins to manifest: *What a roundabout way to be blessed by the tragedy of our twisted father's pain.*

There's more, though—I love Janet, simple as that. I'm tormented by guilt when I imagine looking into her eyes, unable to avoid the sad truth: I caused her to feel prolonged agony—angst stoked by the fear of losing me—and part of her heart.

Will I ever be able to let go of the guilt I feel about that?

And there's something else there: Deep inside, wearing a scary mask, there's a shell crusted with pretense, protecting me in an odd sort of way. Protecting me from feeling the pain that tortures my guts when I step near expressing my love for Janet.

Childhood. Memories.

Now I realize acknowledging my deep love for my little sister brings me too close to the times Dad beat her and I couldn't stop him. I was her big sister. I yearned to protect her.

I couldn't.

I couldn't do anything except watch my father torture her while she screamed.

All I could do was push away the love I felt for her so I wouldn't hurt so much.

So I wouldn't hurt so much.

So I won't hurt now.

I won't hurt if I don't look into Janet's eyes and thank her for her love. As the one who still feels a need to protect her, I won't feel the pain I've caused her.

I won't hurt if I avoid facing the fact that my little sister took care of me, even when the burden of my care became unbearable.

I won't hurt if I push away my love for her.

That last insight breaks my shell of denial, and dawn explodes. The warrior in me has work to do . . .

———

A few days after my epiphany, I stand in my apartment's living room, a warrior shivering with emotion.

The doorbell rings. Responding to my invitation, Janet has arrived. Pensive, I mosey to the door. After inviting her to come inside, we stand side by side, looking around.

Within seconds, my voice explodes into the awkward silence, breaking a shell that is meant to be broken. "Janet, thank you for my life. I wouldn't be standing here if you hadn't saved me from myself."

Janet doesn't hear me. "What?" Maybe her emotions are noisy like mine. Or my voice, which seemed louder than thunder, was really timid and soft.

Planting my feet and leaning in her direction, I repeat myself loud and clear: "You're the reason we're standing here together. You're the one I have to thank for my life."

Turning to face me, Janet opens wide her arms, then draws me close. "You're welcome."

Even though I'd long dreaded that moment, there's nothing more.

For what else is there when two hearts find their way to claim their peace?

FREEDOM BECKONS

My simple, humble self knows only the song of truth.
High notes.
Low notes.
My song is my song.
All birds have a song to sing.

The Wee Tiny Sparrow

A few months short of my sixty-seventh birthday, I stand musing at the door of my sparsely furnished apartment. Now that I've taken care of all preliminaries, I'm ready to move in, poised with key in hand, marveling that I'm well enough to live alone again. And I'm grateful for the opportunity to spread my wings to experience another facet of The Gift of the Circle.

Still thinking, I recall a bold decision made several days before this extraordinary moment: I secured reservations for the forthcoming September with the Moab outfitter I always use to be launched once again on Utah's Green River for a fifty-mile, solo canoeing adventure in the Canyonlands National Park's back-country.

Several times during my years of suffering with Lyme disease, I would suddenly and all too briefly feel well. When that happened, without fail I imagined myself returning to the wild Canyonlands. On one of those rare feel-good days, I even pitched my tent on Janet's deck, checking the fabric's condition, yearning to experience the exquisite beauty and the "people" rocks calling to my soul. Even though I longed to answer their calls, I shriveled back into illness and despair.

While inserting the key in my door's lock, I realize I'm a long way from being well enough to canoe even a short distance, yet I feel certain I'll be ready when the time comes for me to board the plane to Utah.

My pondering aside, I take a deep breath, returning to the moment.

Then, with intention, I turn the key, opening the door to my future.

My heart pounds while I look around my apartment, reminding me that my sole purpose is thriving in the rhythms of life, sharing tender connections with others in every vibrant breath.

Janet, Crystal, Marilyn, The Noble One, doctors, my therapist, and others precious to me stood by my side during the darkest moments of my life. Their steadfast love spoke a truth I couldn't grasp: I matter simply because I exist.

Their loving inspiration led me to this trailhead of sorts—the pathway to restoring my health. The pathway home to loving myself.

Because of those who've loved and shepherded me this far, I now have at least a foothold in an identity that's more reliable than the false one I'd spent a lifetime creating by earning "gold stars."

With a tenuous sense of direction, and without knowing how I'll find my way home to loving myself, I settle into my apartment, beginning to weave the fabric of a dynamic, transformative healing, rife with unexpected challenges.

Mind-body healing strategies continue to be the mainstay of my burgeoning mental and physical health. Complementary, yet critical to my healing, are occasional consultations and treatments by allopathic and homeopathic doctors; in addition, I engage the care of licensed alternative medicine specialists, such as acupuncturists and brain-energy practitioners. Supplements are a daily must, especially to reduce inflammation, support my immune system, and provide robust nutrition to my body long starved by incessant diarrhea and an inability to digest food.

I also continue taking an antidepressant to quell anxiety.

I've gradually discontinued all other pharmaceuticals prescribed during my last psychiatric hospitalization.

Why?

Lithium, a mood stabilizer, provoked hand trembling, signaling potential harm. Instead of consulting the outpatient psychiatrist in charge of my case, I sought the advice of my internal medicine doctor, who suggested I drop my dose by half; when my symptoms continued, I decided on my own to abandon lithium altogether.

There was another factor in that decision besides the disturbing physical effects: I believed my emotions needed expression for stabilization rather than their utter suppression by a drug.

The benzodiazepine I'd been taking for anxiety went by the way after I forgot about taking my scheduled dose a few times. So I figured my anxiety was waning. Carefully testing my theory, I gladly stopped taking yet another drug, ready to address anxiety head on, taking only an antidepressant.

Other than my one-time consultation with my internal medicine doctor about lithium, I didn't consult anyone about withdrawal from psychotropic medication.

How come?

At some level, I was certain what to do. And I expected I would be admonished to the contrary if I consulted anyone from the medical profession. Also, with my history, who would have blamed anyone for expressing caution?

After the fact, I told my therapist and others what I'd done.

That said, when stepping over the threshold of my new apartment, I'm unaware that I still shoulder the explosive burdens of psychological debris. They soon make their presence known, sometimes bursting into my space, rattling their terrorizing threats in my face when a Lyme symptom—or a mimic of one—surfaces.

Before long, I come to understand their origins. After becoming ill, I read countless tragic stories on the internet of those debilitated from Lyme disease. When Lyme rampaged and countless treatments failed, in despair, I transmuted my fear of debilitation into a subconscious certainty. I didn't question that foreboding outcome until I received The Gift of the Circle.

Nor were the internet tragedies the whole problem. A rotten underpinning was at work when Lyme struck, and still threatens to topple me. Since childhood, I've believed I'm worthless—unlovable. Although I'm slowly walking free of that self-deprecating stance, I still have a ways to go. So I harbor a destructive, unconscious belief that I'm not loveable enough for anyone to want to help if Lyme strikes again.

That's illogical, given my contradicting experiences, yet logic isn't at work. I'm a bit like a soldier, shredded by shrapnel from the sudden explosion of an IED, then rescued and carried to safety by those who love her; she heals from physical wounds, yet fears taunt her. She shrieks and trembles when a firecracker goes off while she's merely taking a walk in a park.

My IED?

Lyme, rampaging and shredding what I thought of as my identity. My suicide attempts added more trauma to my experience of chronic illness, fostering a distrust of myself. Being electroshocked to burn away my tragic story heaped more agony onto an already burdensome emotional load.

The burdens I shoulder manifest themselves in radical mood swings, jerking me around even when all is well. I'm surprised by the volatility and force of my emotions: One minute I'm dancing and twirling, thrilled to be feeling so good. Then, a hint of a Lyme symptom, real or imagined, signals a threat. Suddenly my emotions slam me onto my couch, curling me into a thumb-sucking fetal position as I seek comfort from anxiety.

Although I'm unprepared for those emotional lightning strikes, memories of their destructive force urges me to tell my story, entreating me to release feelings in the presence of my therapist, while I'm writing, and at other suitable times.

Insomnia plagues me also. I'm afraid to sleep. Afraid to end my watch. Afraid that, if I do, disease will strike again.

Sometimes I wonder if withdrawing from all the drugs I took to mollify my moods was a good idea. Then I realize most of my feelings are genuinely positive and life-affirming, providing me the encouragement I need to trust in my innate power. And sleep does come when I give up the watch, too tired to care about anything other than getting a decent night's rest.

So, with an antidepressant providing a necessary edge for working skillfully with my irrational beliefs and their emotional signatures, the help of my therapist, and my own determination to heal, my emotions flourish, becoming teachers extraordinaire. They reveal with laser precision what I need to learn about myself in order to experience holistic wellness. And the reward for my efforts to learn about myself, as indeed, I do, is the gradual diminishing of my emotions' furies.

As I move forward, I recognize that my healing battlefront is primarily psychological. The mind-body medicine strategies on my to-do list become sophisticated weapons in ways I would never have guessed. With Brenda's mentoring, I learn to use them masterfully. *You Can Beat the Odds*, her artful book, becomes ragged from use. Dog-eared pages, highlighted remarks, and notes in the back, reminding me where to find important passages, tell of her book's use as my handbook for healing.

Also, my relationship with Brenda has changed.

Now, when I go to see her, I'm intentional. I take charge of the content I bring to our sessions, knowing that I'm pinpointing where I need to focus our attention. My emotional challenges are my directors. Each time I visit her, I arrive with a written agenda.

Sometimes I define a need for figuring out why I feel anxious or depressed in certain circumstances. Often I include a request for her to give me suggestions about refining an imagery or another mind-body medicine strategy. And routinely, I include an imperative that stares at me when I'm sitting in "my" chair in her office—an imperative that knows I must face my past. Although I feel scared when I look at one of those insistent agenda items while Brenda waits for me to speak, I somehow find the courage necessary to burst open painful, pus-filled, psychological wounds because I feel safe in her compassionate presence.

Taking charge was a part of my makeup before I got sick. When Lyme rampaged, I succumbed to being a writhing victim, searching outside myself for power and for answers. Now the determined warrior part of me is taking charge again. I'm beginning to wear the wardrobe of strength. And, my natural tendency to take control is, I will learn, a characteristic of those who survive life-threatening illness.[1]

I'm learning to love myself by mirroring the feelings of those who love me. As a result, I'm beginning to refine my self-caring: I'm eating a lot of raw fruits and vegetables. The meats I consume aren't infused with antibiotics or preservatives. During the day, I rest if I didn't sleep well the night before. And, I continue to make certain I schedule time for working my to-do list.

Preparing an intuitive agenda for my sessions with Brenda reflects concern for my well-being, too. In turn, Brenda trusts my judgment without compromising the integrity inherent in a therapist's injunction: to be truthful or to change direction in a session's content when necessary to keep me growing.

Lyme shadows lurk, all too often interrupting my sleep with terror. Yet I continue to heal, eventually finding inner resources to subdue my fear.

One day in the distant future, after three dramatic experiences—the coup de grace to anxiety's torture—my episodic journey with unnecessary fear will end, although I've much to learn before that happens.

The Land of Dark Peace and The Velvet-Tongued Vulture no longer tempt me.

And I'm learning to appreciate the benefits of slowing down.

Before Lyme struck, my life was going well on the surface. I was successful professionally, blessed with wonderful friendships, and living on the boundary of a wooded preserve I loved. Yet I was restless and a stranger to contentment. My smile was pasted over secrets of my past and an urgent need to outrun mortality.

Vainly attempting to soothe myself, my schedule was torturous. The frantic pace I hammered myself into left no time for the regeneration I needed. I squeezed out silence and stillness of any kind, including my meditation practice. After accomplishing one thing, I was on to the next. There were brief moments of solace, yet agitation quickly stirred me out of a calm that yearned to watch the clouds drift in the sky or the dew sparkle on grass. My feet couldn't rest in the sand long enough to feel the slow rhythms of the earth I cherished. Once in a while I wondered why I was so driven. When silence and stillness threatened to answer me, I bolted into frenetic action instead of waiting to listen.

I'm slowing down now. Although aging has a part in that, most of my downtempo comes from becoming peaceful. As my pace opens space for insights to arise, answers about the restlessness of my past emerge. I welcome them even though they bring their share of healing imperatives. The very answers I avoided long ago now become peace messengers, along with my reactions to the threat of Lyme. Together, they light my way to health, revealing the pathway to the transformation that comes.

Hearing the Green River's call, I earnestly begin healing myself, using the mind-body medicine techniques on my to-do list. And I progress forward using a route determined by my innate intelligence while learning to pay close attention to my intuition—a masterful guide.

Then there's my surging mission—a wave splashing my heart with a tingly, bubbling warmth. A wave that's come to shore knowing there is no other place to be.

I remember standing in my living room awed by my freedom,

having received a Divine imperative to tell my story of healing—a mission wrapped in The Gift of the Circle. I wasn't completely well, and I hadn't been given the skills to write a book, although I'd written over the years, expressing emotions by couching them in academic or business-like jargon. Nor was I given the courage to put my thoughts on paper and read them aloud. And I hadn't been told about the magnificent individuals who will show up to help me.

Jedwin Smith and Rosemary Daniell, two talented and otherwise amazing individuals, infuse their way into my life soon after I moved to the apartment.

While honing my literary skills, Jedwin and Rosemary teach me as much about myself as about writing. More than that, they both inspire me with insightful edits their own naked truths expressed unapologetically in their works. They encourage me to be courageous and truthful, especially with myself.

One day in May, I begin the daunting task of writing *The Gift of the Circle*.

Something happens on that significant day, setting my course as a writer, pointing the way to integrity, my healing North Star . . .

———

I'm sitting in the black swivel chair at my desk preparing to compose something for my first workshop session with Jedwin. I wrestled myself into that chair, fighting an insistent belief that no one will care what I have to say.

I'm focused on the computer screen, fingers poised on the keyboard, waiting for words to come, but no thoughts break through my dense puzzlement about where to begin.

To ease the pressure, I remove my hands from the keyboard and place them palms down on the desk.

Suddenly, I feel something important bubbling to the surface. Leaning my head to the side as if listening, a statement ripe with meaning and of startling clarity erupts into my awareness. I profess out loud what must have come from a deep knowing that my freedom is at stake: "When I write, I will be as truthful as my memory allows. Integrity will rule!"

I pause, taking in a deep breath, feeling fear over my own injunction. The Watcher, who's beginning to show up more often, reassures me:

Avoid worrying about being honest.

Painful stories told more than once will soon lose their power to unsettle you.

Telling them will one day be like speaking of a mere thunderstorm that passed through your life.

Even with this reassuring message from the wise part of me, I'm still not ready to write.

I know the truth is for me. Integrity feels oh so right—natural. And I like natural. More important, being chronically ill and threatened by suicidal death has burned away any need to cover up the hard lessons taught by harsh circumstances. Pretense seems trifling.

Even so, I still hold back from writing.

Seeking grounding support for my intention to be transparent, I reach for my signed copy of Brenda's book that I keep close to my desk. After finding the passages I'm looking for by referring to my notes in the back of the book, I reread, "Those adults who've suffered childhood trauma are at far greater risk of developing serious diseases as adults than those who haven't. . . . Children who grow up in spring-loaded environments, [like me] where their need for vigilance remains fairly constant, have a higher rate of illness overall."[2]

Wanting more assurance, I find a quote in Brenda's book from a discussion about related research she had with Dr. Robert Anda, once an epidemiologist for the CDC: "'The risk factors for the leading causes of disease are not randomly distributed. It's not a roll of the dice, but a rigged game that has more to do with childhood experience than anyone could have predicted.'"[3]

I keep reading, looking for the one statement that resonates with my intention to be honest in my writing, remembering there's a bit more to the idea.

I find the sweet spot in a summary about the major health benefits of opening up about traumatic childhood events: "The tantalizing implication is that we're only as healthy as the secrets we share."[4]

I've opened up about the often violent eruptions of my father's irrational temper. And my mother's unwillingness to stand up for me and my sister.

Yet, there are secrets of adolescent trauma, sequestered by shame, that I've never told anyone.

Pondering, I put aside *You Can Beat the Odds.*

Shame seeps into my awareness.

Suddenly I grasp the understanding that shame has been a master of contortion and deception. Shame has kept my child-hood secrets festering, despoiling my self-worth.

And probably compromising my immune system, too!

In this shame-facing moment, I acknowledge feeling embar-rassment about attempting suicide. Besides wanting to escape misery, I didn't want to feel that way, so I was motivated to do a stellar job at attempting to kill myself.

I'm tired of shame.

Weary from keeping secrets about my past.

Exhausted.

Done!

I take in a deep breath, gathering resolve and courage for what I know is coming. Again out loud, I declare, "I intend to tell my secrets." All of them. I will houseclean my soul.

Whatever that takes.

Freedom beckons!

ENTRAINING
WITH AWARENESS

The language of truth
is born in stillness,
shimmering with the light of dawn.

I begin to write, learning how to express my truths. The process plays an integral and unexpected role in my healing, partnered with the mind-body medicine strategies on my to-do list.

My self-initiated imperative to be open and honest while going live with my life's trauma presents me with grueling challenges, surprising me with stories of my past now free from the constraint of shame. They surface in no apparent logical sequence. Related feelings erupt into my presence, adding to the panic attacks that jerk me around when Lyme threatens.

With an ever-increasing trust in my intuition, when the stories from my past show up, I pause to feel them flood the present: a nodule of shame, making me want to bow my head; a memory of abuse choking my throat with long-suppressed grief; or a realization of a heartrending tragedy left in Lyme's wake, filling my eyes with sorrow.

Each time I face a painful emotional wound, there's a moment of exquisite torture I don't think I can stand, peaking just before I finally decide to open the emotional floodgate and release pent-up feelings. When I do, signs of healing burst into my space like pus exploding from a punctured boil. After wailing, groaning, grieving, or raging, there's respite for a time as quiet tears stream down my face.

Then a sigh.

Then sweet peace.

A softening. A feeling of compassion for myself. Lingering mellow sorrow, maybe. But the excruciating pain is no longer there. And I'm able to find the words to tell my story.

Once I've recovered fully from a turbulent episode and even danced a little, my intuition nudges me once again, knowing precisely when I'm ready to face another emotionally laden challenge. And one soon surfaces.

Managing my emotions is a work in progress. No small task, yet worth every ounce of effort I put into learning how.

While discovering how to manage my feelings, I'm trying to figure out how to master the art of writing. Although my writing is important, the strategies on my mind-body medicine to-do list are the "big rocks" in my schedule, still coming first!

When I tire of the regimen dedicated to prompting my immune system to perform at peak, I remind myself that I do have a choice about how I spend my time. And, I'm quick to remember the reason I set out to discipline myself with a checklist in the first place: To be healthy. To reclaim my life.

No small matter.

The strategies I use are universally efficacious. The research points to that.[1]

Yet the way they play out for me, and would for anyone else, for that matter, is as unique as a finely tailored garment made from a choice fabric—the right fit.

My beliefs about the strategies' potential power to heal are critical.

Bruce Lipton, a cell biologist, devotes an entire book to the effects of beliefs on health. In *The Biology of Belief*, he notes the results of research outcomes related to the use of placebos—and *no*cebos: "When the mind, through positive suggestion, improves health, it is referred to as the placebo effect. Conversely, when the same mind is engaged in negative suggestions that can damage health, the negative effects are referred to as the *nocebo* effect. In medicine, the nocebo effect can be as powerful as the placebo effect."[2]

When I first read about the biology of belief, my jaw dropped as I began to grasp how my negative expectations about becoming debilitated and destitute had affected my emotions, stoking anxiety and thwarting my body's efforts to heal—a bit like dropping a granite boulder on top of a seed trying to sprout.

In *You Can Beat the Odds*, there's a flashing neon-light injunction for me to be as particular about the thoughts I allow to take hold in my brain as I am about people who enter my apartment: "Your brain is like a virtual pharmacy, influencing your body as it responds to your emotions and to your thinking processes. In every moment of our lives, an ever-changing array of hormones and molecules interact, nudging us either toward health or toward disease."[3]

There's much more to monitoring my thoughts than I ever imagined. Keeping my own internal, thought-induced pharmacy in mind, I come to think of each thought as having a signature chemistry that's mine to infuse—or change my thinking. I have my work cut out for me, developing emotional muscle for harnessing runaway thoughts threatening to jerk me around, creating havoc in my body's chemistry, carrying the lethal potential to make me emotionally and physically sick—again.

The Watcher, the voice of my own sagacity, is becoming an invaluable guide for developing emotional balance. Speaking the healing language of wisdom and change, my sage self is showing up more and more often, slowly creating room in my heart for light to play and smile as a result of my dedicated meditation practice.

I didn't expect that scenario.

Following the advice of my therapist, I reintroduced my meditation practice to learn to relax, expecting to reduce systemic inflammation, thereby supporting my immune system and my efforts to heal.

To my surprise, emotional stabilization, critical to my recovery, slowly manifests, too, with the help of The Watcher. When crafting awareness by observing my breath, I discover that I can somehow step outside emotional disturbances and then steady myself with wise advice.

What do I mean?

A quote from *Seeking the Heart of Wisdom*, coauthored by Jack Kornfield and Joseph Goldstein, speaks to the issue: "[Meditation] means collecting the mind or bringing together the mind and body, focusing one's attention on one's experience in the present moment.

"Most fundamentally it is a simple process of focusing and steadying attention on an object like the breath and bringing the mind back to that object again and again. It requires that we let go of thoughts about the past and future, of fantasies and attachment, and bring the mind back to what is actually happening; the actual moment of feeling, of touching the breath as it is."[4]

The authors continue, revealing the birthplace of The Watcher: "Wisdom comes from directly observing the truth of our experience."[5]

Jon Kabat-Zinn, founding director of the Stress Reduction Clinic and the Center for Mindfulness in Medicine at the University of Massachusetts Medical School, offers more: "Mindfulness meditation is paying attention, on purpose, in the moment, non-judgmentally. . . .

"Awareness is something that we are intimately familiar with and yet complete strangers to. So, training in mindfulness cultivates resources that are already [ours]. We don't have to go anywhere or get anything, but we do have to learn how to inhabit another domain of mind that, as a rule, we are fairly out of touch with."[6]

Understanding that my thoughts had much to do with creating my anxious states was a first step. By observing my breath, noticing what my mind was doing when wandering came next. In a certain way, that process fostered the ability to be an observer of the functioning of my own mind.

Much of my thoughts at the beginning stages of healing were related to worrying about the future: *What if my money runs out. What if I have to go into a nursing home. What if . . .* During my meditation sittings, noticing those thoughts arise in a nonjudgmental way helped me to understand that they were detached from reality and the present moment. As a result, I was afforded the spaciousness for developing the insight that I was, indeed, safe and that well-being was truly mine in the moment. And that pathway led to an understanding that eventually made safe the letting go of fears that weren't serving my well-being.

Besides experiencing the real-time results of my meditation practice, research supporting the use of mindfulness meditation to enhance my immune system impresses me, compelling me to stay dedicated to a daily sitting practice.[7]

As the wise part of me becomes increasingly adept at observing my thoughts and feelings without letting them carry me away into fearsome drama, wisdom, expressed by the voice of The Watcher, heals using diverse talent.

And by paying attention to the detailed characteristics of my thoughts and feelings while I'm meditating, I'm training myself to work with them when I'm out and about, otherwise living my life.

Meditating isn't always a walk in the park. Often I'm sleepy and would rather nap or turn the light out for the night than train my mind to be in the present. Restlessness occasionally makes me want to throw in the towel. Then there's the rebellion I feel about disciplining myself to be still and watch.

Somehow I usually manage to put all those obstacles aside by shifting into a state of curiosity. Interest in what's to come lightens me, lifting the ominous weight of discipline. Instead of dread, I'm sometimes able to feel excited, expecting something intriguing to happen while I pay attention to my mind's ever-flowing change.

In the end I come to know how meditating nurtures me beyond developing awareness or enhancing my immune system. When setting aside time to be quiet, intending to help myself heal, I'm sending a symbolic, loving message to my body: "You're important to me. I care enough about you to pay attention to your needs."

The simple insight meditation techniques I use are rooted in ancient Buddhist traditions. I'm not a student of Buddhist psychology at this point, yet I'm aware of one of the foundational tenets: all things change.

That includes my emotions, although sometimes they've felt cemented—especially anxiety.

Gradually, by getting in touch with my mind and body, I experience the fluidity of my feelings, even of anxiety.

One day, I'm meditating, and anxiety erupts. Focusing on the feeling—an area near my heart where acute physical pain manifests, I notice something that changes everything. For a mere split second, I feel calm. I feel the cessation of anxiety and chest pain.

Hope resounds: *Maybe, just maybe, I can learn to lengthen the space between the feelings that have caused me such misery.*

The next time anxiety arises while I'm meditating, I notice more: the intensity of feelings comes and goes, swelling, saturating my body, then receding.

Receding!

The Watcher microscopes the calm between the waves:

You're on to something here.

You can figure out how to create more space between the waves.

Yes, you can!

And remember, paying attention to your feelings eased them.

You've been pushing anxiety away for years.

This particular point of awareness is a boundless treasure born of ancient Buddhist teachings: there's suffering in aversion.

Understanding that concept blesses me. I feel crowned with a halo of light, illuminating the way to a peaceful me.

A peaceful me?

Toward that end, two sequential circumstances taught me profound lessons in emotional management. Learning them was critical to putting my life back together.

The first occurred during an unforgettable experience in a rural setting where ironic humor finds room to entertain . . .

WELL-SEASONED

Funny thing:
Something stinkin' awful
that happens to me
sometimes teaches my wee tiny brain
a good lesson.

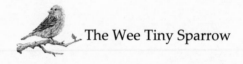

The Wee Tiny Sparrow

The months after receiving The Gift of the Circle, in the early days of 2010, until September, when I leave for Utah, are rich with meaningful lessons. They're intermingled with the emotional challenges of healing and the joy of feeling free to learn and play in the sun.

One morning in early January, my friend Marilyn calls, initiating an unforgettable lesson that will help me loosen the sometimes breath-choking grip of anxiety. At the beginning of our conversation, Marilyn and I spend a few moments sharing what's going on in our lives, then she makes an intuitive, no-nonsense suggestion so like her: "I've got a great idea I want you to think about. How about volunteering at the horse rescue farm that's down the road from my house? Remember, the one I took you to a few months ago?"

"I do. What's going on?"

"The farm needs help. You need to occupy yourself constructively. I think you're a good match for each other."

I promise to think about her idea before ending our exchange.

Although I'm beginning to understand the connection between
my thoughts and feelings, anxiety is still more of a tyrannical force
than I'd like. So I figure engaging in an activity that focuses my
thoughts on something other than myself might be a good thing.
Besides, doing something at a farm in the fresh air and sunshine
is my idea of a great deal.

After deciding to follow up on Marilyn's suggestion, I call the
horse farm's office to offer my services. When I do, I'm dumb-rock
clueless about the special "fresh air" project that awaits me.

———

For decades before I got sick, my morning routine involved
getting out of bed before daybreak, finding my way to the kitchen
to get a cup of bold, hot coffee, and doing handwork while sipping
my brew.

Sickness robbed me of the energy to do even simple things like
that. That's changed, for I've returned to my pre-dawn routine
with a slight variation. In the early-morning silence, while sipping
coffee, I first read devotions to set my rudder for the day. After
pondering what I've read for a while, I pick up handwork, taking
pleasure in knitting or crocheting. Doing just a little revives
memories of healthier times. And there's a reassuring, soothing
normalcy about the process that's encouraging.

Before I go to the horse farm on my first day of volunteering, I
make my way through my morning activities and then dress for
the occasion. First, I don a long-sleeved, white, cotton, waffle-
weave underwear top to brace myself for the low-thirties
temperature outside. Next, I step into light-gray sweatpants and
then top off my upper body with a red, jersey T-shirt and a dark-
gray, fleece sweatshirt. Everything's loose—I can't stand tight
clothes!

Carolyn Martin Graham

After straightening my sweatshirt over my hips, I slip my feet into gray, wool socks and sturdy, brown, scuffed boots, hoping my feet will stay warm in these old leather friends of mine.

To finish off my *"haute couture,"* I wrap a bright-orange, fleece scarf around my neck a few times, feeling oh so snuggly. Orange gloves with black, no-slip fabric in the palms prepare my hands for the car's icy-cold steering wheel.

The final touch?

A red, plaid cap with an extra-long bill.

When I catch a glimpse of myself in the mirror, the smiling, decked-out reflection looking back makes me burst out laughing. Given my recent stays in psychiatric hospitals, there's lush irony in what I see.

I give myself a high-five thinking I couldn't look more insane. *You are a loose fit indeed.*

———

After parking on a patch of gravely gray dirt at the horse farm, I'm getting out of my car when I notice a man. When he's close, he extends his hand, introducing himself as the farm manager.

Looking him up and down, I notice he's wearing scuffed, brown leather boots, too, only his are pointed-toe cowboy boots. A dark-brown, curled-rim, leather cowboy hat crowns a statement of character that's as unique as my own.

From my five feet five inches, I inspect more of his five feet three inches of what I now think is pure rough-critter: a rangy, taught spring, wearing jeans tight enough to keep him irritated, poised to strike like a rattlesnake.

His bowed legs make me think he's got to make room for some mighty big balls. I figure I'm right about that as soon as he tells me he rides bulls in rodeos.

After our lean niceties are over, he fires a question at me: "What'd ya come here fer?"

Waiting for my answer, he leans his head sideways while his

squinting eyes scan me up and down, speaking silent reservations. They linger on my face, which is thoroughly etched with wrinkled stories. I know he can tell I'm carrying some earth time.

Sixty-seven years, to be exact.

Eager to start working, I answer his question with a reply, oozing naiveté: "Whatever needs to be done. I came here to help. Put me to use where you need me the most."

"Okay, then." Taking off without further ado, and motioning me to follow, he swaggers ahead of me to the nearby barn, where twenty-four horses are stalled overnight—in individual stalls. The horses have been let out to graze on green pastures in fresh breezes. When we reach the barn, the farmhand opens the gate to the first stall. My nostrils are blasted with the caustic stench of ammonia.

Grinning, the farm manager bows, pointing with his extended right hand to the evidence left behind of well-functioning equine systems: urine-soaked, hoof-mashed horse manure, mixed in scant straw. I'm stunned by the fetor. By my farm-chore igno-rance. And by the enormity of my beckoning task.

While I muster up the courage to honor my commitment to work where I'm needed most, the farmhand brings me a rusted wheelbarrow with a black, fat-tubed tire at the front, and a wide-bladed shovel. When they're at my feet, he points to the stalls on both sides of the barn then motions me to follow him once again. At the other end of the barn, we exit to an impressive view: a large field humped with countless mounds of moist and dry dung heaps.

Even on this chilly morning, warm, aromatic fumes rising from sunbaked manure, assaulting my already offended nostrils. *So much for working in the fresh air.*

I clearly see the full range of my task and the farm manager smirking.

How lovely, I showed up just in time to shovel shit!

Acknowledging my understanding of my job, I nod to the farmhand.

He gives me a thumbs-up, spins on his heels, and struts toward the gate of the first stall. When we're there, he bows toward the inside, finalizing his mandate. Adding emphasis to his silent directive, he turns his head to the side opposite me, then fires a shot of dark-brown tobacco juice to the ground and swaggers off.

For three hours straight that day, and every day for weeks afterward, I shovel urine-soaked horse manure. My strength and stamina amaze me; I've been down so long I didn't think I had any left. The stuff I shovel from the stall floors has a repulsive stench so potent that I can't think about anything else except harnessing my energy to end my task as fast as possible. Every second I'm working, my attention rivets to each shovelful of urine-soaked manure. I take care not to spill even a speck in an effort to hasten the end of my duty. I overload the wheelbarrow in my zealous enthusiasm to finish shoveling. Wheeling the loads is a real struggle because the overloaded wheelbarrow is prone to swerving and tipping over. Maneuvering takes every ounce of energy and focus I can muster. Then there's the dumping area: I'm forced to go to the far reaches of the field to find empty space.

By the time I finish my work each day, I don't have anxiety—not even a little. And none shows up for hours afterward. My stench-drenched focus on urine-soaked manure anchored me into the present. The level of physical effort required to do "anything that needs to be done" burned off any angst about my untoward commitment and anything else.

After several weeks, I begin to grasp an enormous lesson: When my focus is not on my illness and debilitation, anxiety evaporates. When I'm working at the horse farm, I'm in Eckhart Tolle's "power of now." There simply isn't room for wild-eyed thoughts to enter my mind when I'm focused in the present doing something I know is possible, albeit noxious. The profound physical activity of my work uses up every trace of adrenaline and other chemicals that invoke anxiety. As a result, I'm calm for a long while.

Also, while I'm shoveling, I come to know I'm powerful

enough to triumph at the task at hand—a radically different self-perception than the victim-like posture I wore when Lyme was on a rampage.

I keep going to the horse rescue farm week after week to get a shit-shoveling calm.

One morning, I'm walking to the barn to do my thing when the farm manager angles toward me with his usual swagger, and a smile wrapped around his ears. When he's by my side, he turns his head then fires a stream of tobacco juice to the ground before he speaks. "I been talkin' 'bout you."

Captivated by his aura, I mimic his vernacular: "Oh yeah, what'd ya say? Somethin' 'bout some ole lady comin' out here?"

"Nah. Thar were some younguns hangin' 'round tryin' to act busy. I told 'em how ya work 'til yer done with the job."

I'm struck silent, certain something big is coming my way.

Making me even more certain, I watch spellbound while the farm manager lowers his forearms to hitch up his britches, something some guys do when they think they're heading into a challenge, perhaps making certain their balls are intact.

Anyway, this rough-hewn piece of work cocks his head to the side. Next, for emphasis or reassurance, he fires an especially big wad of tobacco juice to the ground.

Then he leans his head away from me in the first unsure pose I've seen. With slow deliberation, he raises his eyes, telling me he's not real sure if he should proceed. "I told 'em yer . . ."

"Go on. Tell me what ya told 'em."

"I told 'em ya work 'til yer done with the job, even though yer, uh . . . well-seasoned."

TO SHOOT A
BIRD—OR NOT

When I let another bird's rage
ruffle my feathers,
I'm helpless.
I have to ease my quills,
and let go of the anger
before I can fly free again.

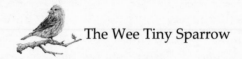 The Wee Tiny Sparrow

Some say life's events are made up of nothing more than streams of co-arising phenomena, interacting endlessly, directed only by one's own conditioned mind. Others say every incident is predestined by an omniscient God.

My belief about the origin of events falls somewhere in the middle of those two extremes.

For me, a Divine Force mysteriously orchestrates happenings in nature and in my life—a force in which I see the presence of purposeful direction. At such times, there seems to be a certain kind of familiar synchronicity magnetizing recent events—like when I received The Gift of the Circle. My powerful learning at the horse farm was like that, too, coming precisely when I needed to develop an awareness about how my anxiety is diminished when I'm in the present moment.

Soon after my potent lesson at the horse farm, a radically

different set of circumstances manifests. Again, at the hand of the Divine, I am informed by yet another life-altering experience. This time, real-time power derived from my meditation practice enters into a stream of events to teach.

When meditating, I've been training my mind to pay attention to sensations of air passing in and out of my nostrils. Sometimes I've focused, instead, on the sensations of my abdomen rising and falling by placing my hand there when I breathe.

Noticing what's happening with my breathing sounds too simple to matter much.

Research says otherwise.

Shallow breathing is known to escalate blood pressure, invite cancer proliferation, contribute to the deterioration of brain cells, create anxious mind states, and compromise immune-system function.[1]

Since childhood I'd been breathing high in my chest without using my diaphragm to fill my lungs to capacity.

Because I grew up in a household with an unpredictable and sometimes violent father, staying on high alert was necessary for my well-being. My home always felt unsafe, so I stayed poised for escape, wary and frightened. Flight mode became my habituated stance into adulthood, restricting my breathing.

Later, terror over losing my income, job, and home exacerbated a habit that kept my hands so cold strangers would shrink back when I touched them. Often they'd grab their own in astonishment, exclaiming, "Your hands feel like ice cubes!" Until lately, I didn't know cold hands are often evidence of unhealthy breathing.[2] Evidence, as in my case, that emotional and physical welfare is being compromised.

Although my well-being is improving now—and I'm no longer in my father's presence—my breathing is still habitually shallow most of the time. Changing my long-standing habit of holding myself spring-loaded tight, poised for flight, isn't easy.

But using my breath as a focus during meditation is helping. Often, when I place my hand on my abdomen, I invite myself to inhale deeply using my diaphragm. In doing so, I'm summoning calmness while engaging one of my body's most powerful detoxification processes to help me heal.[3] Also, I'm gradually conditioning myself to slow down and to relax, counteracting the tense agitation I've unknowingly manifested for decades.

There's something else at work during my meditation that takes life in the story to come. While focusing on my breath, my mind inevitably takes a trip—away from the moment. That's what all minds do. When I become aware that my mind is no longer in the present, I gently change the direction of my thinking—without judgment—and return to my intended focus.

Sometimes when I'm meditating, powerful emotions grab my attention; if they're persistent, rather than allowing them to carry me away, I shift my focus from my breath to search for the thoughts prompting them:

Was I imagining canoeing on the Green River—feeling excited?

Was I thinking this healing stuff is too hard for me—prompting discouragement?

Was I revisiting a painful event—summoning fear, depression or sadness?

When I become curious about my emotions, they soften and fade, confirming the idea that all things change. When they evaporate, I return to noticing aspects of my breathing, calming and balancing myself.

In essence, I'm training The Watcher to be conscious of what's happening in my mind and body while strengthening my understanding that they are inextricably partnered.

And in those split-second moments when The Watcher notices what's happening with my unruly mind—and redirects my focus—I'm artfully sculpting emotional prowess.

I'm reminded of the time when I was eight, learning to play the violin. In the beginning, with my shiny wooden instrument tucked under my left chin and my resin-coated bow stroking the strings, I attempted to create a simple melody: "Mary Had a Little Lamb." The screeching sound pained my dog's ears, her yowls voicing protest. With practice, though, I learned to marry enough attention and skill to tease out a melody that invited smiles and the vision of a gentle, white-fleeced being nestled beside me.

I'm at the screechy violin stage in my healing process, learning lessons, practicing skills, and cultivating awareness.

Even so, my beginner's attempts at discovering my thoughts and their related emotional testimony—as well as learning to calm myself with my breathing—is giving birth to an unexpected awakening.

An awakening to yet another powerful reality and a new way to be in this world.

———

One Sunday morning I'm sitting in my car at a red light.

My mind is distant, drifting. I'm enjoying an intoxicating revelry somewhere, so much so that I'm unaware when the light changes to green.

A blaring horn startles me.

Fear twists my gut, distorting reason.

I freeze, bracing for a crash.

My failure to move forward stokes a cauldron of anger already boiling in the male driver behind me.

Smoking, screeching tires and a bellowing horn signal wrath as he careens around my car.

I feel assaulted. An inferno of rage engulfs my own body. Heat flushes my face. My eyes glint with ice-forged daggers.

Fiery indignation fries my logic.

Sneering, I cock my bird finger.

Vile words beg to scream: Asshole. Dickhead. You dough-headed fuckface. Their goading urges me to give chase.

Yet I don't.

I don't shoot a bird, either.

In a split second . . . everything changes.

The newly conditioned part of me makes the choice not to react. Not to react to the beguiling rage I felt.

My bird finger relaxes. My defused hand then rests on my thigh.

I begin breathing with my diaphragm, filling my lungs, rhythmically calming myself.

After noticing there are no other cars behind me, I listen to The Watcher, who grabs my attention:

Your seductive anger tempted expression.

That's an understatement. Right?

I don't know if I've ever seen your bird finger so ready to fly.

A knee-jerk reaction, you know. One you've practiced to perfection.

You've a different skill to learn. One that will serve you better.

The choice you made to avoid reaction is critical to your health.

Remember, your emotions brew their own chemistry.

You can't afford to create a toxic body with toxic thoughts and toxic actions.

Keep breathing deeply, calming yourself even more.

You're on the right track!

What happens to conclude this episode with rage is nothing short of a miracle.

First, I release residues of outrage in a long sigh, looking ahead when I do. My attention is drawn to the dark silhouette of the driver who sparked my ire. He's gunning his engine, then slamming on his brakes. Halting, jerking, halting, jerking—a tortured mass of human rage and metal driving up the ramp of an interstate highway.

With a kind, gentle voice The Watcher speaks again:

You know well the agitation of the driver who angered you just moments ago.

You also know why you wouldn't want to be in his body.

You didn't want to be in your own once.

You're softening, experiencing the pain of the other driver now that the veil of your own ire has lifted.

Notice the feelings now bathing your heart.

What are they?
Compassion born of your own tragedy.
Compassion born of serenity and wisdom.

When reflecting about the transition of my feelings from rage to compassion, I'm awed.

I become keenly aware that engaging healthy breathing began calming me in the face of wrath. I chose to rein in my emotions rather than allow them to carry me away, weaving the tapestry of peace patterning my meditation practice.

After contemplating that moment, an insight bursts into my consciousness: I have the power to choose my thoughts. The power to steer my feelings in a direction that works to my benefit.

My choices about the way I think and act then infuse my body with either toxic chemicals or those inviting calm, peace, and good health.

I can choose to shoot a bird—or not!

IMPROBABLE CRUCIBLES

Sometimes I find seeds
buried deep in the dirt.
When I am done eating them,
I perch on a twig to rest,
nourishing the earth with their remains.
My wee tiny brain often wonders then,
is life about circles?

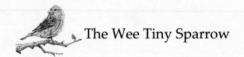 The Wee Tiny Sparrow

The gut often speaks the language of truth.

Over the years my gut sent me intuitive, intelligent messages I ignored. Those messages were sometimes subtle, sometimes not. No matter, I cast them aside, when paying attention to them might have saved me a lot of trouble.

As mindfulness sensitivity to physical cues, The Watcher is learning to respond to my deep-belly messages. In fact, the wise part of me and my gut are becoming close companions, conversing in a rational way.

When a visceral reaction to circumstances prompts consideration, now, more often than not, I review my situation, and then give direction. Even if there's impending emotional pain, I'm prone to act on that direction with serious intention.

During this period of intense healing, memories of my father's abusive treatment often surface, evoking discomfort. Even though I've hidden those memories deep down in my subconscious, the natural healer in me knows I must now open and release them—and other heartbreaking childhood traumas.

I've never faced the full measure of my father's destructive behavior until now. And, I don't have the emotional stamina to process everything that happened between us in one big lump. So, an intelligent inner physician releases a dose of darkness I can handle and then allows me respite to heal one wound before another is opened.

——

My dad was a mixture of extremes.

He wasn't all bad. Yet when I reflect on my childhood, I sometimes struggle to find the good in him.

When I was a kid, my father kept our home life in turmoil. He was as unpredictable as a roulette wheel. Because he probably hadn't had a soft place to land when he was a kid, he didn't know how to provide one. He offered no cushion when I made a mistake, no helping hand in managing the tough stuff.

He didn't know how to love me simply for being the wonderful child I was. I tried to be perfect so he would take me in his arms, tell me he loved me, tell me he was proud of his little girl. The truth is, even if I had been perfect, he might not have given me what I yearned for.

I felt wobbly when I was young, teetering on the razor's edge of a cliff, with no room for a misstep—ready to fall into a black hardness with no one to stop the bone-shattering, heart-wrenching splat I thought was sure to come.

Fear of my father's unrelenting criticism and his beatings caged me in fear.

My mother was caged in fear too. Fear of being abandoned by him for another woman. Fear of being poverty stricken, homeless, and unable to take care of me and my sister. Dad pickaxed my mother's self-confidence with hard, cold words, convincing her she was inadequate. Although he never hit her with his fists, he might as well have.

My mother's principles, intellect, and talent were subservient to my father's reign of terror. Crossing my father to stand up for me and my sister simply wasn't possible for her. And for some reason she deified him, adopting his opinion of her as the final word.

Without knowing what was happening, I did the same thing.

Even so, I couldn't figure out why I didn't like my mother, although I felt her goodness in my bones. She offered the only love and stability I knew, especially when my father wasn't around to interfere.

When my father *was* home, he scrutinized me, arbitrarily striking with pointed criticism or worse. For an insignificant mistake, a gentle child's try at coping with a complex environment, he beat me with a belt or a razor strap.

He beat my adorable, curly-haired, redheaded little sister. I cringed every time I saw him strike her. When he hurt her, he hurt me too. But I couldn't protect her.

When I was in high school, something dramatic happened between me and my father. One evening at the dinner table, I made a derogatory remark about the lima beans I had to eat. My father vaulted from his chair, jerked me up by my left arm with his bull-muscle strength, digging his fingers into flesh that screamed for release. After kicking my chair aside with his foot, he forced me to walk ahead of him to my bedroom in the back of the house, where he shoved me through the doorway, still gripping my arm. With his free hand he unbuckled his belt and then zipped his weapon into the air, snapping the end, preparing to strike.

Somehow, I found the agility and strength to circle him, using the arm that was gripping mine as a pivot, my eyes riveted on his belt. Desperate to avoid my father's wrath, I spun around and around him, pleading, "Please don't hit me, Daddy. Please don't hit me."

Suddenly, something changed. In total silence, he let go of me and lowered his striking arm. Still mute, he put on his belt, then walked slowly back toward the dinner table, his head bowed.

Although that was the last time he beat me, my habit of staying vigilant and poised for attack remained frozen in place.

My current challenges with shallow breathing and anxiety attest to that.

———

I don't know much about my father's childhood. He died in 1992, so I can't ask him questions. Even if I could, I don't think he'd be able to share his experiences. So, I'm left to fumble in the mist, trying to understand him and our relationship.

I do know my father was the oldest of five children. When he was a boy, he shucked oysters and deep-sea fished with a commercial fisherman to help feed his family of six.

Based on snippets of information I heard over the years, he was bullied by other children, and perhaps treated too harshly by his parents. His treatment of me likely mimicked his own childhood experiences.

When acknowledging my father's childhood suffering, I sometimes feel compassion for him. Mostly, though, I feel sorrow or resentment when remembering how his bitter heart didn't know how to let go of his impoverished childhood.

Throughout my own youth, my father tight-fisted praise. And money, except when spending for himself, or providing for one of his many paramours. My father was Clark Gable—handsome and charismatic, attracting women he couldn't refuse. His lavish sexual and monetary attentions to his lovers compromised any chance for being generous with his own family members. All the same, he had much to say about money—about saving, tithing, paying bills on time. To his credit, where those matters were concerned, he followed his own sound financial advice.

Sound or not, his final words to me about economic self-sufficiency were ruthless.

He could have been kind, for I was as responsible about finances as he'd taught me to be.

Tight-fisted, fear-baited bitterness distorts vision, though . . .

———

My turn is coming. I can hardly wait!

When my name is called, I walk up a few stairs and across the stage toward the president of Western Carolina College. With my right hand I shake his while he places my diploma for my bachelor's degree in the other.

My parents are in the audience. I wonder if they're as proud of me as I am of myself. Because my father paid my tuition, I hope he's feeling I'm worth the expense.

After the president pronounces the class of 1965 graduated, I bound toward them as they chat with the dean of women, whom I worship. As I approach, my father extends his right hand. I shake his with my own—expecting congratulations.

Instead, he attacks. "Why didn't you make the dean's list?"

My pride withers—and dies. I drop his hand, but I can't let go of his words. My eyes, now filled with shame, seek refuge on the floor.

After gathering enough strength to stretch a smile across my face, I lift them, peering into an awkward silence. I'm speechless. I don't know what to say. I don't know what to expect.

I don't have long to wait.

With whip-lashing malice, my father attacks again: "Now, that's all you will ever get from me!"

———

Learning to manage my thoughts and emotions began at the horse farm while I shoveled manure, and at the traffic signal as I observed my reactions to another's anger transition to compassion. Those events were merely the beginning of a complex journey. Their simplicity belies the difficult nature of understanding my emotional triggers, the role my subconscious plays in my life, and the motivations that prompt my decisions to feel certain ways.

Managing my emotions will be an active, ongoing challenge during the next few years—and key to my recovery. Deciding to release painful memories, like those related to my father, when they well up into the present will be a significant part of my healing. And my creativity will play a starring role during the next few years when those memories surface. That ingenious part of me will loosen self-imposed judgment, allowing me to tailor the strategies on my mind-body medicine to-do list to my unique circumstances.

Although everyone is creative, I'm blessed with a megadose of the spark that ignites imagination, sending my thoughts into the Aethers, the wide-open space without boundaries. There, I connect free-floating ideas, forming unique concepts. Many times I manifest them.

Creativity was at the root of my professional success. And my eccentric personal life spoke of an artistic flair that gifted me with immeasurable pleasure.

Where did my gift of creativity come from?

From my father. My obstreperous father.

———

When I was a child, my father, a licensed sea captain, always had a small, ocean-going wooden fishing boat he navigated with skill. Using his extensive knowledge of game fish habits he had learned as a boy, he fished to eat in the same way he did when he was young. Saltwater game fish were a staple of my family's diet.

My father was a talented fisherman, taking pride in slapping an abundant catch on the dock when nearby commercial fishermen returned from sea with empty holds and a boat full of disappointed tourists who'd paid to catch the big ones.

Disgruntled, those fishermen frequently dared to ask my father what he used for bait.

"Something *I* make," was as far as he would go toward revealing the answer to his routine, bountiful catches that made him both a dock irritant and a celebrity.

The fishermen, hoping my father would be generous with his secret, used commercially manufactured, bright-colored lures bristling with hooks secured to their underbellies. Some of them had shiny pieces of light-catching metal attached. And some were segmented, causing them to squiggle.

No matter how fancy, they couldn't compare to my father's.

His were made from improbable materials and crafted in the sagging, wooden garage that stood behind our house. Engaging his ever-active imagination, my father was inspired one day to make his own lures while passing my mother as she sat embroidering a tablecloth. His eyes riveted to bright-yellow and orange skeins of floss in her sewing basket.

With lightning speed, a vision of an irresistible lure must have flashed through his mind: A segment of sash chain about four inches long; three pairs of two-inch hooks, wired and evenly spaced along the length, ought to be enough to hang on to a big, thrashing fish. Clumps of six-inch, vividly colored embroidery floss, folded in half and slipknotted into every loop, would completely hide the danger.

I watched him make those imagined lures. I ate their success. Over and over my absorbent eyes observed my father using creative inspiration, crafting practical objects from unlikely materials, like he did when making bait out of sash chain and embroidery floss.

On a larger scale, my father was a visionary, seeing answers others couldn't dream of.

A fiercely independent thinker. He wrote the code for being his own person . . .

Sweltering heat plagued the summer days and nights of West Palm Beach where I grew up. There was no air conditioning to keep the humid heat from pressing down.

The church we attended had ceiling fans, yet they did little to cool the stifling air. To supplement their effort, we used cardboard fans with wooden handles, waving them back and forth during services that seemed as if they would never end.

In those days the church dress code for men dictated long-sleeved shirts, neckties, and a jacket. Undershirts were preferable.

My father took exception.

"Oh Jim, what will people think?" my mother nagged each hot summer Sunday morning as he dressed for church. Ignoring her protests, he donned a short-sleeved cotton sport shirt, open at the neck.

I took all that in with the silent, keen eyes of a raptor. And I somehow recognized that his decisions to be logical set him apart from others, placing him on the fringes of cultural norms. Even so, he was accepted socially and respected by his peers, a community leader.

My feelings about my father are as extreme as he was. When remembering his beatings, I feel hurt. When telling of his ridicule, his drawing the line about financial support, I still feel shame, embarrassment, and suck-in-my-breath fear.

But telling of his creative spirit and his courage to be sensible makes me feel big-sky pride in him. Little-girl pride. Look-up-to-my-daddy pride. And I'm now aware that he paved the way for me to be an independent thinker too.

I know exactly where I learned to step out with courage to express my creative ideas—inspired by reason. I know where I acquired the skills to make logical order of variables, manifesting sensible ideas into real-time usefulness even though doing so sometimes sends me to the fringes of culture norms, too, where I'm accepted like my father was.

I love the creative part of me that is his legacy—the part of me that sees limitless possibilities in the environment around me, the part that expects to find answers in the domain of the improbable, the part that turns my back on the editor that says, "Not possible."

As much as the damaged side of my father betrayed my tender innocence, distorting my self-worth, what was good in him nurtured my inherent creative spirit. Although he did so in an unskillful manner, he's the one who cut me loose from his pocketbook to empower me to be financially responsible and self-sufficient.

Appreciating the positive facets of his nature mirrored in my own saddens me sometimes. Had things been different, our common ground could have given us a place to share. Maybe we could have even had some fun together.

Despite the fact that emotions about my relationship with my father still run strong, there's a certain *isness* surrounding them that's beginning to bud. My new eyes of wisdom are revealing an ombre of perceptions: all of my father—his radical character flaws and his dynamic strengths —has molded me into who I am today. In their own way, his dynamic range of talents and imperfections are a significant part of the richly colored, multitextured tapestry patterning me. The me I'm beginning to love and understand.

UNIVERSAL LANGUAGES

My wee tiny kin are everywhere,
wearing our simple, earth-toned feathers.
We chirp at dawn,
telling of light,
quieting the voice
of even the blackest nights.

 The Wee Tiny Sparrow

Red-tailed hawks often show up to encourage me when I need to feel powerful or when something magnificent happens. They burst the boundaries of convention, connecting me with infinite possibilities as they paint the sky with their russet tail feathers.

My relationship with them and other raptors began some time during the 1990s when I was still living in my tree house.

After finishing my morning coffee and a few chores, I left my home to run, intending to prepare myself for officiating at a wedding. Feeling the need to expand my awareness and access my spiritual connection to the Aethers, I'm running on the shoulder of a road beside a lake, sparkling with rippled sunlight. Opening my mental boundaries into the vast, cloudless blue sky, I seek inspiration and strength for the task ahead.

My mind is floating when a powerful force rockets from the sky and collides with the earth just a few feet in front of me. I'm jolted into the present. My heart pounds. Terrified, I come to an abrupt halt. Drawn to an impressive energy, I feel the eyes of a large hawk pierce the distance between us.

I'm amazed the hawk dares to remain nearby. Attempting to make sense of what's happening and seeing nothing in his beak, I glance at the ground looking for a stunned snake or mouse. There's nothing there either.

While I'm still trying to make sense of things, the hawk lifts himself from the ground with a few graceful wing movements. Displaying the russet mark of a red-tailed hawk, he flies to a low-lying branch above my head, declaring an unmistakable supremacy.

The hawk's eyes and mine lock, magnetized by a shared awareness. While searching his for meaning, I sense that he's a Divine Messenger, sent to bestow a sacred kind of power.

I poise for more of the unexpected.

Suddenly, I feel infused with a shimmering light, pulsing with inspiration. Confidence fills me. I then know I will find meaningful words precisely when I need them when officiating during the forthcoming wedding.

The mesmerizing connection between me and the hawk invites me to remain with him forever. But, I must leave to return home to shower and dress for the early-afternoon ceremony.

Before ending what feels like a conversation, I nod, lower my eyes, and bow with my hands prayerfully clasped, acknowledging him for his magnificence and the gift he has bestowed.

"Thank you," I say aloud. "Namaste!"

———

When visiting my favorite sanctuary for injured raptors, I become oddly still, spellbound by their mere presence. And I'm not the only one. Each time I'm there, other visitors whisper, naturally awed like me.

Hawks and other raptors seem to command reverence. They're magnificent, speaking with piercing, wise eyes. When soaring with outspread wings in the vast expanse of the sky, they express a majestic freedom of spirit, inspiring me to soar in my own way.

On the day I received The Gift of the Circle, I was yearning to spread my wings to fly free of Lyme disease and anxiety, but I didn't know how until I finished reading *You Can Beat the Odds*.

Soon after scurrying to tell Janet I'd found the way to heal myself and then making my to-do list of mind-body medicine strategies I expected would restore my health, I listened to a piece of stirring instrumental music that flooded me with immense joy and gratitude for my recent discovery. Based on the research I'd just read about, I believed the rich, vibrant sounds were healing me—at that very moment.

I was glorying in the experience of restoration when Janet appeared in the doorway to my room. "Do you know that's an old hymn you're listening to?"

"What hymn?"

"On Eagle's Wings. Would you like to hear Michael Crawford's rendition?"

"Sure."

When I inserted Janet's CD into my computer, I wasn't expecting anything out of the ordinary. Yet, I was mesmerized by the voice filling my soul with words speaking of being raised on the wings of a raptor.

The hairs on my arms came to attention.

Tears streamed down my face.

I felt soft and warm. Blessed. Touched by an offering of Divine Hope.

As I begin healing, the silhouette of a raptor soars in my soul on the wings of song. Memories of the raptors in the sanctuary and the Divine Messenger perching on a tree limb fill me with awe and the promise of well-being.

While welcoming the feelings, an unexplained knowing tugs at my heart—calling that will begin to manifest when I first step over the threshold, entering my new apartment.

Over the years, I've experienced profound emotional reactions to music. Until reading *You Can Beat the Odds*, I hadn't thought of the emotionally stirring melodies I'd enjoyed as sonic vibrations with the power to facilitate healing—if the frequencies, volume, and one's musical tastes are taken into account.

In modern research outcomes, music is demonstrating the potential to prompt restoration of both body and mind. In the words of my therapist, renowned health psychologist Brenda Stockdale, "What we know puts music and sound squarely in the middle of any modern day pharmacopoeia."[1]

At the Cleveland Cancer Center, a study revealed that a half-hour music therapy session boosted the immunity of pediatric patients. In another study done elsewhere, classical music proved as relaxing as a high-potency benzodiazepine with critical-care patients.[2]

Music can boost endorphins, reduce cortisol production and inflammation, improve the recovery of stroke victims, reduce the amount of sedation needed for surgery, effect dramatic recoveries in comatose patients, and more.[3]

There's no doubt that music affects my moods.

My emotional state is critical to my healing—every mood has a corollary inner chemistry. My chemistry, in turn, determines the efficacy of my immune system. All of my emotions are important teachers. In short doses, they can work to my benefit; however, if I remain excited, anxious, or depressed for extended periods of time, I will foster an environment inviting Lyme bacteria to ravage my life again.

My positive emotional reactions to many types of music affect my inner chemistry in the same way a medical prescription does with one major exception: there are no side effects. So, I use music as I would a pharmaceutical—to promote my healing.

"On Eagle's Wings" becomes my most important vibrational medicine for a while.

I don't have instructions to regiment how often I need to induce the soaring joy I feel when I listen to the inspiring words and thrilling sounds, so I rely strictly on my gut to tell me.

These days, I pay close attention to my deep belly signals, often referring to a passage in my handbook for healing, *You Can Beat the Odds*, which is now dog-eared, underscored, and decorated with bright-colored page markers: "No organ system next to the brain has more nerve tissue than our gut, prompting scientists to refer to it as our 'second brain.' So the fabled gut instinct is actually an elegant example of mind-body communication. With this evidence in mind, we want to maintain a healthy respect for the messages coming from our bodies."[4]

I'm learning to do just that.

And The Watcher is close at hand when a gut impulse nudges me to listen to music for healing, sometimes imposing much-needed firm direction:

Trust your gut!

Remember, your gut is your internal messenger.

Honor that part of you that knows more than you sometimes think.

You're tempted to feel like you're a crazy person when you want to play "On Eagle's Wings" over and over. Avoid going there. Instead, acknowledge your intuitive intelligence—the part of you that knows exactly what you need. The perfect dose.

Taking in my own counsel, throughout the next few months I play "On Eagle's Wings" whenever I feel the need to until I feel right about ending a healing session. Sometimes I park my car, stop writing or whatever else I'm doing, to dose myself with my vibration-induced chemistry, at an amount tailored by instructions from my gut: a modus operandi I come to use throughout my healing journey with all the healing strategies on my to-do list.

Second to meditation, music is my most powerful medicinal resource, sometimes influencing me even after I turn out my light at night while I listen to Andrew Weil's *Vibrational Sound Healing*. During the introduction, his deep, rich voice, resonating with authority, fortifies my belief that music will, indeed, heal, a critical matter swaying the effects of his recording and others I use in my pharmacopeia.

Sometimes certain music provides powerful emotional leveraging.

While I'm still living with my sister, I have my first experience of using music to extricate myself from emotional turmoil when Lyme symptoms—real or mimicked by cellular memory—terrorize me, mauling the present.

When agitation first strikes, I try focusing on my feelings like I do routinely during meditation, hoping they will fade away.

They don't. So I waste no time doing something else. After grabbing my media player and waist pack, I head out the door to drive to a nearby park, planning to walk while playing music that I hope will restore balance to my unnerving emotions.

Even though my expectations are high, what actually happens is a thrilling surprise.

After parking, donning my waist pack and earbuds and locking my car, I walk down a few steps and onto a track. Pausing, I take in my surroundings, trying to settle myself. First, I see a gray cement ribbon gently curving around sloping hillocks of winter's straw-colored grass. Gazing at the far side of the park, stark silhouettes of steadfast tree trunks captivate me until my eyes flow upward, resting on sturdy, bold limbs hanging in the air. Then, meandering still, my gaze travels outward to the determined branches bordered with delicate, cocoa-brown twig-lace, fringing a vivid, starched-blue sky.

Nodding to the gallant, lacey twigs that brave the elements, I acknowledge the promise held in each tiny tip: *Spring will be here soon.*

While I savor that thought for a moment, The Watcher offers other pensive considerations:

There's promise in you, too, no matter what storms come your way.
Even though you've had your share of challenges, others may come.
You've not earned privileged indemnity.
That's just the way things are.
On the bright side, you're learning skills to deal with difficulties that will make them easier to handle.

Sighing, I nod.

Then, a brisk, cool breeze brushes my face, beckoning me to caper.

I'm already feeling less anxious, so I don't need a lot of encouragement to get going. After adjusting my earbuds, I find a playlist I named Apogee, and start playing the assorted mariachi and bluegrass music, thinking their rhythms will help, if anything can.

First I walk, steps brisk.

Then, I can't help myself.

I dance.

I dance, gyrating my body, raising my fisted hands in the air as the upbeat rhythms make me want to fly.

With reckless abandon, I exclaim out loud: "Yes! Indeed, you betcha. I'm headed to my highest point of development! Apogee, here I come."

Pumping my fist, I mark the moment. Yes! Yes! Yes!

Inspired to hold on to my faith in miracles, I leap into the adventure of a lifetime, continuing to frolic around the track.

After circling for the second time, I imagine being at the head of a choo-choo train, my friends, my sister, my doctors, and my therapist grabbing on behind, playing with me, thrilled to see me thriving.

With music and exercise as playmates, anxiety soon evaporates. Lyme symptoms terrorizing me just a short while ago are gone too!

I feel so much joy I don't care if anyone thinks I'm an old, crazy lady. So I continue to respond to music freely, choo-chooing and dancing to the voice of The Watcher, who can't help chiming in:

Life's too short to shackle your simple, childlike rejoicing.

Enjoy yourself.

Feel pride in your eccentricity.

After all, woman, you've just stepped out of death's clutches.

Play in fields of flowers.

Soar among the clouds with the wings of a raptor.

Dance in the wind where the big birds go . . .

Right on!

Slowing down to walk a bit, I think of something Ashley Montagu wrote in *Growing Young* in the 1980s, long before research confirmed his opinion: "Whether one dances by oneself or with others, it is the positive reinforcements that one receives from this poetry of motion, this feeling of being in tune with the universe, that is so uplifting and constructively beneficial it would be difficult to think of any activity of greater therapeutic value."[5]

Amen!

After remembering that inspiring message and feeling like I'm indeed growing young, my feet start dancing again to the upbeat rhythms of Apogee and my recovering heart.

Feelings of power and gratitude wash over me.

For the time being, I no longer carry the weight of disease or my own victimization.

———

Brenda Stockdale writes in *You Can Beat the Odds*, "Music can make us weep with joy or wail with grief, accompany us on a road trip to get away from it all, or take us back to a time we want to remember, when anything seemed possible. From the soaring symphonies of Hayden and Vivaldi, to strains heard in places of worship and places of play, music is evocative of memory, time and emotion, able to raise us out of a dungeon of despair or release tears like much-needed rain in a desert."[6]

Achieving immediate emotional and physical changes using music becomes a familiar antidote. Other mind-body medicine techniques I use are potent agents of change, yet their results manifest themselves with less sensation and speed.

Music invigorates me, music plays with me, and music helps me release painful emotions.

Speaking of release, I sometimes think we humans are a species of release. We're released from the Aethers into the womb. When the lure of the earth beckons, we are then released from the womb to travel down the birth canal toward an adventuresome journey.

When we take the first breath, we are released from death. For a time.

As each moment passes, we are urged forward into the next, unavoidably releasing the past, propelling ourselves into the future. We release toxins from our bodies to cleanse. And we release emotions to heal.

While living in my apartment, and at the beginning stages of writing *The Gift of the Circle*, I experience a profound emotional release using music . . .

I'm writing about saying goodbye to my mother that mournful day before I moved to Georgia. As I try to write, picturing myself waving goodbye to her, my heart wants to explode and weep.

I'm fidgety, miserable. I yearn to keep writing. But I can't break through the sadness and depression cementing my creative urges into hiding places. And, once again, merely focusing on my feelings, as I've done sometimes, doesn't help.

I keep struggling to find words until my gut nudges me and The Watcher breaks into the turmoil:

Put your writing aside for a while.

Thinking clearly is impossible—until you restore emotional balance.

As you've noticed, merely being with your feelings isn't enough right now.

You need to do something else to release your pain.

Honor that need.

And trust your capacity to change your feelings no matter how powerful they are. They're no match for your determined efforts to protect yourself.

Remember your experience on the track?

I do, but thinking about using my Apogee playlist to help makes me squirm. Then a vague recollection of a mood-changing process I read about in *You Can Beat the Odds* comes to mind.

Because I don't remember the terminology or details of the method, I spend a few minutes reading: "Another way music can enhance your personal healing repertoire is through the isomoodic principle. This technique is based on matching music to an individual's current mood then gradually changing the music to achieve a different emotional state, with physical benefits."[7]

After thinking about what I've just read, my gut tells me I need to get busy and release emotions before they continue rupturing my well-being—and my immune system.

Although my feet itch to get out the door and I'm more than ready to try the isomoodic process, I'm afraid of feeling the festering, gut-wrenching pain smirking in the shadows.

With compassion, The Watcher nudges me:

Go ahead, get your things.

I know you're scared to face your feelings.

Be brave, though.

You'll feel better—oh so much better—when you let them out. Suppressing them elevates sovereignty, their dark powers. They'll continue their subversive torture of you until you allow them to surface.

Avoiding pain is natural. But not always beneficial.

The tormented memories of being sick and suffering for so long are slowly rising like a full-moon tide. The time has come.

Go. Be with your agony.

Reluctantly heeding my own wise counsel, fastening my waist pack containing my media player and earbuds, I move, turtle-like. Then, in the same slow fashion, I lock the door to my apartment and head for a nearby, quiet side road.

Without knowing what's going on, I'm facing one of the most significant events of my recovery.

In moments I'll be releasing a wad of the festering, pent-up feelings I've stuffed inside me for eight years. I've just experienced their power to ravage my desire to write. Imagine what suppressing them has been doing to my insides—and my immune system!

When I arrive where I'm planning to walk, I pause to select music I think will help me transition into a state of well-being.

I'm fraught with feelings that rattle logic, so I make a mistake by trying the upbeat, bold rhythms of Apogee. Despite the mere thought of them making me squirm just moments before, I still think I can jumpstart joy.

Instead, the vibrations that usually make me want to dance prick nerves already raw with anguish.

Searching for a solution, I think of "Nessun Dorma" from *Turandot.* The mere idea of opera makes some people gag. Not me. I'm especially drawn to arias.

Although I don't often know the meaning of the words, a majestic voice singing an aria often turns on my emotional spigot. When Pavarotti sings "Nessun Dorma," tears are guaranteed. After I find Pavarotti's rendition on my iPod, I set replay, knowing once will never be enough to unload the torture I feel.

The rich, full sounds of the orchestral prelude fill me with a longing to come into my heart and be with my pain.

At first, I can't, even though my heart pumps wildly and my chest becomes turgid with emotion.

Again I play the aria.

Finally, Pavarotti's voice and the vision of his outstretched arms compels me to feel.

Compassion for myself erupts.

The knife-edged isolation I've felt for so long doubles me over in pain.

The terrified, little-girl part of me shakes. The little-girl part of me that lost control and slid into an icy, lonely abyss.

A wad of hardened suffering surges from my gut and lodges in my throat. The pressure is unbearable.

I don't understand what's happening. And I can't stop the process.

I feel like I'm going to break apart into shards of tormented flesh and bones.

My mouth opens.

Excruciating pain I wasn't brave enough to feel when Lyme was marauding my life escapes in a primeval groan of agony.

I wail.

Then, suddenly the music I wasn't consciously aware of for a time surges deeper into my soul. The orgasmic emotions imbued in the music, rich with hope and pleading sorrow, embrace me.

Their warm knowing speaks the language of my own emotions that have felt so alien. I feel welcomed into the humanity of man. Understood and cherished. The isolation I've felt for so long feels warmed by a loving friend. A wave of compassion for my own misery bathes my heart with the welcome company of music that seems to know all about my pain without knowing my story.

The compassion I feel holds me close while my wails fill the air. Sirens of grief for all that was lost spill from my tender wounds.

I'm sorry you were down for so long, The Watcher croons.

Feeling sick and useless was unspeakably painful.

I'm sorry. So, so sorry for your suffering in the psychiatric hospitals.

You were too sick yourself to help others figure out was wrong. Those who tried to help you simply didn't know how.

Shock treatments weren't the answer. They couldn't change your reality.

They couldn't give you back your farm or your donkey, Buttercup; restore the job you cherished; lay your beloved Kristina beside you to snuggle; make possible another walk in the woods with Forest; bring your mother back so you could feel one of her big, warm hugs; surround you with the dear friends you left behind.

They couldn't fill your empty heart.

Go ahead, let everything out.

Everything!

Be fearless.

Wail as long as you need to.

Tears aren't the hurt.

Tears heal the hurt.

Then, as the aria ends for the umpteenth time, tears of a different sort stream down my face when the translation to the final words appears like a subscript: *At dawn I shall win.*

At dawn I shall win.

There's both pain and triumph in that message. Trauma and hope. Death and the promise of the stars that shine in the night.

Feeling like I'm holding tight to the hands of kind, understanding brothers and sisters around the globe, I sniffle and blow my snotty nose, while feeling a few hopeful tears being kissed by a gentle breeze.

Sighing, I gentle down into a peaceful, soothing place, parachuting into warm, moist, feathery feelings.

Softer, quieter New Age music then leads me into the welcoming arms of gratitude as I relish moments of freedom from emotional pain. Although I'm still not ready for mariachi and bluegrass, I am ready for Dan Gibson's "Wings at Rest" to cuddle my heart—a heart ready to be serene, even if just for a while. Soothed by contentment, I then play "Sunshine on My Shoulder" and "Country Roads," feeling John Denver take me to happy places.

As I finish my isomoodic journey, I'm a much different woman than the one who started walking merely an hour ago. While approaching my apartment, I realize how the experience of my existence was changed by my feelings. *Zoweee! Music just helped me vomit feelings and their pain trying to smash me into the past!*

As I unlock the door, I'm still musing: *Hmm, music seems like a skilled Sherpa guiding me along the treacherous slopes of emotional pain to the airy freedom of a summit—where all things are possible.*

As a result of dramatic mood changes evoked by different rhythmic vibrations on two occasions, music becomes my faithful companion during my healing journey.

Apogee sparks energy and joy. Timpani drums inspire power. Opera speaks the voice of compassion. New Age music cradles me with lullabies when I need respite.

And the sure chirping of a small sparrow in the morning often awakens me, offering the gift of hope in the dawn of a new day.

THE CARESS
OF COMPASSION

*Emotional occasions . . . are extremely potent in precipitating
mental rearrangements. The sudden and explosive ways in
which love, jealousy, guilt, fear, remorse, or anger can seize
upon one are known to everybody. Hope, happiness, security,
resolve . . . can be equally explosive. And emotions that come
in this explosive way seldom leave things as they found them.[1]*
                                                   —William James

—

A big storm changes things.

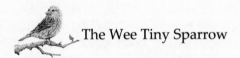 The Wee Tiny Sparrow

After the emotional release inspired by "Nessun Dorma,"
there's more room than ever for gratitude in my heart. Sometimes
I'm so overwhelmed by my abundant blessings that tears moisten
my eyes, especially when I once again acknowledge how many
supported and believed in me, extending hope when I couldn't
feel anything except despair and dread.

Gratitude continues to be the overriding positive emotion I
experience during the early spring months of 2010, living in my
apartment healing and writing *The Gift of the Circle*. Even so, I've
mountains of work ahead to stabilize other emotions that still jerk

me from one extreme to another. Although I'm becoming more aware of what's going on in my inner world, I still don't understand where some of my feelings come from. When their intensity scares me, I sometimes curl into a fetal position and rock myself, despite the fact I've learned coping skills that might serve me better.

Insomnia continues to plague me. When darkness comes, I'm usually too afraid to leave my watch to sleep. Afraid that if I do, Lyme, lurking in the shadows, will attack with vicious malice. When I am able to fall asleep, I often awaken in a sweating, sheet-soaking panic.

Anger twists my gut when I remember the ECT treatments, my outrage flaring. Why did psychiatrists at a well-known university mental health geriatric hospital risk damaging my brain? Risk compromising my memory, or worse, before engaging me in non-invasive therapies, therapies I now know are well-documented for their positive results?

Anger isn't all I feel. In my hurt and disbelief I can't understand why no one asked me why I wanted to die. After all, my attempted suicides weren't secrets. My pulse and my temperature were taken every morning. A psychiatrist or physician's assistant visited me daily to check on my progress. No one probed. And I was too sick to direct my own therapy.

For some reason, I'm not outraged at being misdiagnosed as a drug addict the first time I sought psychiatric hospitalization. Instead, I experience weak-at-my-knees relief—I'm downright awed that I somehow managed to scavenge enough energy, in spite of my weakened emotional and physical state, to act the part of a repentant addict well enough to secure my release.

My panic attacks continue to be incited by anything even resembling a Lyme symptom. A simple case of diarrhea opens the maw of terror that swallows my sanity. Anxiety spews into my space, once again torturing me.

I feel like I'm being terrorized by a scene of impending, yet fantasized, doom: A flash flood roils and hisses, ripping through the canyon bottom inches beneath my feet. Boulders carried by the raging current thunder against each other. Surging waves grab at my ankles, threatening to tear me from the razor-thin ledge where I stand. Angry spume slicks the rocks behind me when I vainly attempt to climb them.

Tight, fear-laden breaths imprison terror pounding in my heart. Everything I have—focus, energy, and emotion—is withered by my efforts to escape certain torture.

Then, silence.

As I breathe a long, uncertain sigh, relief creeps through me, stilling my terror as I realize that I'm okay for the moment. That strategies to encourage my immune system to perform at peak are working once again. Hope glimmers, inspiring my heart to consider relaxing in a hard-won moment.

Although emotional challenges still exist, achieving balance *is* becoming easier. And joy emerges readily sometimes, sounding a call over something as simple as catching a glimpse of a butterfly seeking nectar in a spring flower. My thoughts grab the chance to dance in the miracle of the moment, wondrous that I'm present, full of life.

Also, there's more space between my psychological episodes. When they don't take me off my feet, and I'm able take charge, music continues to be a powerful healing tool. Many times, mindfulness sounds an alarm snug up to the genesis of disruptive thoughts, so I can change their course before they take over. Affirmations, imagery, and other mind-body medicine strategies are also significant players in my stabilization.

Before I tell of their part in my healing, there's a poignant, unexpected facet of my recovery I want to share—mental rearrangement urging expression in the same way a flower needs to offer nectar to butterflies.

———

Once, when my heart stopped pounding, I felt momentary

peace after reliving an imaginary, roiling, hissing episode of chronic illness that leapt from the past. I seemed to be peering from the top of a canyon where I viewed my suffering in high relief . . .

My gut twists. My heart wrenches as I remember my near-death suicide attempts and other events of my illness and the horrific struggle to survive.

Grieving, I wail, disgorging my feelings in the same way I did when listening to "Nessun Dorma."

I mourn once again the loss of my professional status, of Sunny Hill Farm, Buttercup, Kristina, and all the other parts of my life ravaged by Lyme and my inability to cope with severe trauma.

When my pain wafts into the shadows of the past, my heart bursts wide open, revealing the full measure of my dark despair and suffering, not fully unacknowledged until now.

In stark contrast, the reality of my healing makes a brief appearance, clothed in feelings of jewel-toned triumph.

Suddenly a question erupts: *Why me?*

Prompted by the mystery of that troubling question, I shake my head back and forth, knowing I'll never know the answer.

I'll never know why I'm being "raised on eagle's wings" while others wish to be, yet remain shackled to suffering.

During my life, I've flown in the Aethers with ecstatic joy. And I've groveled in the pits of hell—grief stricken—for short periods of time. Until now, I've never understood the full measure of human suffering.

Before Lyme struck, my painful challenges were common-place, short lived. So how could I go beyond sympathy to comprehend the wretchedness, the anguish, of some of my brothers and sisters?

Juxtaposed to their stark, dystopian plights, I'm suddenly humbled by my newfound freedom.

How could I have guessed that, through grasping the depths of my own suffering, I would come to know compassion for myself—and others? Or that I would feel called to tell my story?

And in the mere telling, that I would be led to heal in more ways than I could have imagined?

While I was shackled with illness year after year, yearning for meaning and purpose in my life, how could I have imagined that the crucible of my torture would become, in part, the answer to my plea?

Now, when I feel compassion for myself, I feel compassion for those who can't find their way out of the rubble that engulfs them. I know their angst. I was there, intimately aware of the threat of destruction.

Even though parts of me were broken and shattered by chronic illness, I somehow feel honored that I now hold membership in the distinguished order of survivors who experience the nectar of life in simple things. Best of all, trauma has sculpted me into a different, kinder human being. Those who struggle to rise in triumph in one way or another and can't are my heartfelt companions now. They are treasures of The Gift of the Circle. I won't forget them. I don't want to.

When I weep for myself, my tears carry their pain.

When I dance, I dance for them.

When I sing with joy, they're in my very soul.

And when I come to shine like the sun, may my radiance speak of my love and concern for my suffering brothers and sisters. May my story inspire them to know that we're never hopeless, never useless. Never without meaning and purpose, no matter how desperate our physical or emotional circumstances.

May my story inspire them to know that sometimes the effort made to extend a simple smile and hang on for one more heartbeat can be all that's necessary to be a hero in anyone's eyes.

SUSPENDING DISBELIEF

*Boundaries of our inner worlds sometimes seem cemented
by predisposition. Yet, we partake of life from the breath
of boundless inspiration. Indeed, we are reborn
moment by moment, beckoned to soar with wings of Light,
into Infinite Freedom where the improbable has no sway,
and unfettered wonders manifest, shimmering with joy.*

*A seeker's paradox:
In the realm of infinite possibilities,
the improbable invites the unexpected to manifest
and tease the senses.*

On a summer evening in 2010, while nestled into my squishy corduroy couch, I remember the people rocks perched along the canyon rims of Moab's Green River morphing into companionable groups of ancient speakers. Patient as only rocks can be, they seem to be awaiting our soon-to-come visit, making my skin prickle with excitement.

I continue my reverie, envisioning myself camped on a bank of white sand, warm from snuggling inside my sleeping bag; I remember opening the flap to my tent and feeling a cool breeze startle my bare arms, and then donning a long-sleeved T-shirt before sipping hot, bold coffee, warmth soothing my cold hands. With joy, I recall birds chirping to welcome the otherwise still mornings. My feet resting on the couch actually twitch when I imagine pushing my canoe off from the beach, cold river water shocking my sandaled feet.

Reliving the thrill of dipping my paddle in the water, taking my first stroke of a new day, urges me to keep traveling backward in time. A glassy liquid ribbon, dazzling with the reflections of an ombrous gold and pink sunrise, fills me with awe. I want to dance with the sparkling ripples that flit in my mind, knowing they come as the canyons warm, inviting expressions of the wind.

Still delighting in the magic and freedom of recall, I feel myself drifting alone in the vast wilderness of the Canyonlands, talking to ravens and wrens, my voice reaching beyond the boundaries of convention, relishing the opportunity to be real without feeling crazy. I remember the thrill of sensing a supernatural presence of ancient cave dwellers, once thriving along the Green River, as they seemed to welcome me to the vastness of creative majesty. As my imaginary excursion ends, my heartbeat quickens, for I'm certain now that I'll be well enough to actually return to Utah in the fall.

Little do I know that the grand finale of this period of profound healing awaits me there, to be Orchestrated on a crystal-clear evening as the sun paints the sky in the west, while I sit in the doorway of my tent at the Confluence where the Green and Colorado Rivers merge.

Meanwhile, I'm walking five miles several times a week, with ease and much pleasure, especially when the music on my playlist, Apogee, incites me to riotous abandon. With the guidance of my therapist and my concerted efforts to craft a new way to be in the world, my mental health continues to improve, too.

When speaking about my therapist, Brenda, I'm frequently asked how often I see her: once a week if something troubling surfaces; twice a month if I'm maintaining physical and mental stability, yet have issues needing attention to continue healing. Eventually, once a month is enough.

My relationship with Brenda is invaluable. She's in the moment when listening, alert and focused. Most of the time she understands where I'm coming from when I share feelings or thoughts. If not, she respectfully asks me to elaborate until we're on the same page. Authenticity and kindness permeate her approach, creating a safe haven for being open. Also, her laughter is infectious. Her sense of humor finds merriment in my foibles—and her own—defusing my propensity to seek perfection as a measure of my self-worth. And her pervading commitment to integrity finds a way to tell me with tact the difficult things I need to hear if I'm to heal from the inside out.

There's full-blown irony in being sixty-seven and looking up to her with the innocent awe and trust of a child, and the wisdom of a woman who knows Brenda is a warrior of sorts, standing firm in her belief that I can reclaim my life.

As I continue to seek direction from her, she's as steady as ever. Complete restoration is possible, she announces with words, posture, and facial expressions. Her energy radiates optimism. When I stumble, my state doesn't unsettle her confidence in my ability to heal—to come home to the beauty and peace of wholeness.

Although I continue to take homeopathic antimicrobials, my therapeutic relationship with her, my commitment to processing painful emotions when facing my past, and my steadfast daily attention to the research-based, mind-body medicine strategies on my to-do list are at the core of my recovery.

Imagery is one of those strategies. Although my visual meanderings in Utah create a corollary body chemistry that supports my immune system, there's another, more focused kind I use for healing that is constructed with the intention to kill Lyme bacteria. Noteworthy research results support my belief that they have the potential to be as powerful as any pharmaceutical.[1] Since the beginning of my recovery, I've acted as a mind-body movie director, producing several antimicrobial imageries tailored by my gut instincts, telescoping my medicinal needs.

One I created early in my recuperation remains a favorite, making me laugh.

Why?

Part of the script is a spin-off of a vivid, too-funny memory involving me and cats . . .

———

On a black, stormy night, bridging winter to spring, I'm nestled in my sleeping bag with a pink-flowered quilt spread on top. An air mattress insulates me from the cold wood floor. With my hands clasped beneath my head, relishing the spaciousness of my new, unfurnished tree house, I'm peering at my A-frame, silver-metal ceiling that's supported with two-by-twelve pine beams.

Several weeks ago, my ten cats and I moved up here to live among the branches and leaves of stately, ever-green live oak trees draped with Spanish moss. Except for a space that serves as both closet and pantry, there's nothing but screening between me and the elements.

My cats and I quickly develop a nighttime symbiotic relationship, serving as off-grid heating pads for each other. The number of feline companions seeking warmth from my body becomes a temperature gauge for reporting chill levels to friends curious about how I'm faring: a ten-cat night is one cold enough to draw all of my feline friends toward me. Eight magnetize themselves to the contours of my body on top of the quilt. My hairless and tuxedo cats burrow into my sleeping bag, gluing themselves to my chest and abdomen.

This soon-to-be notable night has a ten-cat chill. The temperature is cold enough to know winter isn't spent, yet warm enough to manifest thunder rumbling in the distance, drawing my attention to the outside. Suddenly, a blazing streak of blue-white lightning splits open the storm-blackened sky. The air inside the tree house crackles, terrifying me. A thunderclap explodes on top of me and the cats. I bolt upright, braced for electrocution.

My cats?

Bundles of fur leap into the air. Forty legs slip and slide in all directions on the smooth wood floor, attempting to escape the violent death threat rudely jolting them from their warm repose. They care nothing of my plight, leaving me to fend for myself.

Mumbling thunder and greased, pallid flashes of lightning signal the rapid departure of danger. Relief that me and my cats haven't been fried floods my veins. Sighing, my breathing slows. Then, giggles tumble from my lips, pulled into an ear-wrapping grin by fear's exit.

Deliverance from death and dancing memories of my leaping, scrambling cats incite deep, raucous hee-haws to echo in the vast airy space of redemption.

While sporadic giggles squirt from my desire to hang on to such glee, my cats, one by one, stepping slowly—cautiously, looking from one side to the other—return to our sleeping spot. As each one reassumes a warming position, a chortle or two escapes as I think of this adventuresome, ten-cat night.

During my recovery, I'm hypersensitive to Lyme symptoms, often confusing real ones with those that are merely psychosomatic.

Once, there's no mistake. A full-blown relapse is signaled by Lyme fatigue sucking my energy into a murky swamp of brain-fogged confusion, stealing my capacity to find words for construction of even the simplest sentences. Explosive diarrhea shoots undigested food into the toilet.

When I can't deny what's happening, I panic. But after settling myself just enough to engage logic, I begin thinking about an answer to my dilemma. I've never tested positive for Lyme, even when a classic bull's-eye on my abdomen pronounced infection. So I don't waste money and time on testing fraught with inaccuracy. And I know antibiotics won't help. They never have. Seeking a prescription for one is pointless.

Instead, I trust my familiarity with my disease history, my

instincts, and the wellness I've achieved so far using mind-body medicine to direct my course of action. The first thing that comes to mind is the need to design an imagery expressly to kill Lyme spirochetes.

Before proceeding, I review the overriding theme of the chapter about the imagination's healing power in *You Can Beat the Odds*: "When you use your imagination, your body experiences physiological changes as if the events were actually taking place in that very moment. We can exploit this natural process and consciously create a . . . chemical reality . . . suited to our purpose of healing."[2]

With that in mind, to fortify my belief system, I revisit the potent research outcomes backing that statement, documenting the medicinal efficacy of imagery and the impressive anecdotal records of those using that process to reverse even the most malicious of disease states.[3]

Also, I find Bruce Lipton's book, *The Biology of Belief*, and reread scientific confirmation of the placebo effect's power to direct the course of the body's chemistry.[4]

After empowering myself with authentic information, I confidently spark my imagination with enthusiasm — and science-based hope. A mind-movie tailored by directions for creating imageries with medicinal efficacy in *You Can Beat the Odds* rapidly takes shape . . .[5]

———

Before calling on my visionary resources, I plant my feet at shoulders' width apart, meaning business.

Then, to bring myself into the moment with the expectation of undeniable success for my efforts, I breathe three long, slow breaths deep into my abdomen. With my attention focused, the biology of miracles begins taking shape. My imagination beckons my ever-ready intuitive fairy helper, born of Light and Wonder.

She appears, shimmering in iridescent hues of violet, purple, and mauve, scenting the air with a spicy fragrance reminiscent of cloves and cinnamon. Her graceful wings take her where she needs to go as easily as a breeze passes through trees in a sun-dappled forest. Dancing, back-flipping, and showering the magical space we share with particles of starlight, twinkling with hope, she displays her eagerness to support me.

No matter how sick I feel, when she appears with such ardent enthusiasm to be at my service, I smile.

"Namaste," we say in turn, bowing to each other.

Using a professional, no-nonsense tone for the benefit of Lyme bacteria who might be listening, I give my fairy helper directions: "Get your clear-blue spray container holding the liquid antimicrobial you manufacture for my benefit."

When she has that in hand, I take a moment, making mental note of my fairy helper's perfect intelligence, identifying with certainty the exact strain of Lyme bacteria infecting me—and her liquid Lyme killer able to cross the blood-brain barrier, one that hones in on Lyme spirochetes and cysts like a merciless super-drone, seeking a target that cannot escape attack, no matter where they hide, whether in cell walls, nuclei, cytoplasm, or muscle tissue.

Then, I warn the Lyme bacteria of the death threat at my fingertips.

Why do that?

Because I'm concerned about the right to life of the Lyme spirochetes. So rather than killing them right off, I issue a heads-up. "On the count of three, when I give the signal, an antimicrobial that will kill you is going to be sprayed on the lining of my stomach. After that, as soon as I inhale, the liquid will be taken into my bloodstream along with oxygen to every cell in my body—seeking, finding, and killing you—if you haven't left me."

"You have three seconds to get out of my body: One. Two . . ."

By now, I'm so engaged in my mind-body movie that I've suspended disbelief, engaging the full authority of my work. I envision electrified Lyme spirochetes leaping and scrambling, pushing and shoving each other in their maniacal panic to escape certain death.

I laugh out loud. And laugh some more, images reminiscent of terrified cats stoking my humor.

"Three!"

Nodding, I give my fairy helper the command to spray the lining of my stomach with her killer antimicrobial, believing she knows the perfect amount to use.

She bows when finished, punctuating her power.

I inhale deeply, imagining her killer substance being transported throughout my body by my blood. Lyme spirochetes wither, collapse, and die. Cysts, spirochetes morphed to escape detection, implode. Microscopic detritus from the carnage is sucked into the current of my arterial system, expanded by the water I drink daily to accommodate cleansing. The waste is then either excreted in my urine, or sweated out through the pores of my skin.

To end my "intravenous" session, I imagine myself in robust good health, standing tall on the beach at the Confluence with my paddle held by the shaft high above my head, triumphant after a solo fifty-mile paddling adventure.

———

I engage that imagery each morning for several weeks. Along with that and all the other strategies working to heal me, I begin to reclaim my energy and my capacity to use my intellect.

One morning, soon after concluding the time with my fairy friend, I feel a need to cleanse my body. Without questioning my gut, I strip and dry-brush myself, paying special attention to my back. While showering, I grimace with disgust, responding to the icky sensation that something noxious is being rinsed down the drain.

Getting into the feeling, I bid good riddance.

When I'm completely satisfied that I've thoroughly cleansed

myself, I friction-dry my body with the rough side of a towel and dress. For the moment, I think nothing about what's just happened, except to praise myself for responding to my instincts without questioning them.

A week later, I feel touch-deprived and go for a massage with someone I've seen often. When the massage therapist folds the covers down to begin working, she exclaims, "There are blackheads all over your back. What happened to you?"

"Toxins leaving, I guess."

I'm too timid to tell her I think dead Lyme bacteria clogged my pores. Yet I'm certain as I lie there that the blemishes on my back are leftover remnants of Lyme bacteria trying to get off my body.

THE ART
OF LETTING GO

Every time I want to fly
I have to let go of something I've been holding on to.
Hard as I try, I can't figure out any other way out of cages
I sometimes make for myself.

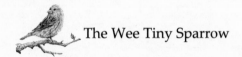 The Wee Tiny Sparrow

The mind-body medicine power tools I use for crafting my health are a gift from my therapist, Brenda. They engage my birthright—my body's awesome capacity to heal.

My unique rendition of these strategies seems to work like bird songs that gentle the early-morning air. They're simple, predictable, and uplifting. With seamless harmony, their design is woven into my miraculous and intricate mental and physiological systems. My body and mind welcome them, engaging me to dance to an overture of flourishing wellness.

When I finished reading *You Can Beat the Odds*, I was stunned, for I knew I held the answer to my recovery. A large part of that knowing was grounded in robust research, documenting the efficacy of each strategy advocated by Brenda for immune-system enhancement. Those research outcomes and others continue playing a significant role in sustaining my belief that I can heal myself and maintain wellness. They help free me of a lurking doubt that sometimes threatens my confidence in my body's innate and miraculous restoration capacity. In fact, her research of outcomes stokes the power driving my recovery and my beliefs. Indeed, these beliefs are the CEO of my health management. On the flip side, they gripped me in the barbed shackles of physical and emotional illness for eight years. One way or the other, beliefs *are* influential.

Experiencing results has helped me to continue forging ahead. And faith in my pathway is bolstered by the sparkle I see in Brenda's eyes and my own as I reclaim myself.

Yet I need more. Even though I'm deeply spiritual and have profound reasons to trust in Divine direction, I have trouble with that and use more than one antidote. One of them is seeking a logical stance before taking action on a concept. My left brain needs sustenance—especially when I'm floundering. So, I look for reassurance about my capacity to heal myself by learning how others have done so. I collect their stories in a sort of mind quiver, armoring myself for challenges to come, supporting my CEO.

Toward that end, as part of my daily to-do list, I often reread portions of *You Can Beat the Odds*. In addition, I read from at least one other resource every day, searching for a morsel of research that validates my body's wonder. In fact, I chose to add that authenticating, immune system–bolstering process to my daily to-do list.

Why?

Given my experiences with so many treatments that failed to halt Lyme disease, I get jump-up-and-down excited when I open a book and read that scientists are verifying the magnificent and eloquent healing systems that are naturally mine. Based on what I now know, I'm certain the chemistry I produce with those good feelings sends messages to phagocytes, the white blood cells that protect me from harmful bacteria and other foreign material, encouraging them to perform well.

So, each day, I seek mind-bolstering information about my body's healing design. I look for a "sweet spot" written by a reliable expert—simple statements carrying profound weight. A sentence or paragraph, they're enough.

I keep going until I reach a sense of closure. As my mind takes in the information framed in robust research, I'm certain all my cells respond to the message, affirming their ability to act in my best interest.

Where do I find resources?

Each book I explore has references pointing to others. A topical search on Amazon yields a plentiful supply of exploratory reading. And *You Can Beat the Odds* is flush with references for investigation. I often refer to one of them: *Opening Up: The Healing Power of Expressing Emotions* by James Pennebaker, professor and research psychologist at the University of Texas at Austin.

I know something about the healing power of releasing emotions. Music continues to help me let go of painful feelings when I'm afraid to face them. And, after expressing my feelings about illness when writing *The Gift of the Circle*, I experience a time of peace.

Yet facing the pain of my losses has sometimes taken hard-to-find courage.

Recalling or even rereading a research outcome documented in Pennebaker's book often gives me motivation to keep going when things get tough . . .

"Fifty students wrote for 20 minutes a day for 4 consecutive days about one of two topics. Half wrote about their deepest thoughts and feelings concerning a trauma. The remaining 25 students were expected to write about superficial topics. . . . The students consented to have their blood drawn the day before writing, after the last writing session, and again 6 weeks later [to test for lymphocytes that control immune function]."[1]

What were the results of the study?

"People who wrote about their deepest thoughts and feelings surrounding traumatic experiences evidenced heightened immune function compared with those who wrote about superficial topics. Although this effect was most pronounced after the last day of writing, it tended to persist six weeks after the study. In addition, health center visits for illness dropped for the people who wrote about traumas compared to those who wrote on the trivial topics."[2]

The follow-up of the test subjects yielded much: "In the surveys that we sent out several months after the experiments, we asked people to describe in their own words what long-term effects, if any, the writing experiment had on them. Everyone who wrote about traumas described the study in positive terms. More important, approximately 80% explained the value of the study in terms of insight. Rather than explaining that it felt good to get negative emotions off their chests, respondents noted how they understood themselves better."[3]

Opening Up concludes with a huge motivator, helping me remember that my writing is more than just telling my story: "Writing, then, should be viewed as preventative maintenance. The value of writing or talking about our thoughts and feelings lies in reducing the work of inhibition and in organizing our complicated and emotional lives. Writing helps to keep our psychological compass oriented. Although not a panacea, writing can be an inexpensive, simple, and sometimes painful way to help maintain our health."[4]

Besides writing The Gift of the Circle, I also do stream-of-consciousness journaling, an immune- system strategy appearing on my to-do list.[5]

So how do I use stream-of-consciousness journaling to open up, let go of feelings, and fortify my immune system?

First, I take care of practical matters, ensuring that I will be completely focused and free to write about whatever comes up. To that end, I turn off my cell phone. Then I shut the door to my room, setting the stage for letting go of anything that comes to mind. But after that, getting started is troublesome. The "screamin' meemies" tug at my bones. All of me knows I'll be sitting in one place facing feelings. Facing stillness and demons. This reaction seems odd to me because I meditate without a lot of resistance, even inviting stillness. But I don't stop to figure out what's going on. Rather, I pay attention to finding ways to soften resistance.

When the struggle to proceed actually threatens to halt my experience, I remember how I've felt when training for long-distance bicycle rides. I seldom relished riding twenty miles with bricks in my paniers to replicate the weight of the gear I would be carrying and build muscle after a full day's work, yet I somehow managed to summon the wherewithal to mount my bike and get started. And after finishing, I felt better—every time. Using that experience as a template, I hold on to the expectation of feeling better after stream-of-consciousness journaling no matter how bad I feel in the beginning. So when the time comes to write, I pick up a legal pad and pen, sometimes squirming and wanting to bolt from myself.

In an irritating sort of way, The Watcher shows up then:

Discipline is good.

Paradoxical, too.

Freedom rides on the pathway forged by discipline's efforts.

Hold on to the research you know about.

Let go of the emotions that will hold you captive to anger and sorrow.

Your immune system will thank you.

And, consider the possibility that the struggle you feel could mean you need to abide in this process of acknowledging and letting go of your feelings.

Best of all, you'll feel great when you're finished!

With that counsel in mind, I take a deep sigh, and giving myself permission to allow my gut instincts to direct the process, I prepare to write for thirty minutes. Once I've begun, I completely engage in expressing myself, keeping my pen on the paper—and moving. Stream-of-consciousness journaling is radically different from keeping a journal in the usual way. There's nothing to hang on to, nothing to reread. The process is about letting go, letting the shit fly. And the results are definitely not for anyone else to see. With pen point remaining on the paper, I release whatever thoughts surface, uncaring about grammar. Spelling isn't important either. Crossing t's and dotting i's doesn't matter. The words flow from gut to paper as I write about the truth of the moment.

I'm no stranger to expressing my feelings, although during the catastrophic events of ravaging illness, I locked down my emotions. I didn't have the courage to feel the pain of rapid-fire, profound losses. But recovery's different. I spew my feelings in different ways. In therapy sessions, walking along the road, listening to "Nessun Dorma," and on paper during stream-of-consciousness journaling.

Lyme-related hurt is still raw and grating the surface of my tender recovery. Often that's what's on top when I begin to write. I look for the hurt. I don't want to cage the hurt anymore. I embrace the hurt. I examine the hurt, walking through dark passages. Each time I do, a nugget of hard, compressed pain softens and puddles into compassion for myself. The emotional charge of painful memories becomes less gripping.

If I don't feel better the first time I write about something, my gut often prompts me to keep writing about the same material in a subsequent session until my related feelings have lost their charge.

Not everything that comes to mind is about the past. Sometimes a current event boils to the surface, so I write about that, "housecleaning," letting go of the issue, dumping every related thought and feeling onto paper.

If I run out of steam, I just move my pen on the paper making squiggles until a thought or feeling emerges. Anything goes— colored pens, pressure, music, tears, profanity, gratitude, anger. When emotions are strong, they provoke the urge to press the pen into the paper hard, and I do. If the need to write big and bold shouts, I do that, too. When the need to "speak" to someone flares, I speak my mind, uncaring about refining my language. And if I feel the need to cry, I release my tears. If I can't cry, yet know that I need to, I find my tablet and earbuds then play music that helps me let go of my feelings.

When I feel a need to establish my power, I get off on music. A concerto for trumpets followed by Handel's Hallelujah Chorus inspires me to describe my prowess in huge, bold, capital letters, addressing every cell in my body, engineering the final outcome of my recovery with me as the heroic victor.

I don't force anything, even writing about good things. The topics I write about are gut-chosen. The techniques are gut-driven.

I don't revisit my writing. To foster the art of letting go, I protect the confidentiality of my experience: I always shred my writing immediately following a writing session. After removing the written pages from a legal pad, I swagger downstairs to the basement, feeling proud of myself for finishing the task. There, in the shredder, I pulverize my writing into crinkled bits of anonymity.

The first time I shredded my stuff, I spontaneously brushed my hands back and forth, saying goodbye to some bad experiences I'd written about. And I've done that ever since, signaling my return to "now" and my intention to create an evening free of emotional effluvia.

When returning to my room, I feel light, knowing I can choose to let go or hold on to feelings.

In fact, much of my health seems to be won by letting go: suspending disbelief, disgorging my feelings to music, or releasing them during stream-of-consciousness journaling.

And, in the end, freedom prevails.

IN THE
CARE OF ANGELS

I can be
a speck of feathers and bones,
or I can be
the wee tiny sparrow
who teaches big ideas.
I am who I think I am.

 The Wee Tiny Sparrow

Joyce, my friend and confidante since 1968 when we met in graduate school, once remarked, after one of us confessed to an unwise excursion outside the boundaries of cultural norms, "God should have given us more brains or less temptation!"

Amen!

Many times during the decades of knowing Joyce, I've followed my insatiable spirit of adventure, taking on high-growth-yield challenges spiced with danger. Just one of them was riding my bicycle from Charleston to Enterprise, located thirty miles west of New Smyrna Beach.

Another equally challenging event, although quite different in nature, came when I chose to speak out about a controversial topic. In 1970, during the first year of integration of the high school where I worked, I stood before the school board to advocate for continuing education on behalf of a black student who was facing expulsion because she was pregnant. Doing so rattled convention and was tinged with danger from those who hated blacks. Many white parents delivered their students to school in trucks, guns mounted on gun racks in the back of the cabs. Their hostility bristled in the air, and I couldn't help wondering if I'd get picked off by one of them.

Then there were secret liaisons with men that could have exploded in my face. When shedding the girdled façade of primness I felt forced to wear before second-wave women's liberation, my rebellion against the idea that good girls don't have sex before marriage drove me into some dangerous, unwholesome circumstances . . .

One time, I was asked to be a co-hostess with another woman for men overnighting on a yacht cruise. At the front end, that doesn't sound like a big deal. The yacht, however, was owned by the principal of the high school where I worked as a counselor. Worse was the fact that the men on the cruise were married. And, although I wasn't expected to share my body, I was asked to wear cocktail waitress attire, suggesting that I would.

During the cruise, while I mixed and served drinks, I noticed through the smog of cigar smoke that the men were playing blackjack for high stakes. At the time, I thought the men were merely doing what some men do. Although I didn't have enough brains to avoid the temptation of acting like a "hot number," I did know public knowledge of my "services" would have created the perfect tornado. And that would have been a minor stir compared to what would have happened if authorities had busted the cruise that turned out to be an illegal gambling venture to raise money for a sheriff's campaign.

I remained unscathed from that experience and many more during my life. My marriage to an alcoholic could have resulted in death. When my husband was drunk, he brandished loaded guns, and threatened me with rape and worse. He thought nothing of grabbing me by the neck and slamming me against a wall.

I've jumped into out-of-the-box experiences, survived a

turbulent marriage and my own penchant for adventure. And I've been enriched by decades flush with splendid expressions of my creative nature and a Divine synchronicity I can't explain and didn't deserve. Since high school, I've believed unseen angels from the Aethers watch over me. And now I know there are Earth Angels, too: Janet. Friends. Doctors. Brenda.

When reflecting, I believe angels shepherded me as Divine ambassadors when I was being ravaged by Lyme disease and mental illness.

Why me?

I don't know, yet their presence seems to have been unmistakable. Is that my conjuring? Maybe. Even so, creating an imaginary presence that makes me feel protected does no harm.

Earth Angels, though, aren't a figment of my imagination.

When I had to give up my home, my friend Rebecca shared hers with me. When I got too sick to stay with her, my sister, Janet, and her husband took me in. During the entire time I was ill, loving arms surrounded me—even when I was too blinded by misery to see them. Even when I couldn't say thank you.

My survival to reach age sixty-seven is miraculous. I've been tenderly cared for while learning the lessons my choices have taught me while cradled in the arms of a Universe I should be able to trust, especially when peering into the past, appreciating the vast protection I've been granted.

Yet I don't trust things to work out for me.

I don't.

Watchful.
Always watchful.
Cold hands—icy cold.
Waiting for another beating.
For more than forty years.
Waiting.

Lyme mutilates my life, leaving tattered remnants
heaped on childhood terror.
Cold hands—icy cold.
Falling in a dark, sharp-edged void,
bracing for the spine-breaking collision with the streets.
Vein-dry poor.
Homeless.

When I was a kid, there wasn't a soft place for me to land. I always felt as if I were wobbling on the razor's edge of a cliff with no room to move, ready to tumble into an abysmal, black hardness with no one to stop the bone-shattering, heart-wrenching fall that was sure to come. My fear of being poor and homeless was real to me, stoked by my parents' unfounded arguments about money late at night when they thought I was asleep. Also, I lived in fear of tripping up, of having the floor yanked out from under me by my judgmental, unpredictable father. My need to feel safe created a need to stay watchful, poised for disaster—and escape.

Without knowing so, that fear-laden watchfulness crept into my subconscious, chilling my hands and shortening my breath. My experiences with Lyme and self-destruction served to cement leftover childhood fear into wads of distrust, despite the tender loving care of the nurturing angels who have protected me throughout my entire life. I think of my meeting Brenda, one of my Earth Angels, as a Divinely inspired, synchronistic event.

Once in a while, before I leave her office, she opens a box of cards. Written on each card is a unique and meaningful affirmation, one on each side. Brenda fans out a selection, offering me my choice. I pick one without seeing the messages. For me, there's magic in that process; part of me believes there's a certain card I'm meant to choose—one with special import—one that's just what I need at a given time.

One day, she holds out a handful of choices.

No surprise that I pick a perfect card that has healing affirmations I will use repeatedly during my entire recovery and beyond. One side reads, "I am safe in the universe, and all life loves and supports me," and on the other, "I breathe in the fullness and richness of Life. I observe with joy as Life abundantly supports me and supplies me with more good than I can imagine."[1]

Brenda makes a powerful research-based declaration about affirmations in *You Can Beat the Odds*: "Affirmations are positive self-statements designed specifically to overcome any negative conditioning from outdated belief systems. They work because we believe what we hear most often about ourselves."[2]

What I believe drives the performance of my cells throughout my entire body. More than any other variable, my beliefs are driving the outcome of healing, the outcome of my life![3]

So how many times will I need to be shown the truth about me and the Universe before I can trust that abundant support will continue to be mine?

Who knows.

What I do know is I can attempt to sway my brain in a direction that resonates with truth based on my experiences. I can do my part by using the affirmations on my card to untangle the terror gripping my gut.

The part of me that's scared so much of the time seems like my little seven-year-old self. She's the part of me that needs to know she's protected and nurtured. She's the one I speak to every day to tell her what I know to be true from my experiences of the Universe.

Before I connect with her, I do my daily self-care routine, brushing my teeth, washing my face, and dressing in something comfortable. Then I go to spend some time with "my kid" in front of a mirror. There's something powerful about using a mirror, about engaging with my eyes that reach deep into my feelings that seem scripted. When I visit with the part of me that feels like a frightened child, I speak out loud.

Why?

I learned from *You Can Beat the Odds* that my own speaking and singing voices have the potential to engage the healing tendencies of my body, especially when the tone of my speech is calm and comforting.[4]

When I look into my mirrored eyes, I first see the haunting, subconscious fear of my kid peering back at me. They beg from the belly. They cry from a heart that yearns to be free. They speak to the woman I want to be.

Can I please stop watching now?

I'm so tired of doing that.

I want to play with you. I want to dance, too.

You can't be with me when you're always afraid of something bad happening to you.

Being separated from you all the time doesn't feel very good. In fact, I hate the way that feels.

I need you to take care of me. Then I won't be so scared all the time.

I want you to love me.

Standing in front of the mirror, hearing that little kid plead with me, sparks a response. I tell her out loud what she wants to hear most:

"You're extraordinary—the most wonderful kid I've ever known. I'm going to do better at taking care of you. And I won't try to kill myself again. That must have been terrifying for you.

"I didn't know I could heal myself or trust that things would work out for us. I gave up on hope. I'm so sorry I put you through all that.

"I know what to do to get well now, and you can rely on me to hang in there until we can dance and play together. We'll do this life together, the two of us. From now on, I won't stop looking for answers until I find what I need. And if I can't figure something out by myself, I'll find others who will help me.

"I'm learning to understand that we'll always have what we need—you and me. One way or another, I'll take care of us.

"That's a promise!"

———

When I'm through talking to my kid, I speak the affirmations on the magical card I chose from Brenda's array (that I believe was authored by Louise Hay although there's no documentation giving her credit):

I am safe in the universe, and all Life loves and supports me.

I breathe in the fullness and richness of Life.

I observe with joy as Life abundantly supports me and supplies me with more good than I can imagine.

———

When I affirm those truths, connecting the woman standing in front of the mirror with the kid I see in the eyes facing me, sometimes I cry. Feeling so alone and helpless for so long has been really painful—and terrifying.

When I cry, I wrap my arms around myself and tenderly caress her, speaking with comforting tones:

"I understand better than anyone what happened to you. You've been through a lot. That's all over now.

"That's all over!"

Every morning, the knowing-woman part of me speaks the reassuring and life-giving truth. The woman who wants to learn a new way of being, the one who wants to be well, the one who wants to live and make a difference in the world. The one who wants to find her voice.

The woman who knows she will, one day, take off and fly.

SEASONS
OF THE HEART

On cloudy days
I sometimes snuggle into my nest
of feathers and clouds to think.
Often my wee tiny brain
wonders if my life is about circles.
Seasons come and go and come again.
And, after every night, the sun shines,
making me want to sing my song.

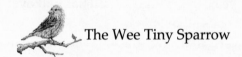 The Wee Tiny Sparrow

Dead leaves fall to the ground, remnants of fall and other seasons, to decay and nourish the earth. Tragedy seeks to nourish the soul with shadows, awakening feelings gone numb from emotional pain.

During the winter, spring, and summer months of my early recovery, memories of the pain wrought by Lyme and my inability to be flexible sometimes sadden me. Yet I'm able to soothe my sorrow by recalling the blessings that flourished then—simple, yet profound gestures of empathy and generosity.

When I became dysfunctional, my friend Rebecca insisted that I move into her charming, small home. Although I was resistant to the idea at first, I soon realized I needed her help—and her company.

Although she encouraged me to bring my aging pets—two dogs and three cats—I knew taking them with me wasn't realistic.

Knowing I was failing, I sought a place for Forest, my eight-year-old, eighty-pound mastiff mix. Gracious friends whose hearts knew of my struggle to survive and my need for him to have a home promised him refuge when I needed to give him up.

As for the rest, I barely had enough energy to care for myself. Continuing to care for them wasn't possible. Besides, Kristina, my sixteen-year-old cat, had been peeing in my bed daily since we'd moved to the country—a sign of unhappiness, I assumed, because her physical health was fine. I didn't feel comfortable with the idea that she might ruin a mattress in someone else's home. Worse than that, I didn't have enough energy to continue washing my sheets every evening.

And there were other problems. A huge tumor, made raw from gnawing, had erupted on my dog Nacomi's skin on one side by her rib cage. Nicholas, another one of my cats, was visibly ill. Both were in urgent need of veterinary intervention that I knew would be expensive, and I was afraid to spend money, fearing I would need what I had for medical expenses. My cat, Rishi, was well, but pushing seventeen.

I'd done enough work placing animals to know that aged dogs and cats are rarely adopted. Those with serious behavior or medical problems never are. And my emotional outlook precluded believing there could be exceptions—like Forest's circumstances.

So, I turned guilt and sorrow into icy, implacable stone in order to do what I felt had to be done. I made the decision to euthanize all of my old companions except Forest.

He stayed with me for a while at Rebecca's until I couldn't offer him even my attention. Kristina and my other pets remained at Sunny Hill Farm until I could gather the courage to say goodbye to them. Although my energy levels were sorely limited, I was still working. Each day, on the way home, I somehow managed to stop by my cottage in the woods and drag myself inside to feed Kristina and the others.

My beloved Kristina greeted me at the door as she'd always done. And every time I acknowledged her loyalty, I was reminded that the inevitable was soon to come. When I tenderly laid my dear Kristina, my companion for sixteen years, enshrouded in a towel in a grave bedded with hay, I suppressed an unspeakable agony.

———

Now that I've been living in my apartment for a while, I feel confident of my capacity to sustain my health and the life of another sentient being—enough to adopt a cat.

Hoping to fill the empty space left by Kristina, I begin a daily search of rescue agencies on the internet.

There's no question about what I want—her duplicate, affectionate and white-coated.

One morning, beckoning from the computer screen, big blue eyes peer at me from a bundle of long, white fur: a female cat for adoption at a nearby kill shelter. My mind races, tripping over my pounding heart. *She's the one. I can tell. Her eyes speak the same language Kristina's spoke.*

Somehow I know the cat I see. I can already feel our magnetic connection. My heart pumps with excitement when I stand at the shelter's reception desk describing the cat I want to meet to several attendants.

When I mention a long, white coat, they nod to each other, knowing the one. But I can't see her. I'm told she's sick with an upper respiratory infection and isolated in the shelter's infirmary, where she's being treated with antibiotics. Antibiotic treatment for a sick animal in a kill shelter is unusual. Resources are scarce; survival of the fittest reigns. After I'm told to come back in a week, I'm filled with gratitude that *my cat* is offered the chance to live.

When I return, dread and excitement play tug-of-war all over my body, for I don't know the fate of my intended pet. I was too scared to call about her before coming. Jittery, and hoping for the best, I ask to see her.

She's alive! Better yet, she's well and ready for adoption.

One of the attendants steps aside from the counter. "Follow me."

She leads me to a private room specially designed for meeting prospective adoptees. "I'll be right back," she tells me as I take a seat on the bench in the back.

Carrying an armful of inquisitive, blue-eyed feline, the attendant quickly returns, then places a magnificent creature into my welcoming arms.

After spending a few minutes with her warm, purring body curled in my lap, I know her presence in my life has begun. *Mmhmm, she's going to be just like Kristina: Cuddle with me when I sleep. Sit in my lap when I'm reading or sewing. Beg me to pet her by purring while rubbing against my leg.*

Blissful, I fill out forms, certain I'll qualify for adoption. After an attendant approves me, I pay the fees. I'm told my cat will be spayed the next morning. "She'll be ready for pickup after three p.m."

———

Tingling with excitement, I open the door to my pet carrier, remembering the time I brought Kristina home after a two-week stay in a veterinarian hospital where she'd struggled to survive a dangerous respiratory infection.

Not knowing what to expect with my new pet, I sit down in a nearby chair, wondering if this cat will run and hide like many do when they're new to a space. Like Kristina, she doesn't.

Although she's unsteady from the effects of anesthesia, she weaves her way toward me, jumps into my lap, and sits, gazing into my eyes. While I'm stroking her silky fur, she tenderly places one pink-padded paw on my cheek, softly speaking the language of a cat grateful to have a home.

"I'm equally as grateful to have you here," I tell her, feeling as though I've been "raised up on eagle's wings." Knowing I've received yet another Gift of the Circle, I wonder what to name this lovely creature:

She's white—shimmering with healing light.

Star?

That fits!

There's something else, though.

Her touch against my cheek—a gentle whisper of love—soft as a feather.

Star Feather.

Star Feather. That's her name!

After stroking Star Feather, saying her name out loud several times so she'll know when I'm calling her, she jumps from my lap to explore.

Turns out she isn't affectionate, and I'm respectful of her boundaries—most of the time. When she hops onto my desk to watch me write, sometimes she curls up on my papers. At times like that I can't stand letting her rule, so I cop a feel.

Although Star Feather isn't much like Kristina was, I'm grateful for her presence in my life and touched when she chooses to be close.

She has a way of polishing bright the thankfulness I feel for my well-being. Sometimes her big blue eyes rest in mine, peering deep into my soul, joining us in the wellspring of the eternal. In those quiet moments I'm reminded that seasons find their nourishment in limitless hope.

Star Feather prompts me to continue appreciating the throng of friends, family, and healthcare professionals who wouldn't give up on me when I'd given up on myself.

———

After eight years of being incommunicative and isolated because Lyme spirochetes had despoiled my brain, disabling my capacity to interpret airport signage and robbing me of the stamina to travel, when I began feeling well enough to fly again, I was eager to connect with some treasures of the heart. Loved ones who had been the essential fabric of my well-being. Loved ones I couldn't believe held me dear during my entire illness.

At the same time I made reservations for Utah, I scheduled excursions to see my niece, Elisa, in Colorado; my friend Shana, in Michigan; and their families.

When poised to "Book Flights" on Expedia, fear jerked my fingers off the keyboard: *What if I get sick when I'm traveling? Maybe I shouldn't go so far from my doctors—and Brenda.*

Wait a minute. Wait a minute, heeded The Watcher. *First, your immune-system enhancements are portable. And you've relied on them for months now to keep you well. "Well" is the operative word here. Worst case: You might need assistance.*

Elisa and Shana are completely capable of orchestrating your support. After all, they're not kids anymore. They're both mothers involved in the complex task of raising children. Certainly they could make arrangements for getting you back to Georgia or for anything else you might need.

Feeling confident after that wise counsel, I announced out loud, "I'm going. I am going!"

With that I struck "Enter," arranging for four days in Colorado with Elisa and four in Michigan, thinking that's more than enough time for me to snail out of my quiet places to experience the sounds and high energy of youth!

When I was with each family, my heart felt their love filling me with the warmth of their enthusiastic welcoming, speaking of their profound support and gratitude simply for my presence.

I cared what happened when I was with each family. I cared in a way that's probably unusual: I merely wanted to be *present*— genuinely with them. They were the main attraction, no matter what else we did. I sought to soak up each family member's uniqueness, listening carefully to what each one had to say with voice and body and noticing the things they did well. At times I had to put aside urges to advise from an elder's hubristic soapbox, choosing, instead, to embrace each family member as a living, breathing work of art in progress, absorbing their intricacies as a consummate gift.

A sneaky kind of sorrowful thought sometimes tried to bore a hole in my delight, tempting me to mourn the growing-up years that had occurred without me. In the end, my happiness at finally being well enough to be with those I love couldn't be corrupted.

Then and now, my joy is usually alert and sturdy, born from a rugged climb upward. Gratitude for having two young families as part of my life goes deep. In a paradoxical way, the tragedy wrought by Lyme refined the shimmering light of these blessings, highlighting their value.

When I returned from my visits with Elisa, Shana, and their families, I was full of wonder that I was, indeed, able to travel on my own and encouraged that I'd be ready for Utah.

As soon as my feet hit the ground in Atlanta, I yearned to see my friend Rebecca in Maine. Fear once again halted my first attempt to make travel plans. Impatience with my frailty taunted me. Visions of being limp-rag weak and being pushed in wheelchairs on tarmacs tempted me to believe I was somehow still sick, despite my recent travel experiences.

Once more, the wise part of me intervened, encouraging me to take hold of this invitation to life:

There's no need to be impatient with yourself or fearful.

You're haunted by your recent past, that's all.

Come to the present. You're fine now.

And remember, your wellness strategies go where you go.

Besides, you know Rebecca. She'd drive you back to Atlanta if you couldn't get there on your own.

You've come a long way for this moment.

Trust yourself!

And so I did, declaring out loud, "I'm going."

———

For two weeks Rebecca and I savored the laid-back way we

have of being with each other, reminding me of one of the many times we drove to St. Augustine, a sixty-mile trip from Rebecca's Florida home.

While we were there, as usual, we hit up our sweet spots for warm lemon sugar cookies and fresh, custard-filled Napoleons. On that particular trip, for some unknown reason, after eating the Napoleons our energy drained away, leaving us listless and silent. During our drive home, while fatigue weighted our bodies, neither of us felt nagged by the need to talk. When we were almost there, Rebecca turned, parting the muddled river of self-absorption. "How long have we been married?" Boisterous laughter woke us from our sugar-smogged state, etching a wonderful memory.

Our level of comfortable companionship, so evident then, pervaded my stay with Rebecca. Although I loved the times we explored the area, my main attraction was being with her. The best times were spent on chilly evenings, sitting by the fire near her wood stove, reading, chatting, and enjoying long stretches of comfortable silence. To add to the ambiance, my heart was warmed by nuzzles and kisses from her dog, Tipper, and body rubs by her cat, Truffles.

Saying goodbye to Rebecca at the end of my stay hurt. I was only comforted by the plans we made to see each other again.

———

When I returned home from Maine, I considered driving to Florida to see my friend Joyce. In the end, I decided to wait until later in the year.

For the time being, I'm taking great pleasure in reliving the feelings of being embraced by the arms and hearts of some of the beautiful human beings who were with me during my suffering.

I rejoice in knowing hearts that hold no judgment—hearts that welcome me home to the truth of their love.

FLEXING
WITH VARIABLES

Fear: A dreamless virgin's pimp.
Wisdom: The song of dreamers dancing with the shadows.
— The Watcher

Learning to write from the heart is challenging.

In May I took my first writers workshop, taught by author Jedwin Smith, hoping to develop skills much different than those I'd used in my professional past. When looking over the first piece of my work he edited, I wondered if I was up to the task—every page bled with red ink!

Even so, I've followed Jedwin's advice to "keep writing," aiming to improve, yet he continues to decorate my writing with corrections and suggestions. He does, however, throw in a red-letter compliment now and then that I believe to be authentic. That's enough to keep me going.

Before I spend concentrated time honing my skills using tenses, participles, first person, second person, third person, and the other elements that play out in literary art, I have a long-awaited trip to take on Utah's Green River. I'm scheduled to go in the water on Sunday, September 11. All during the summer, I wonder if the people rocks are as anxious to see me as I am to see them. And I have a hard time believing I'm well enough to endure the rigors of an adventure. Only seven months have passed since I walked away from The Land of Dark Peace and The Velvet-Tongued Vulture.

Yet when the middle of August comes, I begin seriously planning for my trip.

First, I take my paddle off my living room wall where she's been poised for action since I moved into my apartment. Figuring the airlines won't let me carry her on board, I prepare her for shipping by lovingly swaddling the blade, throat, and grip in bubble wrap. After slipping her into a cardboard shipping tube, UPS sends her to the outfitter, Tex's Riverways, to keep in their room-sized safe until I arrive in Moab.

My paddle has been a steadfast companion on other trips there. Her feather-light, eight-and-one-half-inch blade moves a lot of water. She's well-fitted to my height and arms' length, agile and flexible under my command—a perfect friend, quiet, dependable, and patient. Worthy of respect and care.

Once my paddle is on the way to Utah, I gather my clothing and gear for my own trip. I neatly place everything on my checklist in a corner on the floor of my bedroom. For a wilderness experience, I need to see my stuff to assure myself, over and over again, that I've remembered critical items. If I mess up, I'll end up buying what I need in Moab—an expense I don't want. When I get there, I intend to purchase only eats, a multipurpose castile soap, a denatured alcohol canned heat to use in case my propane-fueled stove fails to function, and plastic bags to protect my food boxes and gear—that's all!

Months ago, I acquired a backcountry permit to canoe in Stillwater Canyon in Canyonlands National Park. I'll be required to have that with me for rangers' inspections when I'm on the water. I place the permit along with my well-used, waterproof copy of *Canyonlands River Guide* in the bag I'll be carrying on board the plane. I want them in hand so I'll be sure to have them when I arrive in Utah.

My flight leaves the Atlanta Hartsfield-Jackson airport on September 9. I'm completely ready to go several weeks ahead of time.

Because I'm so well-organized?

No, because I'm excited! I've been wanting to return to the Green River for years. Now I can. More than once I rein in the thoughts that keep rushing me to Utah before I even board the plane.

I think everything's a go until checking my email on August 28. The subject of one message unsettles me: "Tex's Riverways – Please Call Us."

Sucking in my breath, I wonder why. With dread, I read on: "I'm writing you today to inform you of an event that has occurred that will affect your upcoming river trip plans. On August 19 a major thunderstorm and flash flood occurred that did substantial damage to the road we use to access the Green River at Mineral Bottom, the starting location for all of our Stillwater Canyon trips.

"The bad news is that this road closure looks to be something that will take several months to repair, and there is no chance that it will be ready for use in 2010. The good news is that we are finding ways to accommodate most, if not all, of the reservations we have currently booked.

"Please contact us as soon as possible so that we can discuss your options. (To discuss this situation via email would be quite difficult, and we kindly ask that you call us at your earliest convenience.)"

When I call Tex's Riverways, I'm told I have three choices: Cancel. Launch at a point north of Mineral Bottom and extend my trip distance from fifty to a hundred miles. Or, canoe on the Colorado River for forty-seven miles—about the same length I'd planned on the Green River.

Pausing, I consider my options.

"Canceling isn't an option, and doubling the length of my trip doesn't work for me either. Tell me about the Colorado. Are there plenty of places to camp?"

"Yes, especially this time of year. The water level is low."

"What about white water? Is there any between the launch site and the Confluence?"

"No. The river is flat—all the way."

"Okay. We're on. I'll take the Colorado River option. Keep my launch and pickup dates the same."

———

Every time I've been in the backcountry of the Canyonlands, I've learned from nature's metaphorical messages. This time, before I even arrive in Utah, my teaching has begun. In the way of the wild, the destruction of the access road to Mineral Bottom invokes my need to practice something important: to thrive in life, one must accept the invitation to flex with variables.

Resiliency is a noteworthy character trait of high-functioning, long-term survivors of the Holocaust, sexual abuse, pernicious cancers, and other potential insults to well-being.[1]

Before Lyme struck, I was resilient. But when the disease marauded my life, I became brittle and silent, unlike the Carolyn Graham I once knew. I couldn't tolerate what was happening in the moment, nor did I realize I was being cared about and cared for by those who loved me. All I could see was the "washed-out road to Mineral Bottom" and the destruction of my carefully constructed, erroneous identity.

What do I mean by all that?

The best way I can think of to explain is to identify a few items from a survey developed by Al Siebert, PhD, who interviewed hundreds of survivors of catastrophic events: "What he learned was that most survivors are ordinary people, who faced extraordinary situations and rebuilt their lives by tapping into their deepest strengths and abilities."[2]

And he was able to identify common characteristics contributing to their long-term mental and physical health. Using those common characteristics, Dr. Siebert created the Resiliency Quiz, published with his permission in *You Can Beat the Odds*.[3]

After answering the questions on the quiz using my current state of mind, my score was: 65–80 = Better Than Most. Then I answered those same questions based on how I processed the radical changes in my life when I was ill, anxious, and contemplating suicide. My score: *40 and under = Seek Help!*[4]

The survivor characteristics identified on Dr. Siebert's quiz that were sorely lacking when I was mired in the results of extreme trauma are worth remembering. They're worth paying attention to—without judgment, for they give me a template for change:

"I'm usually optimistic. I see difficulties as temporary and expect to overcome them."[5]

My mindset was the opposite when Lyme disease became an issue. Because of what I'd read online about suffering from Lyme disease, and my own catastrophic patterns of thinking, I saw nothing but the maw of doom, certain to swallow me no matter what I did. Without knowing, I donned the shroud of hopelessness and compromised my capacity to heal.

"In a crisis or chaotic situation, I calm myself and focus on taking useful actions."[6]

I didn't know how to calm myself, nor had I learned the coping skills required to process extremes. The coping mechanisms I developed during my adventuresome challenges were useful under ordinary circumstances. They were no match for the repeated assaults to my life by a ravaging bacteria. I needed help.

"I'm able to recover emotionally from losses and setbacks. I have friends I can talk with. I can express my feelings to others and ask for help. Feelings of anger, loss, and discouragement don't last long."[7]

I clammed up, holding my feelings inside with the death grip of silence though there were many who would have listened willingly. Friends. My sister. And I could have found a therapist to help me had I sought one early on. Before then, when suffering from events in my life or puzzled by a behavior, I'd routinely sought input from therapists. When my life fell apart, I simply didn't have the courage to face my pain until I started working with Brenda.

"I'm good at solving problems. I can use analytical logic, be creative, or use practical common sense."[8]

When I was terrifying myself with my own thoughts, logic couldn't function. I was preoccupied with thoughts void of trust: *How will I manage to pay medical expenses? Who will take care of me when I'm older and sick? Who will want to?* There was nothing in my thinking about trusting the Universe to provide for me, although that's precisely what was happening during the entire time I was disabled.

"I feel self-confident, appreciate myself, and have a healthy concept of who I am."[9]

Feeling lower than a pus-eating maggot while I was sick was excruciatingly painful. And maybe, at heart, that's how I'd always felt about myself.

My self-confidence is improving now. Thank goodness!

Therapy sessions, affirmations, and learning to understand that I'm cherished, important, merely because I breathe is taking me to a new level of self-love. Opening to the compassionate realm of nonjudgmental self-acceptance is playing out in new levels of self-care, like healthy eating. I'm beginning to embrace all of who I am: my high-functioning self and the part of me that flounders.

And though I'm unaware of what's happening, I'm preparing myself to deal with my secret past; compassion is inviting me to release gut-rotting secrets. A new level of self-love and acceptance is laying the foundation for a major psychological healing that will pay out in the near future.

"I can tolerate high levels of ambiguity and uncertainty about situations."[10]

I couldn't when I was ill. Sometimes I still can't. That's an aspect of myself that needs tons of work. I tend to anchor myself to the idea that things have to be a particular way for me to be happy. And that I have more control over variables than is possible. Knotting my happiness to desired outcomes is problematic. The art of letting go is one I intend to develop.

Now is the time to practice—when my life is going well, a time when I have the opportunity, for I don't know what my future holds. Maybe Lyme won't take me down again. Or maybe so. Death most certainly will. Without a doubt, I'll once again be asked to cope with painful circumstances.

For as long as I can remember, I've acknowledged the lessons I've learned from heartbreaking events that passed. Now is the time to learn from challenging situations as they arise.

Because I've been so invested in canoeing on the Green River, changing the venue to the Colorado is a big deal. Even so, that could be an offering, a time to cultivate resiliency in simple circumstances. A time to learn how to think using authentic pathways, uncluttered by rationalizations. A time to take hold of my good fortune and the opportunity to thrive in a changing landscape. A time to learn to be flexible.

And why not?

Little by little, I'm weaving my experiences of tragedy into a multitextured tapestry, appreciating the masterful teaching of demanding events and the way they've enriched my life. How else could I have learned that time spent in good health is a precious commodity, inspiring gratitude and good self-care? How else could I have realized that tapping into the present is rich with the opportunity to experience reality, and that wasting time in the past or the future lamenting or worrying is fundamentally destructive? Yes, I sometimes need to revisit my past to learn or heal, yet doing so is only productive when that's my clear intention. And, yes, I need to deliberately contemplate the future in order to make reasonable plans for myself.

That's much different than the random, unaware thoughts that took me over and over again into emotionally stormy places that disabled logical thinking.

As for my upcoming trip to Utah, once in a while, my mind tries to sneak in a video by The Watcher, making up a story of disaster on the Colorado River with me in the starring role as a victim. When fear tries to pimp my dreams of triumph in the wilderness, I pause to reflect: *Right now is a good time to practice flexibility. A time to use my head. A time to adapt and trust myself.*

The Watcher can't help but speak.

No bullying, though!

No need for that.

You're in good condition—strong enough to drag a loaded canoe onto a beach, keen enough to react with speed and skill if nature should challenge you. Your stamina's fine, and you're limber. This trip you've planned is a realistic challenge, even if you are sixty-seven.

You've checked out the critical details with Tex's Riverways—a trustworthy outfit, to be sure. If you didn't think so, you wouldn't have used them every time you've gone to Moab.

You might as well start muscling up this "resiliency" thing.

Besides, the people rocks are waiting for you. You haven't seen each other in a long time.

As a worst-case scenario, until you're on the water, you can always back out. So what if you lose a little money—no big deal.

Out loud I declare, "I'm going!"

AT THE
CONFLUENCE

In the Aethers, the Seeker becomes the sought
as the river of life
flows through the canyons of the soul,
echoing the majesty in the journey.

—The Watcher

Glowing in a cloudless blue sky, a bright sun excites the day on a September afternoon as I step off the Tex's Riverways' gear-loaded bus, towing a rack trailer stacked with canoes and kayaks. While looking around, taking in the familiar scenery, warm breezes whisper, telling me the temperature is somewhere in the eighties. Ripples shimmer and dance on the nearby Colorado River, celebrating my arrival in the Canyonlands.

I walk to the rear of the trailer, where someone helps me unload and carry my rented, seventeen-foot aluminum canoe to the river's bank. We place the bow partially in the shallow water facing downriver, ready for action.

My heart races as I haphazardly load her for the time being with my camping gear, drinking water, food, and portable toilet, balancing the weight. Then I stow a spare paddle made of aluminum and black plastic under the thwarts. Before stowing my own in the same place, I tenderly brush my hand down her smooth, varnished, wide wooden blade, appreciating her steadfast service and companionship on our many waterborne adventures.

Although I'm eager to be on my way, I decide to take advantage of a briefing offered by Mike, an employee of Tex's Riverways. So I meander to a large piece of driftwood, sit down, and wait for him to finish helping others unload their boats and gear.

Opening the ragged, waterproof copy of *Canyonlands River Guide* I've used on my four previous trips here, I locate the pages illustrating the topography of the fifty-mile stretch of the Colorado River and the immediate surroundings where I'll be traveling solo. Mike soon joins me.

I look as calm as he seems, but my heart's still racing. This river trip isn't going to be a walk in the park. In this wild arena they never are. There are always mental and physical challenges to stretch my limits: All too well, I remember being blasted by unexpected gusts of wind. Churning waves pounded my canoe, threatening to capsize me while I desperately paddled to a canyon wall for protection. Or the time when I stepped out of the canoe and was sucked into silt that held me captive until I figured I should float my upper body and frog-kick my legs—keeping my canoe in tow—so I could free myself to swim to a firmer bottom. And once I paddled an entire day in cold, unrelenting rain until my body became hypothermic, begging to sleep. Weak and knowing I had to warm myself, I pitched my tent on a narrow beach and crawled into my sleeping bag after drinking a cup of hot water. My body soon warmed to normal temperature, but the ensuing night was sleepless; staying on watch was critical to make certain the river didn't rise and sweep me away in the current.

Now, though, I'm barely on the other side of eight years of severe illness. Although I've trusted my status enough to get me here, there's still the final word. The face of reality can be different than the face of dreams.

Because I know a test awaits me, I feel anxious, so I'm impatient during Mike's briefing. I have to prod myself to pay attention simply because I've only been on the Green River, not the Colorado.

With untroubled deliberation, Mike turns the pages of the *Canyonlands River Guide*, pointing out several places where there are little-known and secluded Anasazi ruins or rock art along the way to the confluence of the Green and Colorado rivers, my destination. He flips the pages to the last one before the Confluence is depicted. When he points an index finger to a spot shown on the river, I'm expecting him to tell me about a ruin: "The Slide's not dangerous—just a little white water you should know about. When you get there, about a mile from the Confluence, keep your weight low in the canoe and your bow into the waves. You'll be okay."

Fear explodes in my gut, shattering my tentative self-confidence, but I hide my feelings, wearing the appearance of a poised master while I stand and thank Mike for the briefing.

Then I walk toward my canoe and stand beside her, gazing at the river, seeing only a fear-glazed ribbon of water. *The Slide. The Slide! What Slide?* my angry, terrified thoughts screech. I was told by one of the supposedly knowledgeable Tex's Riverways owners that the water from this launch site to the Confluence is an easy, downstream paddle with nothing rough.

In fact, *that* information happened to be the deciding factor in my being here!

Now what?

———

When making reservations for this trip on the Colorado River, I knew I'd be taught in the language of nature's metaphors. Nature is a grand teacher here. Still standing by my canoe, wondering what to do, I hear the river encouraging me to take the risk: "Bend. Change is inevitable. Even rocks change."

Hmm. I came here to learn. To grow myself. To say goodbye to the memories of being a victim of disease.

I've dreamed of arriving at the Confluence as part of a triumphant mind-body journey, declaring—with assurance—that I'm back now; I'm grateful for my well-being. I'm ready to design my future that's beckoning with meaning and purpose.

The Watcher emerges into my quandary:

You're a canoeing expert. That hasn't changed.

You may not have canoed on the Colorado River. You have, however, soloed fifty miles on the Green River.

Others are paddling from here to the Confluence, despite the Slide. You've used Tex's Riverways four times before.

Why?

Because they've proven to be worthy of your trust. Dependable. Concerned about your welfare. If you were facing significant danger, their employees wouldn't be putting you and others in the water.

Even though fearful thoughts attempt to interrupt and make a racket, I hear the voice of reason.

No way I'm backing out.

No way!

I've come a long way, baby, for this.

Into the wilderness of challenges to come, I proclaim out loud, "I'm going!" With a decided nod to logic, determined to triumph over my fears and whatever other challenges come my way, I attend to last-minute details, tidying and securing my things.

After moving the canoe farther into the water, leaving just enough of the keel anchored on the bottom to allow access to my stowed supplies, after removing the paddles and laying them on the beach, I reposition some of them, weighting the stern slightly more than the bow for good steerage.

Seven plastic gallon jugs of water, weighing a total of about sixty pounds, are the heaviest of my stowage. I stack them near the bow to counterbalance my weight in the stern. Next, I position the heavy stainless-steel toilet snug against the water bottles. Then I neaten the two boxes loaded with food and cooking gear side by side behind the toilet. Near the stern where I'll be kneeling, I position the bags holding my backpacking tent, air mattress, and clothing.

With a narrow-gauge rope, I create a web on top of everything, securing my excursion's necessities in case I should capsize. (My canoe has sealed air pockets in the bow and stern and will float near the river's surface even when filled with water.) Weaving in and out of water jug handles and other things, every so often tying knots on the thwarts, I protect my supplies.

I usually take only the bare essentials on my Utah river trips—no books, no camera, no gadgets, no watch—no distractions. I simply want to be in the wilderness—in the raw—with my experience. This time, though, I make an exception: a waterproof notebook and pen advertised as "an outdoor writing product for outdoor writing people."

Wishing the friends who gave me the notebook were with me, I put their gift, snacks, and a few other items I want handy inside a small, clear waterproof bag, clipping the handle around the thwart nearest the stern. To make certain I'm comfortable when paddling, I place a garden kneeling pad on the bottom of the canoe to cushion my knees and to prevent scraping them against the sand and pebbles that inevitably collect there. Finally, I slide the spare paddle under the thwarts and place mine on the starboard side, blade resting on the bottom, throat leaning on the stern seat. Except for one last task, I'm ready to go . . .

After a couple of days and nights on the water, I'll become part of nature's rhythmic continuum. My habitual way of defining the passage of time with calendars and a watch will evaporate into the wilderness. Soon, in evenings to come, I won't be able to remember what day of the week has passed.

Needing some way to keep track of the days on the river so I'll arrive at the Confluence in five days for my scheduled pickup, I tie a piece of rope to the stern thwart using a bowline. When I'm done, I stand back to etch my plans into my brain: *The night before pickup, there will be five knots. Got that—five.*

Finally, I'm ready to shove off.

Fear shrivels my courage. I shiver from head to toe.

I don't remember being this frightened on my other trips here. Is the Slide getting to me? Is this too much for a sixty-seven-year-old? Don't even go there. That's crazy. Irrational fear isn't going to rob me of this experience.

I trumpet my determination again: "I'm going!"

Ready to be on my way despite my fear, I move to the starboard side of my canoe near the stern. Facing the bow and bending over, I place one trembling hand on each gunwale to balance myself. Cautiously, I step into the center with my left foot, keeping my weight low to make certain I don't capsize.

My right leg, poised on the river bottom, ready to push me off, shakes. My strength and courage is leaking into the shallow water.

Phew, I've never felt fear do this.

I hope I'll have enough strength to push myself off.

What if I can't get my canoe into the water? Now, that would be embarrassing!

Once I'm in the water a while, I'll probably feel better.

Taking a deep breath, and summoning all the strength I can muster, I push with my right leg. There's just enough muscle left to get my canoe waterborne.

After lifting my right leg into the canoe and kneeling in front of the stern seat, I feel the river cradle my craft, soothing my fears. Gently, the current, an enthusiastic companion, joins me in this amazing place. After taking hold of my paddle, I float downstream, relishing the contrasting colors that give each a loud voice: Bright, pointed green tamarisk leaves, displaying themselves along white sandy beaches, speak of invasion and disruption of the natural evolution of the canyons. Rust-red sandstone cliffs, framed by a cerulean-blue sky, tell of shadowed majesty sculpted by trauma. The bright silver of my aluminum canoe, gliding along the muddy river, declares my adventure is, indeed, underway.

Perched along the canyon rims, rotund stacks of people rocks show up, greeting me, seeming to lament the time that's passed since I was last here. Sighing, I settle some more, feeling like I've come home. *Interesting—I often feel more comfortable on water than on land.*

Leaning over the starboard gunwale, I check the water line: *Looks like the weight is well-balanced. The stern's cutting a little deeper in the water than the bow. Good. That should help me steer.*

Okay, I'm ready for business.

Placing my right hand on the grip of my paddle, the left on her throat, I bend at the waist, thrusting her forward along the starboard side of my canoe. Then I dip the wide, flat blade halfway into the river. With a determined pull, using my shoulder and core muscles, I take my first stroke on my journey of magic and metaphors.

"To the Confluence!"

———

Early on the morning of my third day in this magnificent wilderness, I'm drifting on a ribbon of glass with one leg draped over the side of the canoe, exhilarated by my surroundings.

I glide on the water with little effort, savoring the landscape and my feelings: Shades of green foliage bejewel the rock-strewn canyon walls, finding purchase in places that sometimes seem incredulous. More groups of rotund, terra-cotta people rocks line the rim of the rock walls. I laugh when my childlike imagination sees three fat, old women in pantaloons bending over to moon me.

I marvel at giant rock pillars that stand tall in the wind like stately Indian chiefs. Intricate canyon formations invite exploration that I decide to pass on. I hear the silent voice of the Canyonlands reminding me in nature's unique way: "These majestic surroundings are being redecorated even now by the gentle breezes and slow-moving current of the river. We've been through a lot, just like you. The splendor you value has been sculpted by many different kinds of circumstances—ones like you are experiencing now, and those decidedly more violent. Flash floods, earthquakes, and volcanic eruptions have shaped our grandeur too."

Trauma has the potential to create a magnificent work of art.

I couldn't grasp that concept when I was sick, though looking back, I know I've "heard" the truth. The ease in my pre-Lyme conditions didn't sculpt compassion or a deep appreciation for simple things. Nor the intense gratitude for my life, sparkling in my eyes and spilling over in abundant generosity and joy.

So far on this trip to the Confluence, I've experienced only mental challenges related to the Slide. Other than that, every waking moment has offered a gift of wonder, intensified by my gratitude for being alive—for being here. Exhilaration stokes a wide-grinning high.

Without warning, everything changes.

Compassion fills me so full that I burst wide open, bow my head, and wail. Suddenly, I'm no longer alone on the river. Those who want to thrive, yet can't, swell my heart. They're with me— all around me. I can't help wondering again: *Why me? How come I got well when others can't seem to heal?*

I don't feel guilty, though.

Instead, The Watcher speaks: *Life can, indeed, have disparate, dark moments.*

At once I know this journey isn't just for me.

Into the echoing canyons I call, "You out there, you out there, you out there. I know how you feel, how you feel, how you feel. I know. I know. I know. You're welcome to come be with me, come be with me, come be with me. This journey is for us. For us. For us!"

I revel in knowing I'm not alone on this adventure. That those who want to rise, yet can't, are somehow experiencing my love. I yearn for them to find solace in what I've learned: Majesty in the journey beckons no matter how desperate our conditions. Meaning in suffering merely awaits recognition. And the soul beckons us to seek answers in the nectar of simple things.

———

Noisy water in the Canyonlands signals warnings: "Be alert. Pay attention. Get ready for action!"

Sometimes the commotion means water is merely flowing under canyon walls, etching new shapes. At other times, the water babbles when being pierced by rocks or when shallow and scraped by pebbles on the river bottom. Water protests with a roaring voice when large volumes are pushed downhill through narrow, strangling spaces between canyon walls and large boulders.

On my journey to the Confluence, the river and canyons have prompted captivating conversations with my senses and days empty of significant challenges. That is, until noisy water interrupts, silencing my fascinating experiences with the shrill voice of menacing fear—the Slide!

Although I suspect my fears are unwarranted, I have difficulty silencing them. Repeatedly, the Watcher comes to my rescue with advice that eventually turns into something like a mantra:

If you keep this up, your whole trip could turn out to be about the Slide.

The noisy water you're hearing is urging you forward.

Stay in the present. There's no danger in this moment.

You're not close enough to the Slide to be concerned. Stop going there before you get there. Stop practicing for an imaginary disaster.

Remember: the outfitter wouldn't have put you in the water if danger existed.

Remember: you're an expert!

You came here to learn and grow.

Trust yourself.

You're worthy of self-trust!

More than once, I have to make a determined effort to wait until I get to the Slide to experience the Slide. After I put aside my fears for the moment, I'm able to dissolve my boundaries of self-identity and become, once again, at one with the exquisite intricacies of wilderness and my journey.

Frequently, I refer to the eighteen-year-old topographical river guide that I should have replaced. When realizing my map isn't current enough to be completely useful because many land formations have disappeared, I pay attention only to the directions the river meanders and the large, slow-to-change landmarks to keep myself referenced.

Late one afternoon I'm sitting on the stern seat drifting downstream, figuring I've canoed about ten miles each day. Glancing at my sunsets-gone-by rope, counting four knots and comparing my surroundings with what I see in my river guide, I confirm my position on the Colorado: *Now I must be getting close to the Slide!*

Taking my paddle in hand, I begin to stroke. My skin tingles with fear. My senses sharpen. Slowly and deliberately I move toward the real thing, ears poised to hear noisy water. When I round a bend in the river, out of sight, but clearly audible, I pick up the too-loud sounds of turbulent water.

With my eyes piercing the distance, seeking sight of my dreaded challenge, my heart races. *Here we go. Get ready!* Snugging my life jacket closer to my chest, and dropping my knees to the floor of the canoe to lower my center of gravity to prevent capsizing, I keep my canoe moving toward uncertainty with steady, rhythmic paddling.

Rounding another bend, whitecaps appear in the distance: *the Slide!*

Scanning the river ahead, and closing the distance between me and the rapids, my brain attempts to compute my risk. With short, quick strokes, I direct my canoe toward the least amount of turbulence.

The churning current rushes me faster than I wish.

Poised with my buttocks against the seat, my paddle just above the water, ready to direct the bow into the waves, I close the distance between my challenge, still unable to tell the character of the threat.

Suddenly, I see the dimensions of what I'm facing.

Relief gushes through me: *I can handle the Slide. I can do this. I can!*

Exhilaration explodes into laughter: *I made such a big deal over nothing. I'm going to be safe. I'm going to be safe!*

Hunkering down, I get ready for a ride on the rushing current as my bow enters the rapids.

Waves slapping the side of the canoe jounce me around.

With urgent core-body strokes, I keep the bow facing down-river into the turbulence.

My canoe is lifted skyward.

The river greases a fast ride down the Slide.

My canoe glides onto still, flat water, yet I'm far from still inside.

Absolute delight stokes a childlike plea: *Can I do that just one more time? I wish I could. Again and again.*

Then another thrill rushes into this already memorable day: *I'm going to reach my goal. The Confluence is barely a mile away. I'm going to get there. I am.*

I really have done this river thing. Forty-seven miles. Solo!

I beach my canoe on a firm part of the white sandy beach at the Confluence, then stow my paddle. Holding on to both gunwales, I step out of my canoe and pull her farther onto land.

When I'm certain my craft and gear are secure, I reach my arms into the Aethers. Filled with gratitude for this long-sought moment, I call out my triumph: "I am safe! I am well! Yes, I *am* well!"

With my arms still outstretched, and my eyes thanking Divine Grace, a wonder as big and bright as the blue sky above fills me, for I'm certain my hard-won health is a Gift. Yes, I've worked for this moment and there have been many Earth Angels shepherding me, yet I feel in my bones that the overriding direction has come from Divine Inspiration, where infinite freedom beckons. As this journey in the Canyonlands' wilderness is coming to an end, the bestowal of wellness and the opportunity to create a new life speaks of miracles.

On the wet sandy beach next to my canoe, I dance and sing to the rhythm of joy in my heart.

Along the canyon walls, the observing people rocks echo a standing ovation to my own.

Yes!

Taking a deep breath, I savor my surroundings. Gratitude paints a vivid kaleidoscope of sights: rivers greeting one another with splashes and curls, red sandstone or gray shale guiding their passage, and an unclouded sky wrapping us in a surreal connection. For a moment I rest, reveling in stunning, effervescent beauty.

When I'm satiated, I scan a gray-white sand dune that's a few feet away from my landing site. Identifying an inviting spot, I pitch my six-by-eight royal-blue tent with the door facing where the Colorado and Green rivers merge.

After stripping and taking a bath beside my canoe, I put on the clean clothes I washed then dried the day before.

When I've gathered cooking supplies and food, I sit down on a nearby piece of driftwood to sauté black beans, garlic, tabasco sauce, and tahini in the frying pan custom made for my Jetboil stove. The aroma stokes a hunger already begging to be fed. Even so, I wait until the mixture is steaming hot before scooping up my eats with slices of red bell pepper.

Robust flavor bursts in my mouth with every bite. And a mixture of salted nuts and dried, sweet apricots serves as dessert.

After washing my frying pan, face, and hands in the river, I dry everything, feeling the rough, thin terry-cloth towel prick my sunburned face. When I've hung the towel on a gunwale to dry, and stowed my gear, I stand and look around again, my heart drawn by a sense of magic capering in the air.

As the last day of my journey with the river and canyons begins to close, I hear a calling to be decidedly present.

After making certain all is well with my canoe, I amble to the door of my tent and sit down at the threshold, folding my arms on my knees, willing my senses to be fully alive to absorb the beauty of my surroundings and whatever else is to come.

Soon, the sun leisurely grants a cooling shade while drifting behind a cliff in the west. The remaining rays paint the canyon wall across the river in gentled hues and shadows of terra cotta.

An incandescent three-quarter moon rises, towing stars shimmering in deepening shades of indigo.

Overhead, silhouettes of tiny bats flitter in my vision. Wings of a large bird whoosh in the air above me. I wiggle my toes in the warm, fine, white sand while the Colorado and Green rivers murmur gurgles of greeting as they join, traveling to a shared destiny.

Mystery and unmistakable majesty speak of the improbable inviting the unexpected . . .

Lyrical, classical flute music echoes in the canyons, dancing in the breeze.

At first I'm too astonished to understand what's happening. Then I know.

With the rivers, the moon, the flute player, I, too, was summoned to be here. Summoned to be here for the clarion call of the Canyonlands echoing my own knowing: "This phase of your healing journey ends here. Well done, child of the wilderness. Well done!"

Embraced by exquisite beauty and tender, Divine Caring, I reverently and humbly bow my head and weep.

PART III

MAJESTY
IN THE JOURNEY

*Choosing to embrace both the joy and the anguish of one's past
sculpts majesty in the journey.*

THE WATCHER

Attention. The quality kind—that's my thing.

I become powerful when someone makes an effort to be with me.

During the months Carolyn calls Majesty in the Journey, she begins to lengthen the time she spends with me.

I like that.

I'm especially grateful that she finds so much value in me that she wants to know me in a deeper way. That's a significant step, because I know being still is a challenge for her.

I'm not the only one who appreciates her efforts. At some level, her mind-body knows what she's doing, and nods a thank-you in her direction.

Sometimes Carolyn's gut and I get so close a sliced second couldn't fit between us.

There's one thing, though. I can't stand the name she uses for her second brain: Gut. What a crass way to refer to such an intelligent and eloquent part of herself.

She can be irreverent. A rebel.

I'm not like that, so I've come up with my own name for that part of her:

Intuit.

That's a great play on words, even if I say so myself.

Intuit—C's into it, sees into it, or Carolyn's into it.

And she gets into it all right during Majesty in the Journey.

She starts out writing her book thinking she's just going to tell about her recovery from Lyme disease. But she was wrong about that.

As she writes, Intuit takes her back to exquisitely painful memories of the things that happened to her when she was Lyme-sick. More than that, Intuit nudges her deep into her subconscious to find refuse from her childhood. She goes into her past because she's becoming aware that she's carrying a big load of emotional detritus. At one time, all that stuff looked to her like a benign sanitary landfill. She forgot that they have to be vented to prevent underground explosions from ripping the earth.

Intuit gently leads her closer and closer to her buried past until she can literally smell the stench of the remains left by childhood trauma.

Until recently, she didn't realize how much refuse she had locked inside her heart. She didn't know what to do with anguish sometimes, so she stuffed her feelings into an unvented space that wasn't made to hold hurts.

When healing from childhood trauma, Intuit lets her know how far to go each time she steps into the past so she doesn't explode her heart.

And my part?

I watch her with care and compassion, and when her emotions rage, I wrap her in the loving arms of the moment, letting her know everything's all right.

By the way, she's often astounded at the strength of her feelings.

Because she's spent so much time getting to know me, eventually I give her a gift of exquisite value: awareness that her feelings are not about the present, and that they will recede like when she first began feeling her anxiety wane. And, each time she notices them receding, she trusts me more. She builds on that trust, just like in other relationships she's had over the years. And, because I'm always with her, she feels supported like she never has before.

That's something wonderful, for that precious kid inside her needs a sense for my ever-present and protective power — awareness, my forte.

Also, during her Journey, I have the honor of joining Intuit to tell her she's coming home to herself — to wholeness. Her heart becomes like a butterfly bush dancing in the breeze, ready to burst into bloom. Little by little, she nourishes herself with compassion, opening up loving, succulent blossoms of joy irresistible to others.

As the love and compassion of her nectared heart bears fruit in relationships, she's embraced by a love so profound her gratitude shimmers in the air.

Now that I've filled you in on what's going on, and what's to come with Carolyn and me, I've got a big job to do. I'm going back to the moment.

To Watch.

PRESENT TENSE

In any journey, there is risk; any deepening of character necessitates a loss. Nonetheless, initiating such a journey remains a watershed, an outpouring of unanticipated grace, and indelible opportunity to drink from the deep well of your life.[1]

—Saki Santorelli

I'm sitting in the front of a classroom attending a workshop sponsored by the Atlanta Writers Club.

The English professor leading the workshop makes introductory comments and, at some point, criticizes authors who use nouns as verbs.

What's she talking about? Nouns used as verbs pepper the English language: Work is a noun and a verb. Sight is, too. Hmm. I'm confused.

That's not the only thing I don't get.

The professor asks participants to write a few paragraphs in first person, present tense, and then, another paragraph with the same content, using third person, past tense. I can't remember the English conjugations of verbs. Not only that, I have no idea how using different tenses and pronouns can affect what I say in my writing.

I hope nobody's noticing I'm not writing anything.

I feel dumb as a rock.

I finally get the gist of what the professor means when two talented writers volunteer to read their work. Their skill sucks the air out of my green-tinted, puffed-up hubris, blown up because I'm a "writer."

How will I ever learn to write like that? I wonder if I've made a mistake to even think about putting together a book.

I shrivel into the knowledge that I've got some work to do before I'll know anything about writing skillfully from the heart.

During the winter months before I took my trip to Utah, I'd joined the Atlanta Writers Club. In April, I'd taken the AWC-sponsored workshop from the English professor that left me doubting myself.

When reading April's AWC newsletter, I noticed information about an eight-week workshop author Jedwin Smith was scheduled to teach. When I signed up for my first one with him, I had reservations colored by my past as the daughter of an irrational male tyrant: *Will I be able to relate to this guy, Jedwin?*

I've got some personal stuff to write about—can I learn to do that with a man teaching me, critiquing my work? This whole idea feels risky. I need to start somewhere, though. And Jedwin's got some impressive credentials: two Pulitzer Prize nominations, a movie contract for one of his books.

In May 2010, I take my first eight-week workshop with Jedwin.

During the first session, I'm mute with caution. In fact, I spend most of my time making myself as invisible as possible while observing what's going on with him and the other group members.

Holy cow, this guy's a buzzed-cut ex-marine. Wonder if he's in touch with his feelings. He seems humble, caring—definitely not a mainstream, cookie-cutter type. I like that. I like that a lot.

Odd how right this feels—like a safe place to start to learn how to write.

During the second meeting, I read what I *think* is the introduction to my book.

I've never written anything and then read my work in front of a group for critiquing. And this group has more male members than female, making me especially timid.

When my turn comes to read, The Watcher reassures me: *This isn't about your dad. Your observations of the group are telling you something important. Trust your gut. Jedwin and the others—all of them—appear eager to help each other succeed as writers. They don't feel like the type who would hurt you deliberately.*

Even though The Watcher has melted some of my fear, my mouth goes desert-bone dry when I get ready to read. My anus is so tight an empty fart couldn't escape.

Then I hear The Watcher issuing reminders: *You're not reading in front of your father. You're at the Eagle Eye bookstore.*

Anchor yourself in the present.

Keep going despite your fear.

After I read, keeping my head bowed, I raise only my eyes to peek at Jedwin and members of the group.

No one's scowling, or looking bored.

Jedwin says something like, "Look around. You've captured everyone's interest. No one's snoring."

One of the men in the group buoys my confidence with a thumbs-up: "Keep writing." In a tone colored with respect set by Jedwin, some of the group members offer helpful suggestions that I write down to use later when editing my manuscript. My tense shoulders, plastered to my ears, lower, dropping to a relaxed position.

I'm sure glad that's over.

Breathe!

I guess I did okay.
I just need to keep writing, like that guy said.

Thus began my journey as a writer, seeking to learn how to transform the thoughts in my head and the feelings in my heart into a work I hope will, one day, make me feel comfortable calling myself a literary artist—a writer.

But I've got a lo-o-oong way to go before that happens . . .

———

After returning from my trip to Utah, I start my second workshop with Jedwin, one week late. He remarks that I look different.

That's because I am different.

My trip has transfigured me—made me more aware of the Divine nature of my healing. As I think back to my Divinely timed experience at the Confluence, memories of the flute music infuse me with the desire to continue to learn to write, for the remembered magic of that synchronistic moment feels like a message of encouragement for something that is meant to be—or, perhaps, must be.

Not having a clue where my decisions about writing will take me, I commit to an emotional housecleaning of sorts. I realize I need to revisit some of my past to take my healing to a deeper level. I'm eager to unload the shame, guilt, and sorrow that have burdened me for too long. And, before the painful memories wrought by the effects of chronic Lyme disease decay into toxins that poison my system, I decide to open up and let those memories tell me more of what I need to hear.

Also, there's a poisonous secret I need to tell—some profound shame I need to unload. I need to dump the shame that's shackled me with self-hatred in order to cleanse myself of the detritus from childhood trauma that's been rotting inside me, exploding into mental and physical illness.

I'm bone-tired of our culture that's dying from pus-driven secrets.

I'm bone-tired of holding on to secrets that are chanting for release. When everything's out in the open, I'll heal at a deeper level, I know I will. I'll reclaim my birthright: an airy freedom from lurking depression and self-hatred.

I dream of being loved after I've told all my secrets—loved, not in spite of what's happened in my past, but rather because my past has sculpted the beautiful canyons of my soul that chiseled the lines in my face, speaking of love and compassion.

I hope for a new me with lightened burdens.

And maybe, just maybe, if I release my secrets in writing, reclaiming love for myself, someone else will be inspired to seek a pathway to freedom. Could anything be better than that?

Committed to being wide open and dead-level honest, I begin to write *The Gift of the Circle*, innocent of where my journey will take me . . .

A FLEDGLING

I fly somewhere, thinking I know why.
Really, though, I never know the reason.
Each wee tiny second is a mystery.

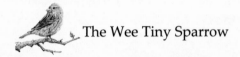 The Wee Tiny Sparrow

Jedwin turns out to be much more than an author and writers coach.

He's an extraordinary teacher, an insightful, red-penned editor. Yet, his remarks are framed with tact and kindness. They are offered as deferential suggestions, honoring my right to make the final decision about my work.

He's fluid, this guy, Jedwin—not frozen in a need to be right.

A quiet wisdom whispers in his eyes. His face speaks of his rugged journey—a life sculpted by radical highs and lows. His gentle smile tells me we're joined in common ground.

During his weekly workshop sessions, I read something I've written aloud. When I finish, and before I look at anyone else, I peek at Jedwin. Every week he's the same: Authentic. Predictable.

I'm beginning to feel safe when I'm around him.

He tells me what I need to hear for improving my writing.

But that's not always what my need-to-be-perfect self wishes. In fact, at first I get so rattled by his and others' suggestions for improving my work, thinking is impossible. Instead, a silent replaying of my responses to even the positive remarks screams into my ears. Yet, ever so slowly, I learn to take evaluations in stride.

After reading something aloud, fear and doubt pound in my ears. When I sneak a look at Jedwin, once in a while I see his fists raised in the air. His eyes are dancing with shared triumph—teacher and writer. That's when I know we're doing well together.

That's when I'm certain he's a gift to me.

———

Then there's Rosemary Daniell.

She, too, is an author and writers coach.

In *The Woman Who Spilled Words All Over Herself*, she describes her passion about literary art: "A spiritual quest as well as an aesthetic one: an unexpected rainbow, a journey of the heart."[1]

I meet Rosemary when attending the Atlanta Alpha Babes Zona Rosa writers workshop, one of the many Rosemary has spawned across the globe to nurture women writers.

When I arrive at our meeting place, her sister's house, and ring the bell at the front entrance, Rosemary opens the door, and enters my life.

I'm stunned by her presence.

Smiling, ruby-red lips welcome me, proclaiming a bold authenticity. Black boots with roses on them tell me this woman's courageous—unafraid of herself. Her cleavage speaks the language of a powerful feminine anarchist.

Electricity charges the air.

Get ready!

An adventure beckons here.

When first meeting Rosemary, I know very little about her, but merely being in her space, alive with expectancy, excites me. Lines in her face tell me she's "well-seasoned" like me.

After attending a few Zona Rosa meetings, I come to know that she's coached more than two hundred published authors. And, I come to believe that working with her one-to-one would be a rare benefit to me as a writer—and a woman. So I begin scheduling appointments for consultations.

When the time comes for me to announce my presence at her sister's front door for my first conference, internal discord threatens to shatter my self-confidence; my feet get an itch to run like hell.

Who do you think you are, meeting with someone like Rosemary?

But I like her. I want to know her better.

I know she's got something for me that's important.

Hold yourself together.

The Watcher chimes in: *Carolyn, we're all the same. A pauper, a queen, an author, and someone seeking to learn how to be one.*

Feeling settled by that truth, I knock on the door and begin a multidimensional relationship with Rosemary Daniell. Indeed, an adventure.

When Rosemary and I sit down together on the white couch in her sister's living room, she has in hand a portion of *The Gift of the Circle* that I sent to her several weeks ago.

Before we get down to the business of discussing my work, we connect in the "pink zone, the Zona Rosa,"[2] the place where our individual boundaries dissolve—the place we share as women sojourners along the sometimes-challenging pathway of being authentic females.

In a seamless way, we move on to my work, which has been splashed with purple ink. Her suggestions are useful, and having a second, professional opinion is wonderful. Yet the most important thing I get from Rosemary on the day of our first one-to-one meeting comes after I've said goodbye, certain I did the right thing to meet with her.

Ambling down the driveway to my car, I hear Rosemary call my name: "Carolyn." I turn around and look at her. "Carolyn, honey, I'm excited about what you're doing with your writing."

"Thanks, Rosemary."

As I turn around and continue toward my car, a giant grin stretches from ear to ear. Even my insides smile.

How did she know I needed to hear that?

Extrasensory antennae that reach to the stars!

From the brief time I've just spent with Rosemary, I sense she's bonded with her truth in a way that makes her incapable of delivering bullshit.

When we were talking on the couch earlier, I told her about my passion for being open and honest in my work. Eyes sparkling with the energy of mischief and anarchy, she acknowledges her understanding: "I call that the thrill of the truth."

Reflecting on what she said, I feel understood and supported.

Rosemary "gets" me.

I can trust what she tells me.

Because I now have a strong sense of Rosemary's bold authenticity, I let myself feel her parting remark, a remark timed with the perfection of one who sees and feels the silent realm of unspoken needs, expressed in her words "a blessing of my writing hand." Her enthusiasm for my writing mission stokes me with so much excitement, I explode onto my manuscript as soon as I get to my apartment.

More than once, I pause to reflect and to feel gratitude transform into humble wonder.

I'm blessed. So blessed to have Jedwin and Rosemary in my life.

Gifts of the Circle, both of them.

FIFTY SHADES
OF GREEN

During the months that I live in my apartment, Jedwin and Rosemary continue to decorate the drafts of my manuscript with red and purple ink, teaching me the craft of writing from the heart. They each give voice to a unique, powerful quality. A quality that mystifies me.

I wonder how they teach the mechanics of writing while giving me space to be creative.

Maybe because their corrections are delivered with kindness.

And they celebrate the times when I write something good. Raised fists. Smiles. Plenty of ink on the good spots.

In my writing nook above my desk, a large, magnetic bulletin board is mounted on the wall. A big piece of white paper, held with magnets, waits for the time when Rosemary or Jedwin writes a note affirming my growing skill. When that happens, I get scissors and cut the comment from my manuscript, apply glue to the back, and paste the remark in a collage with others. Once in a while, I read each one, feeling them light me up like fireflies in the night.

Sometimes one of them expresses a positive opinion that has an especially powerful impact. I go nuts with those, decorating them with bright, foiled stickers that sparkle with inspiration, encouraging me to write long after the exact message has faded from my memory.

The feedback I routinely seek comes from Jedwin, those who take his workshops, Rosemary, members of my newly formed critiquing group, and sometimes my therapist when I need clarification about mind-body medicine.

Initially, sitting down to write takes a lot of effort. The weight of self-doubt threatens to flatten my enthusiasm for my writing and my mission.

Who will read this stuff?

Who cares what I have to say?

Start typing.

You'll find out one way or the other.

Jedwin often says, "Just keep writing."

To do that, many times I need something outside myself to motivate me.

Music becomes a dynamic influence in my writing process.

Because I'm still using music as a way to alter my moods and help me continue to heal from Lyme disease, anxiety, and depression, I know about vibration's power to alter my emotional state.

Marching drum music sometimes escorts me around my apartment while I raise my feet and stomp them on the floor, determined to dissolve the conflict between my desire to write and my belief that thinks I can't.

Chin up. Chest high—fists, too. Get your arse up, sister.

Strut. Strut. Strut.

That's the way.

You can do this, yes, you can.

Strut yourself right over to that keyboard and sit down.

Just start typing.

Somehow hearing Rosemary Daniell blessing my writing hand in those last words, I address the keyboard.

Music morphs me. "In character," I transition into a dimension of feelings created on the stage of my past. A creative process surges. I feel and grasp words that seem to float around me, offering possibilities for expression. When my heart swells with emotion, my body seems to synchronize with the rhythms in the air, emoting onto the keyboard with the swaying movements of a concert pianist.

But sometimes music isn't enough to give me the courage to write. When the time comes to reach inside and open up about the more painful events of my life, I move away from my desk and put my keyboard on the kitchen counter.

I stand. I stand to keep from being squashed into submission by memories that want me to hang on to them. By memories that want to stay like fetid, slimed grease, hard to bring to the light. Finally, after gathering the strength to go on, feelings tinged with sorrow and anger erupt. Determination to speak out fuels my fingertips as I pound the keys, seeking peace with my past.

———

A number of things play out as I learn about writing. I often find that I get caught up in angst about finishing my work. Knowing that my goal-driven nature too often neglects the richness wrapped in the gift of process, my therapist, Brenda, frequently reminds me to stay in the present and lavish myself with the joy I find in the present creative moment.

And something else: I hear other writers talk about finding their "voice." I don't know what that means until I find mine in June 2011—a full year after my first workshop with Jedwin.

Since the time I started writing *The Gift of the Circle*, my voice has been waiting for me, guiding me toward her while I stumbled and tripped over the mechanics of expression. Overusing the vocabulary words I learned in high school in preparation for the SAT kept us apart. Descriptive modifiers filled my sentences, and I had to learn to avoid molesting my writing with the style I used when preparing research papers or working in academic settings.

With patience, my voice waited for me to find her while I searched for confidence in my writing skills.

One morning, I sit down at my desk without wrestling with myself, and start to write. I know something's changed.

I experience the signs of transformation:

Words are coming easier. I'm beginning to believe I've something to say.

Well, maybe.

I'm moving into myself.

When I find my voice, I'm beginning another workshop with Jedwin. He thinks something's different when I hand out copies of an earlier chapter, "An Angel's Smile." He knows I've found my writer's stride after I read my work. That's the good news, for we both know I'm in for overhauling earlier writing to reflect the changes in the way I now express myself.

Soon after finding my voice, a ritual emerges that shapes the way I routinely prepare to write.

As a young child, my grandmother took me to Catholic services. Wonder at seeing a white-robed priest float down aisles jeweled with tints of stained glass, imbuing the air with incense, brought into being my love of smoky scents and the spiritual quality they sometimes carry.

Wanting my work to be crafted by the sweet fragrance of spiritual inspiration, I light incense. As smoke swirls in the air, I open my hands and entice the scented tendrils to imbue me with Aetherial mist.

Asking for the words to express myself, I then take a Native American talking stick from her resting place and lay her across the top of my computer screen, where I feel her encouraging presence. A presence that beckons honesty and a steadfast determination that refuses to quit when the going gets tough. A presence that tells me to reach beyond my ordinary senses to find the parts of me waiting for the life I breathe into words.

When I sit down in my writing nook, I never know where I'm really going as I open up and start to write. Only a rough outline with subtopics and a basic idea guide me. When I started to tell about using affirmations as a technique to help me heal, I didn't know I'd go on a journey that would take me to the pain of being abused by my father. When I started to write about thanking my sister for my life, I didn't know I'd figure out, in the process, why thanking her was so difficult. I didn't know I'd open up to love her even more.

While struggling to believe in myself, to believe I have

something to say, to believe I can develop skill as a writer, I don't know that, one day, I'll find comfort in writing—a refuge when emotions threaten to corrupt my sense of well-being. And I don't know that opening up to write about my past, being honest with myself and others about what happened, will help me find my way home to a reunion with myself—a reunion that fills my skin with the wonder of loving who I am for where I've been.

———

When I know I'm going to write and read aloud about being sexually exploited when I was in high school, I pay close attention to the psychological dynamics of Jedwin's workshops. During the first few two-month sessions, I read aloud something I've written every week. Otherwise I'm a silent observer:

Am I safe to share, to open up here?

Jedwin and the group are kind and accepting in response to what others read.

Even so, I'm not ready to expose myself.

Not yet.

When I first started writing *The Gift of the Circle*, I wrote about a canoe trip I took near where I docked my houseboat in the late 1970s. The only thing scary about telling that story was reading aloud what I'd written—a major accomplishment—especially so because the group membership was more than half male. My father's hypercritical nature has lurked in the shadows when I've been in the presence of a group of men. No matter what they were like, I couldn't get past that. So being surrounded by males was not something I would have deliberately chosen.

Looking back as I write, I *know* Divine Timing and Grace chose Jedwin's workshops as the perfect place for me to be with exactly the right people to heal a gaping wound. As I move forward reading my work, I'm at ease when receiving feedback in words immersed in the deep, rich tones of testosterone.

In a way, I'm being taught to value my inner self. To move

beyond the idea that men only value my body. I'm learning that I'm worth something simply because I want to learn to put my heart's breath on the pages I bring to our workshop sessions.

Over the remaining months in 2010, and into 2011, a core group of writers continues taking Jedwin's workshops, creating a sense of safety in the known. My trust in Jedwin and the group ripens. I begin to take risks, exposing my inner world and the way I express my ideas.

Laughing at myself is one thing. Writing something to make others laugh is scary. I'm ready to try. And I'm ready to get emotional with the group. Humor is the first thing I use that hints at tumescent feelings still begging for expression—urging the birthing, urging the therapeutic release of stories and the emotions that sculpt them. A naughty, a tickling part of me always eager for mischief, wants to roast my past at a public affair—a workshop session.

Thinking I have a funny story to tell, and hoping others will think so, too, I try my hand at humor by writing "The Naked Truth."

PRACTICING

Sunlight in the Aire
gives voice to wisdom,
a raptor's message:
"We're always practicing something."

At that, my wee tiny brain
snaps to attention.
What do I want to perfect?

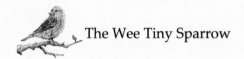 The Wee Tiny Sparrow

Making Jedwin's writers group laugh while reading "The Naked Truth" stokes my courage and my sense of mischief. Using bluegrass and mariachi music in the background to enhance my misbehavior, I write another story from my past that's rife with ribald memories.

I sag when I'm done reading that one, thinking there's nothing else about my life that's interesting to write about. Shrugging my shoulders, I press on anyway, remembering my underpinning mission for composing a book and the encouragements from Jedwin and Rosemary to "keep writing."

I find there's a lot more to this writing thing than learning about syntax. Growing into the emotional task of writing about myself is more challenging than anything I've ever done—more adventuresome. I'm stretching the limits of my mind-body connection while being still, sitting in a chair at my desk, rather than exerting myself physically. Nonetheless, the expansion of my emotional boundaries is profound.

Odd how sitting in a chair is stretching my physical limits.

Keeping myself in one place while writing about emotional stuff— that's harder than pedaling a bicycle uphill against gale-force winds.

While experiencing an adventure in my past on land or water, I've never been able to predict the full measure of an outcome. I have known, however, that I'd grow, become stronger, more powerful. The physical treks on land and water were growing tools, sculpting my emotions and my mind-body connections as much as muscle.

True to the way I worked before I became ill, I still want to grow myself by taking risks, even at age sixty-seven. And writing *The Gift of the Circle* presents emotional obstacles that surprise me, involving me in a profound adventure with myself. The path is at once rugged and thrilling. Obstacles like self-doubt—*Can I really do this?*—and knowing I'll be risking the acceptance of others and myself when I vocalize my truths often threaten my ability to move forward. Internal conflicts erupt and tend to block my way as painful parts of my past beg to be heard, yet protest when I try to bring them into the light.

Once in a while, after climbing an emotional Everest, I feel an intoxicating triumph when I finish a piece of my work. And that dynamic coupled with the support of others inspires me to keep walking with the tough stuff.

Although I realize writing has a powerful influence on my emotions, in the early stages of learning how to write, I don't have a clue that writing *The Gift of the Circle* will be as much a part of my healing as anything else I've done.

Taking one step at a time, I'm engaging in an adventure—one of majestic proportions.

———

During the fall of 2011, my daily agenda of mind-body medicine techniques keeps me well. Writing is important to me, yet my eye is riveted on continuing to heal from the residue of chronic illness.

Although my physical health continues to thrive, my contentment is dependent on how my body is doing. At times, a feather touch of a Lyme symptom still shatters my peace and thrusts me into terror. When that happens, I wonder if the Lyme spirochete is at work, or if I'm mentally creating a set of symptoms that might as well be the real thing. (I believe the emotional and physical symptoms are the same, even though their origins may be different.)

Despite the fact that I'm still having panic attacks when my health feels threatened, they're less extreme and don't last as long as they did in months past. The time I've spent with my therapist and cultivating The Watcher's presence is paying off in a big way: my moods are stabilizing. Also, The Watcher is becoming more insistent and self-assured during the emotional mess of a panic attack. I'm learning to rely on that part of myself to light the way out of the tangle of irrational thoughts that drive my hysterical fear.

Daily exercise is still a constant part of my wellness routine. The Watcher uses the results of my physical regimen to soothe me back into peace when fear strikes:

Look at what you're doing. You're walking five miles at a stretch.

A sick woman couldn't do that.

You're thriving.

Trust your wellness.

Feel your joy.

You've come a long way for this.

When I have a flare-up of Lyme, real or imagined, I resist taking remedies until The Watcher breaks through the pseudo-protective layers of denial.

You're scared, little sister.

You think you'll open the way for Lyme to rape your life again if you take homeopathic remedies — if you admit you need them.

You're in charge now.
This isn't a fight.
There's no fight when there's nothing to battle.
Yes, you still have some healing to do.
Be patient with yourself.
Taking a remedy will make you feel better one way or another. Your mind needs to know you're wise.
And, remember, this won't be forever.

Even if I take remedies for only a few days, they help me find security in the present when I can't believe in the reality that I'm healthy for the long haul.

———

One winter evening, during a discussion held following a group meditation, Nadav, a young man oh so wise for his age, makes a simple yet profound observation:

"We are always practicing something."

Hmmm!

No matter what I'm doing, I'm practicing something.

Every single second I'm practicing—perfecting a certain way to be.

So what do I want to perfect?

Nadav's short, content-rich statement prompts me to remember Norman Doidge's comment in *The Brain That Changes Itself*: "Neurons that fire together, wire together . . . neurons that fire apart, wire apart."[1] Absorbing the full import of Nadav's observation, I start "practicing" a new intention to drive my healing routine.

What do I mean?

There's a part of me still working to avoid Lyme disease. Even though I've been doing well, I want to sculpt neuronal pathways I believe will serve me even better.

So, instead of doing my wellness routine to avoid Lyme, I prompt myself to use the immune system–enhancing techniques to invite health and well-being, envisioning a vibrant woman, fully engaged in life and writing my book. At the same time my internal description of myself changes from someone recovering from Lyme to someone learning new skills—an important shift beckoning an overall sense of well-being. With a comfort permeated with integrity, I begin calling myself a writer. I've written long enough, squirming through all kinds of emotional challenges, and have earned the right.

And, while "practicing" a new way to see myself, the light of emotional freedom sculpts more of my time—my birthright coaxing me home to myself . . .

BONES IN
THE DESERT

From the Aire,
I see bones in the desert,
the remains of a stark reality.

—The Watcher

During the remaining months of 2011, I often reflect back to the year before, remembering when I began to enjoy longer periods of contentment as the mood changes that had jerked me around for months softened. The dimensions of my dark moods shrank, too. I began feeling more joy, less depression, slackened anxiety, and a lessening of the kind of manic excitement that felt more and more like a conjoined twin of anxiety. The constant gratitude I felt burgeoned a sense of well-being that stretched my once-shriveled hope, and I started to trust that I could make a difference in the world. Also, the wholesome parts of me, absent for so long, returned little by little, escorted home by The Watcher. And, I began to expect goodness to manifest.

As Daniel Siegel says in *The Mindful Brain*, "Attunement internally emerges as we sense the primary 'who' beneath the secondary chatter of our busy top-down minds. It is this internal attunement with our primary self that yields the powerful feeling of coming home. As poets have so often urged us to consider, we live so far from this person who has loved us for so long but has been so blindly ignored: our primary self. Welcoming that self is the celebration of life that mindfulness invites us to join."[1]

Although I'm continuing to make marked progress in my healing, completely filling my skin with all of me is a long way off—several years, in fact. I have yet to write and read much of my story out loud. And experiencing Rosemary's effervescent encouragement that colors me with belief in myself is in the future.

More sessions with my therapist, Brenda, often prompted by the emotions that find their way to the surface as I write about painful topics, are beckoning. And a flare-up of Lyme is on the horizon. And another adventure in Utah awaits me.

Meanwhile, Brenda's unwavering focus on who I am—rather than on the trauma of my past—lights my pathway into the future. There's a part of me that knows there's something ahead worth seeking. I'm like a flower facing the sun, ready to bloom.

The Watcher's sense of timing is impeccable, knowing when I'm ready to face "bones in the desert." They're there. I can't deny their dry rattles. They won't give me peace until I release them into the soft morning dew of a new beginning—until I open up to look at them in an honest way.

Every second a new beginning.

I remember thinking that at some point during my healing.

Every second is a reason for celebrating, and an opportunity to release pain.

As Jack Kornfield and Joseph Goldstein write in *Seeking the Heart of Wisdom*, "There is deep joy that comes when we stop denying the painful aspects of life and instead allow our heart to open to and accept the full range of our experience: life and death, pleasure and pain, darkness and light. Even in the face of the tremendous suffering in the world there can be a joy that comes from our ability . . . to open to the truth."[2]

———

Even though I had a bull's-eye on my abdomen circling the site of a tick bite—reason enough to test positive for Lyme—more than a year went by before I found a doctor who knew enough to make a diagnosis on the basis of clinical symptoms. Tests for Lyme are notoriously inaccurate, and I always tested serum negative.

Before I found a Lyme-literate physician, I searched for information on the internet. Horror twisted my guts when I read about the disease's symptoms—and then realized I'd found the reason why my life was withering.

Information on the internet about Lyme was rife with tragic, hopeless stories of those who were in a chronic disease state because they didn't get a correct diagnosis; they didn't begin treatment within a few weeks of infection.

Like me.

Because no one with chronic Lyme told of recovery, I concluded that I was already a hopeless case under a death sentence.

Seeing little hope for myself and having adopted the posture that I would *euthanize* myself rather than exist as a worthless sack of wasted dreams, I started hoarding drugs that I thought would take me out.

———

I have to stop here. Thinking to write is impossible.

My guts are twisted—tangled into suppressed screams.

Let go, Carolyn, implores The Watcher.

Let go.

Cry. Wail.

Go ahead, baby.

Losing everything was hard for you—torture.

You were forced to leave your mom.

Your farm, Kristina, Forest—everything. You lost everything.

There's no shame in feeling the way you do.

No shame in crying. Not everything that happens to us heals overnight.

You're doing a great job restoring yourself.
Keep letting go of this stuff.
Keep letting go.

———

Impossible moments still interrupt my ability to write about anything other than my overwhelming emotions that spill onto the keyboard. But releasing my feelings on the page soothes the anxiety that's distancing me from my story.

There are still tears, but my thinking is working better and the music I've started to play in the background keeps me open, vulnerable, and able to function.

What a journey this is!

———

In Jedwin's groups I'd already risked writing and reading aloud stories that, while being humorous, also made it clear "I'd been around the bend." Having seen no judgment from Jedwin or his group of writers, during the fall of 2010 and winter of 2011, I now risk being more vulnerable.

I write about the catastrophic events surrounding Lyme's destruction of my life, including my suicide attempts. And as I read the results of my efforts aloud, emotion threatens to choke me, and I teeter between my past and the present.

Even so, when I'm finished, I *know* I've unloaded layers of excruciating torment. I've walked through the torturous past—but this time, unscathed. And, their moist eyes embracing me, I know I now have fellow writers to walk with me.

———

Once, after flipping through the pages of my work Jedwin returned after editing, I'm startled by one of his editing remarks. A red mark slices through the word "euthanize" where I've referenced my attempts to go to The Land of Dark Peace.

He inserts "kill"—a red-penned replacement that's more than a suggestion.

Kill myself?

At first, I'm defensive when facing the truth.

The Watcher knows something doesn't ring right about my reaction.

In an explosion of stark reality, I see that by using "euthanasia" I'd constructed a belief to absolve myself from the shame and guilt I knew I'd feel if I owned up to the fact that I had wanted to kill myself. And I was attempting to protect myself from the judgment of others, too, when retelling my story.

So you want to be baseline honest in what you say and write?

You want honesty returned?

You got that in spades.

Busted!

Somehow, when processing my use of a word, I found my way through a maze of reality that ended in a profound insight: although dire at times, my physical illness never caused my emotional extremes. My *reactions* to what happened were what threatened to destroy me.

RETROFLECTION

Sometimes,
I shat where I shouldn't have.
All birds do that.

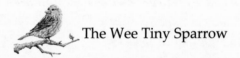 The Wee Tiny Sparrow

A retroflective device is one that has the capacity to reflect light back to the source—wisdom honed by the nature of life.

Nature mirrors Light in metaphors. Authors, friends, loved ones, and sometimes people I don't know act as retroflectors when they offer pure honesty, uncluttered by ulterior motives. Sometimes my own brain reflects Light when a burst of insight clears a foggy myth.

After facing the fact that I was, indeed, trying to kill myself, I thought more than ever before about my suicide attempts. Somehow, the wise part of me emerged from that musing, knowing I needed to seek the truth about the repercussions of my actions on others.

I came to realize that constant anxious thoughts abraded contentment and drove me into the arms of insanity—not Lyme disease. And my attempts to kill myself had caused deep pain for Janet and others who loved me.

Until then, I'd obscured the pain of others with the delusion I didn't matter much. And if I didn't use the words "kill myself," I could escape responsibility for my actions.

Being selfish and self-centered are aspects of the psyche that exist only in the world of the sane. In my insane world, all I had experienced was an all-consuming desire to escape emotional torture. There wasn't room for anything else.

When I thought of my mom and sister, my therapist, friends, others who cared about me and what they might feel if I killed myself, I was so bereft of self-love I couldn't imagine anyone else loving me enough to care. I remember thinking something like, *They all know how to cry. They'll cry out their grief and quickly get over losing me.*

———

Feels so awful to once again see how impoverished I was.

In a way, the intense pain I now feel in this retroflective mode is a gift.

The pain describes the distance I've come.

Gratitude for being alive once more fills my heart and spills from my eyes.

The gift of Divine Light; Ruach, the spirit of the Living God, my breath.

They humble me.

The pain I caused others splits me wide open, bares my heart.

I weep.

Yet, in the weeping, I release more agony and feel the love of others. That very love imbues me with the ability to forgive myself. In a moment of clarity, I know those who love me would want me to do just that. For they've long since forgiven me for shatting on them. They're just grateful to have me around.

Even though I know I've been forgiven, I go on to face more "bones in the desert." I want to be aware of the effects my suicide attempts had on others. I must find out.

For there's no other way for me to fully accept myself. I need to know what others felt so I can, perhaps, love myself in the same way others love me, despite the pain I caused them. I want to know so I can embrace all of me with integrity, caring about myself even in the face of my glaring imperfections.

In a session with Brenda, I ask her to tell me how she felt when my sister called to tell her I was missing and probably attempting to kill myself. She becomes vulnerable, sharing her own pain, and what she says stuns me: "You broke your word. You signed an agreement to seek help if you had suicidal thoughts."

I feel awful when I empathize with how she must have experienced my betrayal of her trust. My word has always been sacrosanct. In betraying Brenda's trust, I betrayed one of my deepest, most cherished principles for relating to others. Even worse, I betrayed my own sense of honor.

Maybe hearing the truth isn't easy, yet knowing where I stand is fair play. Fair is safe for me.

I offer my gratitude to Brenda for her honesty and I offer her my apology, although that doesn't seem enough. Yet, when I look at her, I know that's all that's necessary, for her eyes speak of compassion and understanding.

Then, I move on to more "bones." I ask Brenda what others feel when someone they love commits suicide or tries to. I'm not ready to ask my beloved sister how she felt when I tried to kill myself. I'm still too raw and emotionally unstable for that challenge.

Brenda gives me a hint of my sister's experience: "There's never a way for loved ones to feel a 'clean burning grief' when someone commits suicide. There are always questions: 'Why didn't we see that coming? Where did we go wrong? Why didn't she talk to one of us?'"

I understand. And wonder if others who try to kill themselves are masters of deceit like I was. Determined to end my suffering, I was equally determined to stop anyone from getting in my way. I hid my pain with an emotional mask too dense for anyone to penetrate.

When my session with Brenda comes to an end, relief that all of this is finally in the open floods me. After relief, empathy for those who love me emerges that I at once believe is a preventative, emerged from my own asked-for intervention: the truth.

As I leave Brenda's office, I feel immense gratitude that she is willing to keep seeing me in spite of my suicide attempts. Many would have considered me to be too much of a professional liability.

I'm somber as I get in my car, yet peaceful. Then my thoughts somehow make their way to memories of my cat, Kristina. I'm sensitive about the way I feel about Kristina. I don't want criticism for my profound love of a cat.

While driving home, I decide to seek relief in trusting Brenda with a truth that still haunts me. Knowing honesty must prevail, I decide to spend an entire therapy session with her talking about the way my beloved Kristina died.

After doing just that, creative threads of thought loosen, weaving their way into an unexpected healing tapestry that prepares me to take the plunge with Jedwin's writers group to expose my love for my cat and the guilt I feel about ending her life. And in writing that story, an unforeseen twist emerges in my healing journey . . .

KRISTINA—
IN MEMORIAM

Homo sapiens is a species of release. An endocrine system releases hormones urging creation. Orgasmic release seeds a flowering fetus. A mother's womb releases an infant into a circle of adventure. A painful heart pleads for the soul to release hardened, toxic memories to soften and expose compassionate insight.

—The Watcher

Laser stares are palpable. They sometimes feel like sandspurs pricking the skin, or like a flake of gently landing snow. They can raise neck hairs and tingle spines. They always wear the wardrobe of their intentions.

Memories of two intense stares, one directed at me from a tiny animal and another from my father, weave themselves together in my soul's effort to release painful memories from bondage— my soul's effort to make more room in my heart for compassion.

How odd, sometimes, this healing journey of mine.

My mind's mysterious weaving threads of thought here and there.

Infinibytes of memory in constant motion—seeking balance.

My inner wisdom knowing when to release painful memories, darkness urging light.

———

Inside an animal shelter, feeling concentrated energy at my back, I turn to face a ten-week-old kitten staring at me from behind the door of a cage. I'm attracted to her confident expression. Within a matter of minutes I sign her adoption papers, pay the adoption fee, and christen her Kristina, beginning our sixteen-year journey together—before I even place her in a carrier to start for home.

———

Kristina.

She never goes through a moving-in adjustment period. Trusting her intuitive directive, she acts as if she hears a GPS message: "You have arrived at your destination." She sashays out of her carrier and into my living room, displaying the regal confidence of a tigress.

Two days later Kristina is hospitalized, fighting for her life as a virulent upper respiratory infection threatens to kill her.

Daily, I go to the veterinary clinic to hold her on my lap for a few minutes. Looking at her while stroking her tiny, limp body wrenches my heart. For such a little one, she fights to live with the spirit of a warrior.

After two weeks of struggling, I notice life and vitality peeping through her eyes. She begins radiating energy that feels like the light of dawn misting away the night.

One cold winter day, she is well enough to come home. Before I leave my house to pick her up, I position a heater by a folded blanket on the floor near the living room daybed where I sleep to provide a special welcome I hope she'll understand.

When I get home with Kristina, I place her carrier on the floor and then open the door. She waltzes out and heads straight for the warmed blanket, somehow knowing that's hers. As she stretches out her little two-pound body, I appreciate her *haute couture*—a fancy white coat festooned with pink decorations.

We nuzzle stares, seeming to know we're meant to be with each other.

———

For sixteen years, Kristina decorates my home with her multi-faceted personality, rich with feline character. She greets me at the front door when I arrive home after work, plays hunched-back-kitty peekaboo, making me laugh, and sometimes speaks a piqued language of unhappiness that needs no interpretation. One time, she delivered a silent, yet vociferous message of discontent to a male guest who was reposing in the spare bedroom, slowly awakening, appreciating the freshness of a new day.

Kristina ambled into the room and bounded on top of him.

He thought she was greeting him with exuberant delight—until he felt something warm and wet flooding his belly and upper legs.

Thinking Kristina might be urinating on him was too bizarre to consider. The sensation of wet, clammy sheets plastered against his body soaked his synapses, short-circuiting his killer instincts. That gave Kristina just enough time to escape into hiding and avoid being splattered against the wall.

Using her piss-driven logic, she had delivered a clear message: "I don't want you here. Get out of *my* space!"

Kristina delivered those skillfully designed communiqués her entire life.

When she was nearing the age of sixteen, we moved to Sunny Hill Farm into the home I built in the backwoods of Central Florida. I knew she wasn't happy there, because she peed in my bed, increasing the frequency as Lyme disease began mauling my life. We were so much a part of each other I think maybe she got what was happening to me.

Lyme disease was robbing me of energy. Getting dressed for work was a formidable chore. Driving to and from my office was an ordeal. Taking a shower and getting my pajamas on was a major challenge. Yearning for solace with barely enough energy to crawl into bed, my feet were often offended by wet, clammy sheets.

Rebecca, knowing my health was deteriorating and taking care of myself was becoming problematic, offered me a room in her home. When I decided to move there, I made some hard decisions about my cats, dogs, and donkey.

Kristina.

For a flicker of a moment, I considered trying to find a home for her. A cold, hard reality sliced through my dreaming: an old, bed-wetting cat wouldn't be adopted. And I was too exhausted to even make an effort at placing her.

Although Rebecca opened the door of her home for me and my pets, she didn't know the extent of my problems with Kristina. I couldn't take her with me in good conscience.

With an aching heart, I decided to euthanize her.

From inside a carrier on the back seat of my car, Kristina keens with relentless heart-piercing wails every second of the seemingly endless twenty-five-mile trip to her death. Unable to bear my sorrow and stay with her while she is euthanized, I leave her and a white cotton towel for the vet to wrap her in for burial. As I turn my back on Kristina and walk away, she continues to wail. I'm so close to her, I feel like I'm dying too.

Later in the day, I pick up her lifeless body and make the somber drive to Rebecca's home, where there's a grave awaiting in the backyard. Tenderly, I place Kristina's feather-light, enshrouded body in a hole layered with straw. Using my hands, I cover her with Mother Earth. That's all I can do.

I shove memories of her life and death into a vault of emotional numbness trying to protect myself from the pain of losing her. Yet my guilt and shame for betraying her trust and the relationship we shared for more than sixteen years still haunts me.

———

When I'm writing about Kristina, remembering losing her hurts like walking barefoot on splintered glass.

I wish I could hold someone's hand while I write.

I loved Kristina.

I couldn't cry when she died.

All I could do then was shuffle one foot in front of the other, trying to survive.

Now, I feel the pain.

Now, I cry.

Now, I heal in a curious way . . .

———

I'm fourteen years old, standing in the living room wearing only my bra and panties eating a snack I've just grabbed from the kitchen.

I think I'm alone in the house.

Feeling a stalker's stare, I jerk my head around.

I see licentious malice calculating an attack.

The eyes of a rapist.

They're my father's eyes.

I don't know if I've seen his eyes like that before.

I do know to escape.

Danger raises the hairs on my neck as I scamper away from my father, seeking safety from his violent intentions.

———

I have vivid memories of my father beating me with belts, a

razor strap and deprecating words. I don't know if he molested me. I do know he could have.

I feared my father and didn't like to be near him, never knowing when I'd say something he didn't like or when he'd strike. Even as I write this, I feel he's watching me, so I have to keep repeating to myself that he's not here. That he can't hurt me now.

Warning sirens, never-ending warning sirens, wailed in the background of my childhood. In or out of my father's presence, he was a lurking menace—a silent, powerful stalker.

I think people like him must have been twisted as children with rebar-bending cruelty. They often unwittingly ravage those they love the most with their burdens. They may bear the fiery weight of guilt. My father did. In his actions, he as much as told me so.

———

After adopting my cat Star Feather in 2010, I'm often confused about who she is because she reminds me of Kristina. So much so, sometimes I think the two of them share the same eyes. So much so, I know the time has come to release the secret burden I've carried about my part in ending Kristina's life.

Even though I feel embarrassed about grieving over a cat, I spend a whole hour with Brenda pouring out the story of Kristina's life and death. Her compassionate eyes tell me she understands the tears streaming down my face. She reminds me that I could have thrown Kristina in the woods, abandoning her. Or, I could have dumped her at a shelter, where she would have faced a certain death.

Since I've released other memories that were getting in the way of my getting well, Brenda's thoughts have space to work in me. I begin considering the possibility that maybe I'm being too hard on myself. I begin understanding my pain. For the first time since Kristina's death, I feel a sense of compassion and forgiveness for myself. With my writer's hand and my creative mind, I begin to weave an intricate tapestry, persuading darkness into light by threading together the memories of two disparate beings: my father and Kristina.

In a burst of insight, perhaps invited by my meditation practice and my intention to heal, I realize I've an all too intimate understanding of the guilt I believe my father shouldered.

I realize my feelings about my part in Kristina's death—knowing another suffered because I fell short of the standards I hold to be right and good—were chiseled by the same tools that sculpted my father's guilt. I get a glimpse of my vulnerability to circumstances and how frail I can be. And I begin to understand that I did the best I could. I begin to see that my father did so, too.

Then, the delicate compassion I felt as I forgave myself for my part in Kristina's death begins to influence the way I see me and my father. I believe he suffered in much the same way I did. I feel his suffering for the first time, and I feel another level of forgiveness for what he did to me. I feel the angels reach out and gently take from me some of the memories I no longer need.

When they do, my heart seems to make room for Kristina's memory to nestle in a cuddly place and grace my life, once again, with her feline majesty. And, because of Kristina, compassion for my father opens space in my heart for me to love him a little more.

And my father despised cats.

IN SITU

Remnants of the past hang in the balance,
preparing to nurture the future.

During the first part of 2010, I constructed each day to ensure I made time for the mind-body wellness strategies that were helping me heal myself. And, as 2010 comes to a close, there's a major change in the way I look at crafting each day's schedule. Without realizing what's happened until months later, the hub of each day becomes writing *The Gift of the Circle*—my mission.

Now, because my mental and physical health has, for an extended period of time, stayed true to my expectations, I've developed a strengthened trust in my ability to stay well. That being so, I feel safe in easing the way I use mind-body techniques to sustain my well-being.

Stream-of-consciousness journaling changes from a process I use every day to a strategy I use on an as-needed basis to help myself maintain emotional balance. No surprise that's the first one I stop using daily. Strange, how I still fight myself every time when I get ready to spill my feelings onto paper. Interesting that I always felt better once I get rolling—otherwise, there wouldn't have been any point in continuing.

Instead of listening to music in a focused, deliberate way, I now play background music that makes me feel good, knowing all the while my body is entraining to vibrations that are encouraging my immune system to work efficiently.

I still use music to split open emotional barriers, and to release feelings that want to express themselves when I'm writing about poignant topics. Underlying the use of music in that way is my belief that revisiting painful events in my life, opening up and releasing feelings about them, invites health and well-being.

Affirmations take their place in the form of a daily morning ritual. Facing a mirror, I reach across space to connect with myself—my expressive eyes. I rest with them for a moment then construct an affirmation from what I sense they're telling me I need to hear.

Sometimes I use the same affirmation for several days, and other times I move on after using one only once: *Hmm. Those eyes of mine seem to speak for my gut. I know The Watcher would rather I become dignified and use another word besides "gut" for my second brain. But, for now, I'm staying with "gut." I like the earthiness and slightly crude designation for my intuition. Too funny here. The wise in me is still a bit tangled up with rebellion.*

As to imagery, each morning I stand with my arms outstretched to receive Divine Healing Inspiration as I craft a mind-movie that I often use for an extended period of time.

These days, I *know* there's still Lyme bacteria present that needs to be exterminated. So I've been imagining my eager, helpful fairy visiting me each morning with her potent antimicrobial in hand. After we work together, I continue by picturing myself healthy and well with my canoe paddle at the ready, soaking up the sunshine at the Confluence in Moab.

Earlier in the year I used imagery throughout each day; now, once in the morning seems to be enough. (Sometimes I use homeopathic antimicrobials, sometimes not. I feel my way based on symptoms I'm experiencing and do what seems best; there are no standard medical tests that can tell me the level of infection that's present in my body.)

Exercise?

I love exercising, yet I don't go for walks every day now. Three, sometimes four, times a week for an hour seems to be enough for me. Often I walk for much longer, creating an afternoon's adventure; I no longer keep track of the miles I walk as an indicator of wellness. Now, I'm more into the process, walking until I've had enough; then I go just a bit more to stretch my limits some.

My therapist has warned me more than once about pushing myself too hard, reminding me that, when I do so, I can elevate inflammation levels, initiating a state of trauma, and compromising my immune system I'm trying to support.

Sometimes I walk slowly with a jeweler's loupe in hand to peer into flowers and their mysteries hidden from the naked eye, their glory expressed in jewel-toned iridescence. Their intricate architecture offers a sweet expression of beauty. In whatever way they express Divine Creativity, they dose me with joy—a natural antidepressant.

Breathing from my diaphragm still isn't automatic. I continue to stop breathing, or my breathing is often rapid and shallow. However, I'm making progress: my body's now telling me when I stop breathing—more often than I ever thought possible. The Watcher catches me when I start to fire up my frustration at myself for being so slow to learn how to do something as basic as breathing from the diaphragm.

Getting impatient with yourself isn't going to help you.

Your whole system is habituated to shallow breathing.

You're learning and changing.

If you stop expecting things to change in a certain amount of time or a certain way, you'll feel better about this.

Try extending compassion to yourself.

And, applaud yourself for making the effort to change.

Even though I've believed for a long time that releasing feelings helps me heal, I didn't see, until recently, that I sometimes try to force them away rather than allowing them to surface—keeping myself stuck—especially when I feel anxious. And I've found interesting how the need to grieve produces high levels of anxiety if I don't let go and cry—maybe even wail.

Because of my strengthened relationship with The Watcher,

I'm understanding more about my resistance to feelings, and I don't hold on to them as long as I did not too long ago. I can't say I welcome the exquisite torture that comes just before releasing tormenting feelings, yet the process of letting go has become easier. And now that I'm not so jammed up with feelings, there's room for more logic to insist on letting go.

Logic birthed in wisdom seems to be lighting my pathway to healing. Becoming aware of my feelings is teaching me that the pain preceding an outpouring of emotions isn't going to last forever—only a few seconds.

I'm finding that letting go of emotions takes a lot less energy than trying to push them away or hold them captive. Releasing them most often brings me a measure of peace and unclogs my brain so I can find resolution to what's going on—a positive reward for the effort.

The Watcher continues to strengthen in character. I'm religious about meditating daily. Because I've experienced so much benefit from the self-awareness I'm cultivating, I often meditate for an hour now.

Sitting longer, being aware of my breath or what comes and goes in my mind, is indirectly training me to see into myself to come to know the part of me that controls most of my behavior— my subconscious, which some experts say controls from seventy to ninety percent of behavior.

That said, I'm fast making discoveries in that vast domain of silent power. Until this past year, my subconscious was largely unavailable to me except in therapy sessions. Because I've become more aware of what's going on there, I have the opportunity to make changes in my brain so as to take an active part in creating more of my reality—a different way for me to be in this world.

Now that I'm trusting myself to maintain my mental and physical health, I'm ready to consider taking another big step toward reclaiming my life—my freedom . . .

PREPARING
FOR FREEDOM

*My wee tiny heart
needs to be with other birds.
They know how I feel.
And when I get lost,
they help me find my way.*

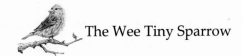 The Wee Tiny Sparrow

In December of 2010, I begin looking at the housing market on the internet. The year's lease for my apartment will end soon. I'm beginning to think I'm well enough to commit to a mortgage. For a buyer, the housing market couldn't be better.

Sometime in early December, ready to purchase a place of my own, I set out on an adventure, intending to spend the day in a historic district that has attracted my attention. In times past, when I've roamed around there, I've thought I'd like to live in the area. Old cottages converted to shops, cafés or coffeehouses with sidewalks in front along a narrow, tree-lined street have invited me to linger.

Planning to spend the day exploring in a serendipitous way while looking for a realtor's office, I take off, my memory-laden, beat-up woven-ash backpack loaded with lunch, water, and an extra jacket.

When I get to the downtown area of the historic district, I feel very much alive and well. The crisp, cool air stokes my expectancy that something wonderful is about to happen.

Exuberant, I get out of my car, don my pack, and lock up, thinking I'll find a realtor on the main street. When I don't, I go into a canoe and kayak store located on a side street to ask if there's one nearby. A clerk tells me there's one to the left of their exit, less than a block away.

When I arrive at the realtors' office, no one's there. But knowing I've found *my* realtor, I don't want to seek out another one. Refusing to feel disappointed that things didn't turn out the way I expected, I leave my name and phone number on a piece of paper wedged in the doorway. I then walk to a nearby park to eat my picnic lunch and people-watch.

———

The first place my realtor shows me is intriguing: a loft situated on the southeast side of a red-brick, repurposed high school.

When she opens the door, the original, amber-shaded wood flooring greets us with stunning character.

I fall in love.

Rays of sunlight stream through three large windows. Their warmth embraces me, and I feel as if I'm being welcomed home.

I look at a few other places the same day, but nothing else gets my attention. I keep remembering the thirteen-foot ceilings, windows overlooking green space from the second floor, and the non-cookie-cutter nature of the loft. After thinking about my options overnight, I know the loft is for me. Because I don't dicker with the bank's fair "as is" asking price, the closing is then scheduled thirty days out.

———

After writing and reading Kristina's story, I further test my emotional safety in Jedwin's workshops. Besides him, there are six of us who always participate—a predictable core. Even though others come and go, that core makes for a consistency that shapes my feeling of security.

Suggestions for our writing continue to be offered from a sincere desire to help each other become skillful in order to publish. And Jedwin holds nothing back about his personal journey with alcohol addiction. His openness creates a bedrock of heartfelt support for all of us, opening the door to explore.

I've continued to pay close attention to what he and the others have said during critiquing, all the while developing my courage to disclose the *real* me. The person with grit who's determined to tell the truth about who I am and where I've been. The person who knows that one day I'll be telling this group about being sexually exploited. The person who hopes my story will be useful to others, the little girl inside who hopes the group will still like me when I'm done.

———

I write the next portions of *The Gift of the Circle* within months of each other and before I move into my loft in the spring of 2011. They're difficult to write, telling of the tragedies in my life wrought from chronic Lyme disease, my disturbing experiences in psychiatric hospitals, and the story about being sexually abused when I was in high school—something I've never told anyone except my therapist. While writing each of those pieces, the strength of my emotions astounds me. They feel powerful enough to explode my guts. They *are* powerful enough to stun my brain.

Fear.

Fear sometimes overpowers me when I write, turning my brain into a muddy soup where the words to express myself are impossible to find.

I remember what my therapist says about imagery in her book *You Can Beat the Odds*: "The reason [imagery] is so powerful is that as you imagine yourself in any given scenario your body responds as if you were really there. The part of your brain that's engaged in this process doesn't distinguish between what you imagine and what is really happening."[1]

The Watcher extends empathy:

No wonder you get scared.
You're replaying the most frightening experiences of your life.
This time's different, though.
You're not stuffing your feelings into your body.

First, I tackle writing about getting Lyme, the least threatening of the topics, and the easiest to share with others. There's no shame in getting sick—just a lot of sadness. I believe if I can just get that written, I'll be able to read the whole thing aloud without sobbing.

The first time fear halts my writing, I decide to change the topic from Lyme to exploring my feelings in the moment; the challenges I experience as a writer each time I open to face my past are at the core of the obstacles I'll face whenever I go there. And, they seem important to share—as much a part of my recovery as anything else.

I focus on my emotions and spill them onto the page, imagining readers surrounding me with loving kindness, understanding what I'm saying, and extending compassion.

How lovely to have a cadre of readers with me as I write. Feels like the times Mom wrapped me in her arms, hugging me against her soft breasts when I wailed about a skinned knee.

If my emotions are disruptive yet not completely overpowering, music helps me express myself—helps me, sometimes, to release enough of my emotional burdens to clear my head for writing. Often, after I've released some emotional steam using music, I find the pathway to my heart. My writing then comes from an impassioned place that's unsheathed and tender—the core of what I know about myself.

But once, as I write about my experiences in psychiatric hospitals, fear shoves aside all my reasoning capacity. All I know to do is leave the place where the fear started—my apartment and my desk.

I don't start to think again until I'm twenty miles north, driving on an interstate highway, when The Watcher finally gets my attention:

You're terrified.

You're not in the hospital now. No one is going to shock you.

Those experiences were hard for you.

I'm sorry they happened.

Pull over when you find a parking area.

Good.

Now cry. Release all those pent-up feelings.

After I've blown my nose and settled down, there's more:

You can't make your apartment and your desk evil places to be.

Return to your work.

You can do this.

Feeling restored, I regain emotional strength and take charge of writing and facing my demons. For I know when I'm finished with this portion of *The Gift of the Circle*, shame will dissolve and leave my insides with the freedom to heal in the deepest possible way.

CRUCIBLE OF LIGHT

Sometimes I didn't fly in perfect form.
Remembering, I sing the low notes of my song,
releasing shame from my wee tiny soul,
making room to love myself more.
Can a little, earthy-toned bird like me
experience such regal splendor?
I think so.
All birds can.

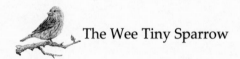 The Wee Tiny Sparrow

While continuing to write, I face up to the catastrophic effects of Lyme disease, the reality of my misguided treatment in psychiatric hospitals, and the psychological wounds wrought from a troubled childhood, bringing about radical, positive transformations in ways I could never have imagined. I stand up to the emotional pain echoing in each of those horrors, if only for brief periods of time. That's all I can handle—brief periods. A few hours at a time to visit the past while hanging on to the fragile thread of the reality that I'm in the present. I'm no longer sick, I'm not waiting for shock treatment on a hospital stretcher, and I'm no longer involved in a tragic sexual relationship.

Writing slowly, as I dissect those tragic events of my past, I grieve. I grieve for my loss of Sunny Hill Farm. I grieve because I was treated with a medieval protocol in the psychiatric hospitals where I sought solace and understanding. I grieve for the price I paid in my personal life because a twisted person took advantage of my innocence, and need for acceptance and affirmation.

While I listen to a CD by Tara Brach, clinical psychologist and insight meditation teacher, she makes a remark about grieving that goes something like this: "Grief can only be fully experienced when painful events are completely embraced, acknowledging in full measure that they happened."

For me, grieving helps me let go of the past and makes way for a future that's unhindered by "dragging anchor" on the bottom of a place I can't change. In a symbolic way I can feel, because of my nautical experiences, that I'm ready, to "weigh anchor" by healing the past in the present. I'm more than ready to be "underway" without dead weight dragging me into mental and physical illness again.

Over and over again, I open up to experiencing painful memories. Although they're often mere scraps of a whole, they are the full measure of what I can see and bear at a given time. My grieving is balanced by spaces in between to feel gratitude and joy as big as a wide-open sky for who I'm becoming.

Indeed, I'm astounded by the power and breadth of the emotions I feel; I'm also intrigued by the layers that keep surfacing. My wise self, prompted by Divine Timing and Grace, takes me to the next step on my journey homeward, holding me with compassion for my tender soul as I open festering wounds. As I heal, I keep getting stronger—ready to muscle the next heavy emotional challenge that bolts into my awareness, insisting to be transformed.

And there's a certain emotional ordering that takes place.

First, I write about the least emotionally threatening of the three: my journey with Lyme disease. Next, I tackle writing about my grim experiences in psychiatric hospitals. The third topic is virgin territory, so to speak. Other than conversations with my therapist, I've never spent time dissecting the emotional and physical consequences of being sexually exploited. Instead, *shame* has blinded me from the truth—shame and the fear of facing the maw of pain I thought would swallow me whole if I faced reality.

Shame. Shame has enshrouded my beauty—hidden me from myself.

Shame is a major component in the emotionally laden memories of mental illness and abuse. Shame makes aggressive attempts to shrivel me into a dried-up wish for expression when I write. Yet I keep going, building emotional strength, knowing all the while that freedom from shame beckons. My open arms await the time when I'll feel worthy enough to embrace with abandon— even love—the Crucible of Light wrought from tragedy.

Another way I order my healing process has to do with transparency.

As I write, I first process my feelings in the safety of my manuscript. In the privacy of introspection, insights teach me. I'm my own unedited, sympathetic storyteller and listener, and as I share intimacies with myself, I soothe my soul. Sometimes I ask an imaginary reader to hold one of my hands or to place a comforting hand on my shoulder. In the process of opening to reality, I start to forgive myself for the desperate things I did when I was sick. I start to forgive others who hurt me, and to forgive myself for who I am—who I *really* am. I begin letting go of shame and open to loving myself more.

The intricacies of abuse and mental and physical illness, many unseen until writing, become topics during sessions with Brenda. Now, feeling completely safe with her, I can open and go full bore, holding nothing back. When I do, she often shepherds me to a new level of self-awareness, grounding me with compassion for myself. Watching her react with compassion as I tell her the most awful parts of my life, I learn to reflect her reactions in my own. I learn a different way to think about what happened to me. I learn to treat myself with kindness and understanding.

In Brenda's office, layers of shame make their gradual departure, leaving no trace of regret. They were never meant to be there.

With her wise counsel, I fill my soul with more and more of who I am. There's something sacred about being gifted with a portion of someone else's lifetime—a gift wrapped in Divine Grace.

I'm preparing myself in a gradual way, building the emotional muscle I'll need to reach my goal of becoming open and transparent. Once I've processed my emotions in private, then with Brenda, I'm ready to go on to a bigger challenge: reading my writing out loud.

Scary stuff, this going public.

I'm tired of keeping secrets. Tired of giving them space to thrive and rupture my insides, destroying peace and contentment.

Tired of their brutality.

Tired of accepting or creating false assumptions about myself.

I'm weary of rejecting myself—rejecting who I am because of what I've been through.

Shame has separated me from myself way too long—judgment, too. A macabre marriage, licensed to destroy.

Adventure—calculated risk-taking—has been a hallmark of my life.

And I've got adventure right here and now dealing with this emotional stuff.

I'm trekking to the summit of my Everest.

By now, I've been sizing up Jedwin and his writers group for a while, feeling more and more emotional safety there. Even so, reading emotionally laden content aloud will still take some doing, as I'll be practicing being transparent about my past. And each time I prepare myself to read, fear threatens to silence me.

I feel just like I did when I was standing on the shore of a turgid Green River for the first time, trying to summon the courage to proceed onward.

Will I be able to read without sagging into a soggy mess of tears?

Will fear silence me?

I'm ready to find out.

I'm going!

Each time I read a chapter that's shame or grief laden, I swallow emotions to keep from wailing. I can't keep them all down. Some rupture my façade, shattering my self-confidence for a few moments. Tears stream down my face. Snot drips from my nose. Even so, I manage to summon the courage to go on to the end.

When I finish, I wonder: *What are you all thinking? Do you still like me even though I'm snotty and red in the face?*

All I see are pairs of eyes speaking the silent language of the heart—compassion. Then, a few members of the group give voice to their feelings. Some give me suggestions for improving my writing skill. Either way, their supportive reactions are a gift of untold measure, and another layer of shame moistens my eyes, fills my nose with snot, and gets blown into a tissue to be discarded.

Indeed, I don't have to do this alone.

Indeed.

PERCEPTIONS

Wisdom evokes transformation of beliefs,
the architect of perceptions.
Perceptions cloak experience
with the wardrobe of emotions.

— The Watcher

I'm now aware that I believed I'd be scorned if I got real with others about my past and my feelings. While some might censure me, I find many are understanding and compassionate, welcoming my authenticity and applauding my courage.

I begin to mirror the acceptance and compassion of Jedwin and the writers group, just as I've learned to mirror my therapist's thoughts and feelings. They encourage me to drop the shroud of shame so I can see who I am. In their reflections, I begin to understand the truth. I'm even beginning to honor myself.

The wide counsel of The Watcher informs:

You've rejected yourself in spite of your many skills, your courage, your depth.

Rejection is a despot. When rejection rules, acceptance withers, merely playing dead, avoiding a deathblow.

Know that the Spirit of Revival, always eager to dance and sing, can't be silenced.

Because of the reactions of Jedwin and the writers group, I come to believe there's at least a possibility I'll experience similar responses from others as I venture forward in my new transparency.

I sometimes still feel naked. Yet I also feel protected, loved beyond measure.

In a way, I'm clothed with Light—a Divine prescription for healing.

Amazing how Divine mystery seems to shimmer in my presence, beckoning me toward the glowing, crystalline facets of a new reality.

First I reach for a different way to be, then I'm shown the way.

And my inner wisdom insists on a grand finale that calls on my newfound emotional strength, demanding that I summon the courage to act. Each time I act, I give myself further reason to trust my inner resources. Each time I act, I stretch my boundaries, feeling the freedom that comes from refusing to be a victim. I "stand tall," reclaiming my power.

After writing and reading about Lyme disease and the events that shredded my life, I'm prompted to return to Sunny Hill Farm in December of 2010—to face my loss, to grieve, to consider a lingering dream of returning. I want to make peace with memories of my time in the woods. I know that, when I do, there'll be more room in my soul to consider the options of a boundless future.

Indeed, those options are smiling in the distance, ever ready to welcome transformation and a new way of being.

———

I'm in Florida, driving west on a two-lane, ruler-straight, ten-mile stretch of asphalt linking DeLand with the rural community of Pine Lakes and Sunny Hill Farm.

I've been in Florida for a few days now, staying with my friends Jeff and Dan. I love hearing the stories of their time with Forest, the eight-year-old dog they adopted when I became too sick to care for him. Jeff and Dan are special friends, indeed. We go our separate ways during the daytime and connect for suppers and evenings full of interesting conversation.

In a few days I'll be staying with my friend Joyce. We've shared more than forty years of friendship. We've both survived extreme threats in our lives. She's recently endured chemo and radiation treatment for rectal cancer; I've survived multiple suicide attempts.

Once I'm with her, I know I won't want to do anything except enjoy her company and that of her husband, Billy, and being in her home where mutual friends come and go. I'm looking forward to hearing Joyce's laughter—the laughter I could have lost. To talking for hours about the past, about the things we've learned, about anything that comes to mind, with no room for pretense as always.

Profound threats to life have a way of cutting facets into the simple things in life, artfully crafting them into treasures of untold worth.

Meanwhile, I'm on my way to Sunny Hill Farm for the second time. Two days ago I drove to Pine Lakes, rode by the property that was once mine, and made a hasty departure, my emotions too strong to tolerate for any length of time.

That was the first time I'd returned since the day in June 2003, when I turned my back on my dreams of living in the woods and drove down my sun-dappled driveway, numbing myself to the tragic reality that Lyme disease was ravaging my life.

But this time, I'm determined to embrace my feelings, no matter how strong they get, to walk on my once-owned land, and to let the memories of my time in the woods play out.

At the corner, where I turn left off the highway, heading east and back into the Pine Lakes community, I stop at a convenience store. I'm going after the same sweet treats I used to buy when returning home from work: one red fireball and two pieces of bubble gum. With the fireball burning my mouth and me laughing at myself for being such a silly kid at age sixty-seven, I drive back into the Pine Lakes community, still a unique cultural island.

Within a quarter of a mile, pastel-colored mobile homes crowd together. They grimace from neglect: Black mold and dirt, streaked by condensation, cling to their oxidized sidings. Torn screens, hanging limp in the cold, tell of the widespread poverty in Pine Lakes, poverty that has no mind for repairs. Although poverty is widespread, homes in better condition soon greet me, relieving my empathetic agony over what I've just seen. For a couple of miles, a mixture of cinder block, brick, and well-kept mobile homes graces my vision, contrasting with the trash strewn along both sides of the road. When I lived out here, my excitement over owning a five-acre piece of land bordering on a preserve blocked out the trash-spawned revulsion I now feel. Shiny aluminum beer cans, crumpled white plastic bags, glass liquor bottles, and an assortment of other trash thrown from vehicle windows sneer at the idea of recycling—a redneck rendition of a sanitary landfill. Draped across the inside of windows or waving in the clear blue sky, Confederate flags decry the peace I'm trying to manifest. This place tests my desire to be nonjudgmental. Stirs up the cauldron of my own angry biases as I reverberate from the same kind of anger I feel surrounding me. I'm a rebel wanting to fight a rebel!

As I continue to drive down the road, my mind flitting from one thought to the next, I remember bringing my mother to Pine Lakes. The first time I drove her out here, I had just signed the contract to purchase my five acres on Red Oak Drive. Feeling like a little kid, I wanted to show my mommy my special treasure.

Her dislike for the area was evident. The farther back we drove off the main highway, the more tense she became. Glancing to my right, I noticed she was pushing on the "brakes" with her right foot, trying, in vain, to keep from going deeper into the woods.

Her fear-based reaction pissed me off: *Here we go again. Another part of my life I can't share with Mom. She doesn't understand me. She never did.*

But I'm not the person I was ten years ago—full of confidence and knowing I could handle extreme challenges. Although I'm reclaiming my personal power, I feel vulnerable out here. *What if*

I get stuck in the sand? What if someone takes exception to my poking around? Out here, guns are a fifth appendage for everyone old enough to shoot one.

With unstoppable power and the advantage of surprise, The Watcher interrupts my thoughts and the fear that's stalking my ability to reason: *I think maybe—just maybe—your mother felt the same way you're feeling now. Your mother didn't understand parts of you. And you didn't understand parts of your mother, either.*

Thunderstruck by The Watcher's message, I pull off the road for a few minutes to think. Until now, I thought the misunderstanding wedged between me and my mom was one-sided. For the first time, I consider Mom's background and how that colored her vision. She was a sophisticated urbanite, with no experience in the backwoods of anywhere. Born in 1911 in Ossining, less than forty miles west of New York City, she was raised in a downtown, burgeoning city environment. After she graduated from high school, she took a train to and from the Big Apple to attend Normal School, preparing to teach.

For the first time I see and feel Mom's perspective of Pine Lakes, and I see at least some of her perspective as a mother: *If I were riding in a car and a daughter of mine were showing me this area, telling me she was planning to live out here, I know I'd be concerned about her well-being.*

For the first time, I understand the anxiety my mother didn't know how to manage.

I see Mom in me, and that we were more like each other than I ever thought.

That's the way of The Watcher—to pry open rigidity, to release a self-absorbed way of looking at things in order to consider different points of view.

After a few moments of reflection, I continue down the road to the place where the pavement ends. The road then becomes a narrow, rutted dirt trail squeezed by either black mucky marshes on my left or woods dense with palmetto bushes and leaning sand hill pines on my right. Even though there's a marsh bordering the trail, patches of the trail dehydrate into sandy nightmares capable of grabbing tires and sucking them into the maw of big trouble in dry weather like now.

Before I make the hard right onto Red Oak Drive where I once lived, a mile of relentless jouncing takes me deeper into the woods. Along the way, I glance to my right at a white sandy hill, remembering the time I saw a four-foot Eastern diamondback rattler crawling into a pile of woodland debris. I shiver. Then I come to a dry patch of sandy trail that makes me wonder if I should keep going. I didn't come this way a few days before, but I should have figured this was here since the weather's been so dry. Determined to keep going, I gun the engine and swerve through the sand, barely able to keep moving as dust billows behind me.

When I finally get to *my* five acres, I pull my car into the driveway just enough to keep from blocking the trail. The land has been joined to five acres on the east. All ten acres have been stripped of trees and foliage. A horse and goat graze on the grass now growing there.

I grieve the loss of the shapes, sizes, and shades of green that once made the land magical. Sometimes I'd sit and notice the sun glisten on some dark-green, waxy leaves that grew near the gate to the driveway. At other times, I'd stand in the middle of a pine grove, feeling the russet-brown needles on the ground cushion my feet while I gazed at the sky above. Once in a while, I'd lie in a hammock, tied between two scrub oak trees, resting in their gracious shade.

A sound spooks me. A jolt of fear interrupts my thoughts. Again I realize I'm not the person I was ten years ago. I'm scared, knowing I'm a stranger in an area that doesn't welcome strangers. Even so, I intend to walk to the top of the hill to see the cottage I built.

First I call out to find out if anyone's home. No one answers.

The land bordering the western boundary of Sunny Hill Farm was once cleared to reveal the property line. That strip of land is now overgrown with low-lying shrubs. When temperatures are warm, dense undergrowth harbors an abundance of pygmy rattlesnakes. They're not a threat on a chilly day like today, but I can't help myself. I make noise with my feet and legs—shuffling the leaves on the ground, kicking and shaking bushes, as I walk the five hundred feet to the top of the hill to gaze at the cottage.

I don't feel sad when I look at the home I built. I feel surprised. *I don't belong here anymore.*

When I came here ten years before, I had the energy to work at fitting into a culture suspicious of someone like me. I had the courage to build my own place and live in the woods alone. I had the grit to face and welcome the wild.

Snakes? I knew they'd be here. Bears? Them, too. Rabid animals? I figured they might show up. But ticks carrying Lyme disease bacteria—never in my wildest imagination.

Without reluctance, I turn my back on Sunny Hill Farm. This time, I leave because I want to. This time, I have a choice.

As I walk down the hill toward my car, a dark speck crawls up the right leg of my gray sweatpants. I jerk my head to take a closer look. Trembling with fear and disgust, I flick the tick into the air.

I'm all ass and elbows scurrying to my car.

I can't get away fast enough.

Odd how a creature, vile and heinous in my eyes, grants me closure and a certain peace about saying a final goodbye to Sunny Hill Farm.

I'm outta here—for good!

SEEDS
IN THE DIRT

My simple life is full of surprises.
With my wee tiny eyes I sometimes see rare birds in crazy
places.
I've watched cuckoos eating the eggs of other birds.
Once in a while, pecking in the dirt, I find a seed.
After hopping with excitement,
I burst my morning song into the air,
telling of dawn after a dark night.

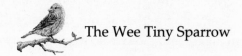 The Wee Tiny Sparrow

During the early-morning hours of June 24, 1943, I was welcomed into the world by my mother and those attending my birth. My mother and I had labored for only a few hours, both of us eager to continue our time together—face to face.

Swaddled in white cotton flannel, I soon took one of her nipples into my small, pink mouth to feed the bond that mothers and babies nurture. My father soon joined us after sneaking up the fire escape at the back of the hospital to where we lay with me cushioned against my mother's warm, ample breasts. Both of my parents gazed at me in dewy-eyed wonder. A dreamlike serenity embraced my family then.

But the world I was born into was a different matter. World War II was keeping the Grim Reaper busy heaving bloody masses

344

of humanity into the world of questions with no logical answers. Nazis overtaxed the already-burdened Reaper, warning of forthcoming toil with dark, gaseous smoke that smudged the skies over Germany as Jews, gypsies, homosexuals, and other political and religious "undesirables" disappeared in showers of grief and betrayal. And there was yet another eugenic massacre happening then—the slaughter of individuals who were also thought of, by some, as pariahs: 270,000 mentally ill men, women, and children were exterminated, "pest control" wrought by German psychiatrists—with no mandate from Hitler.[1]

Germany wasn't the only country with medical professionals interested in cleansing society of the "burdensome" mentally ill. While the Germans were "sanitizing" their population of the mentally handicapped, the concept of eugenics was advocated in the United States by some of the country's intellectual elite. "Alexis Carrel, a Nobel Prize–winning physician at the Rockefeller Institute for Medical Research, proposed that the insane should be humanely and economically disposed of in small euthanasic institutions supplied with proper gases."[2] Another leader among the American intelligentsia of that time, a neurologist and professor at Cornell University, advocated that "feeble minded children, nature's mistakes, be killed upon reaching the age of five."[3]

Not everyone shared those vindictive, dogmatic opinions. Yet, the eugenic scorn of some misguided and unfeeling elites impregnated the culture into which I was born with a heightened level of a long-standing loathing for the mentally ill, birthing a malicious, destructive paradigm of shame that weights the souls of those experiencing mental illness.

Like me.

———

When I was a child, my father suffered from severe depression, but I didn't know that then. Nor did I know his abuses of my mother, me, and my sister signaled mental illness. At some level, my mother knew, for in acts of passive-aggression, the truth of her beliefs sometimes erupted when my father angered her: with a scorching, fiery voice frothing with accusation, she called him a schizophrenic behind his back—a figurative slander used then to hurt someone.

Sometimes, when I, too, had angered her, she unwittingly damned me as well. Eyes blazing, an accusing finger jabbing in my direction, with a hissing voice spitting venom, she struck: "You're just like your father!"

My child's mind drew conclusions from her remark that Mother never intended, for she wasn't mean-spirited. Yet I secretly began to fear that one day I, too, would be "insane" like my father. That one day I'd shoulder the burden of scorn in my mother's voice. A voice mirroring a culture rife with condemnation for the mentally ill—the untouchables.

In 1983, soon after my fortieth birthday, anxiety crept into my life, threatening to steal my freedom. When extensive medical testing revealed nothing physically wrong, I asked to see a psychiatrist.

He delivered a certain kind of long-dreaded diagnosis: "You have anxiety disease, a genetic disorder, predominately female, a chemical imbalance. There is a simple solution, an antidepressant." That was a strange twist, for most likely my proclivity for anxiety, by nature or nurture, had originated with my mother. So, in that way, I was more like her than either of us thought. Within six weeks, the drug the psychiatrist prescribed did, for the most part, quell my torment. Yet, there was no prescription to help me love myself. And none to keep me from feeling disgraced—to keep me from being afraid no one would like me if they knew I suffered from a mental illness.

Fearing scorn for those like me, I kept my diagnosis and suffering hidden within a soul yearning to be free of shame. I wanted to be loved just as I was, an imperfect human being, yet I didn't know how to ask. I didn't know that I didn't need to.

Except when talking with my sister, a few friends, and my psychiatrist, the fear of rejection and self-loathing locked me into a deadly silence about my challenges with anxiety.

In 2002, neurological Lyme disease struck, disrupting the analgesic effects of the antidepressant I'd taken for close to twenty years. Anxiety, unabated by medication and stoked by Lyme's rampage, escalated into unbearable agitation. In an attempt to help me, my psychiatrist prescribed benzodiazepine, and a high dose of another drug to induce sleep.

For eight years thereafter, while still sick with Lyme, a combination of antidepressants and antiseizure medications were also prescribed from time to time by different healthcare providers, to help mollify anxiety and insomnia.

Day and night, a benzodiazepine was the illusory foundation of my emotional well-being, dividing my life into tenuous six-hour segments. An untrustworthy pseudo-power. And—predictably—the addictive sedative betrayed me.

In the late spring of 2009, the dosage I was taking suddenly failed to quell my anxiety just as my body became tolerant of a dangerous dose that couldn't be elevated. At the same time, the medication for sleep failed. Raw from insomnia and anxiety, without consulting anyone, I made a confused and unfortunate decision. *If the drugs aren't working, there's no reason to take them.* So I didn't, giving no thought to the potential aftermath of an abrupt withdrawal from medications I'd taken for eight years.

Soon, my body and emotions screamed their objections. My legs twitched, my heart raced. My anxiety escalated, tormenting me with an intolerable wild-eyed violence.

Even in that dark, frenzied state, I somehow saw a glimmer of sanity that spoke of my need to be hospitalized. Yet, I struggled with the idea. In my mind psychiatric hospitals were stamped with black-and-white imprints. On the one hand, I believed in my blinding naiveté that they could lead me to the ultimate cure for anxiety. On the other hand, I believed they would hammer home the dark shame I harbored.

———

A male crocodile with a hot poker stuck up his ass wouldn't be more disagreeable, I thought while peering at the psychiatrist sitting beside my bed—way too near my face—my mind turning to horny-skinned, pop-eyed reptiles. Of course, I wasn't in the best of moods. That wasn't the first time nor the last I'd been consulted by a psychiatrist after admitting myself to a psychiatric hospital. Each time I was interviewed during intake about my need for hospitalization, my explanation would ooze from my mouth in a thick staccato: "Anxiety. I-need-help-with-anxiety. I've-had-issues-with-anxiety-since-I-turned-forty. Now-I'm-becoming-agoraphobic. Even-needing-to-leave-my-bedroom-panics-me. Every-second-is-a-struggle. Lyme-hasn't-helped-any. The-antidepressant-that-eased-anxiety-for-twenty-years-stopped-working-when-I-got-sick. I've-tried-others. They-don't-work. The-benzos-did-help. Not-anymore. I-stopped-taking-them-without-easing-off. Is-that-why-my-legs-twitch? I'm-miserable."

Because I simply didn't know then, and I was too ill to take charge of my own therapy, I wasn't clear about what I thought was the origin of my anxiety. I only knew my depression and my desire to kill myself were rooted in my inability to cope with anxiety's torture. And my gut-eating fear of the related feelings themselves were cannibalizing my insides and my sanity.

What came next is difficult to explain—and scary. Writing about the sequence of events following my pleas for help takes me into a fiery hell. Yet, I choose to go on, for each time I release this painful part of my past, I heal some—with the ever-present support of The Watcher.

Remember, you're in control now.

You're not going to be locked up. You're not going to be shocked.

Yes, for a time you're going to feel just like you did when you were hospitalized. When you were hospitalized, you had no idea how that part of your life would end. Now you get to feel the full range of feelings: from terror to the thrill of meeting a challenge.

So keep going. You've got cojones, as Jedwin would tell you. You're on the right track. When you open up often enough, you'll become desensitized to that part of your past—like merely remembering a stormy day.

And when you're done?

Celebrate!

For you'll be reminded that you found an immeasurable treasure in unlikely circumstances . . .

———

The first time I admitted myself to a psychiatric hospital— touted as one of the best in the country—I'd pled for help with my anxiety. In so doing, I likely contributed to my unfortunate outcome when voicing my concerns about the effects of Zanax withdrawal.

My long-term suffering from anxiety was completely over-looked. I was diagnosed with depression and substance abuse. And assigned to a substance abuse unit, where I was required to participate in a twelve-step program.

Although I wasn't at my best the morning after being admitted that first time, what clear thinking I could summon led me to the conclusion that claiming a misdiagnosis wouldn't get me placed in another unit. And after a night of sleeping without a pillow and a much-needed blanket because none were available, I wasn't sure a reassignment would be any better than where I was.

So I served my time for ten days, earned my release with the required behavior, and promptly admitted myself to another hospital, one specializing in geriatric psychiatry, where I came to meet the aforementioned reptilian psychiatrist and, once again, pled for help with my anxiety—the help I so desperately needed.

The geriatric psychiatric hospital's website description of potential services for patients included medications, an interdis-ciplinary team approach, and Electro Convulsive Therapy (ECT). The interdisciplinary team approach, in particular, was noted as being rooted in the desire to return patients to an overall state of health. For me, all of those treatments were used as the modus operandi during both of my inpatient hospitalizations—especially an interdisciplinary team. Indeed!

Language at play, sporting chicanery.

One team member was a horticulturist, wearing a white coat. When I was desperate to learn how to cope with anxiety, he taught me and other glassy-eyed psychiatric patients about plants: How to cultivate a bonsai. How to root plants from cuttings. How to graft a sprig of one fruit tree to another of the same species to produce a variety of fruits from just one tree—voilà. I could have been taking a seamanship course only to be instructed to piss in the wind to survive a storm at sea.

Two other white-coated team members offered equally useful activities: an occupational therapist led armchair yoga sessions for coping with anxiety and depression. The other, a music therapist, appeared on weekends.

I felt elderly—demoralized—as I selected from a basket either a tambourine, castanets, or two sticks to synchronize rhythms with other patients. Indeed, I felt like an explosive devise being toyed with.

Why didn't someone know how to disarm me?

Why didn't someone help me feel safe enough to reveal my anguish?

Why didn't anyone ask me why I wanted to die?

Those weekend rhythm sessions were the only connections, even if frail, that I made with other patients.

I've often wondered about the other patients who were sitting beside me then:

Were they afraid of dying alone in a nursing home one day?

Had any of them lost loved ones, soul mates?

Were any of them anguished about burdening someone with their care?

Did any of them have secrets—putrid stories of childhood trauma— tormenting them in ways they didn't understand, or intense fears threatening them because of chronic illness like me?

There were no groups, no therapists, to help us find our way through the dark shades of isolation in hopes of leading us to feel compassion for each other, to know we weren't alone with our pain. To know that even in illness—or maybe because we were suffering—some of us, at least, had the capacity to be empathetic, to leave our own miseries behind to comfort someone else.

And the psychiatrists?

After meeting the reptilian one, I saw him only when he stood peering at me from behind a console ready to induce a grand mal seizure with high volts of electricity. His physician's assistant saw me, however, for fifteen minutes each morning to inquire only about my status related to medications and the ECT.

The psychiatrist supervising my third hospital stay came daily in the early-morning hours, wheeling a podium. His focus: the computer on top of the podium. All I could see was the back of his head as he refused to make eye contact. As he failed to understand my need for human connection.

———

Before I agreed to ECT, I was told the treatments were safe. "However, short-term memory loss is a potential side effect. Usually not permanent, though."

I wasn't told that statistics tell of far graver possibilities—even death.

Using what little data has been gathered on the effects of ECT, as of 2009, the death rate was "one in two hundred for the majority of patients who are elderly, a rate that hasn't changed since the 1950s."[4]

Hmm.

Scary stuff.

Was I elderly then—at age sixty-six?

There's more: I wasn't told the "undisputed" fact that the potential benefit from ECT treatment is short lived, lasting no more than four weeks![5]

Guess that's why the psychiatrist releasing me at the end of my last hospitalization told me there was the possibility I'd need to continue ECT once a month—for the rest of my life.

And there's yet another pertinent fact that was omitted: according to research outcomes, ECT isn't known to be effective treatment for anxiety.[6]

That said, during my last stay in the psychiatric hospital specializing in late-life depression, although my anxiety still lingered, my mental health did improve somewhat. However, the cause-and-effect issues are muddied. When I began my second two-week round of every-other-day ECT, I was also introduced to lithium for mood stabilization. And I was reintroduced to the drug I'd once taken for sleep, a benzodiazepine to quell anxiety, and a tricyclic to help me achieve a normal state of emotions.

After release from my last hospitalization, I continued ECT twice a week, eventually tapering to once every other week, with the expectation I would be treated once a month and continue indefinitely.

While receiving ECT, I continued to take the prescription drugs that were used during hospitalization, not knowing what was helping me feel less anxious—the drugs, ECT, or both.

Soon, healing from the aftermath of each ECT experience was taking up the better part of each two-week interval. Although my anxiety wasn't completely at bay, I was continuing to feel better. I wanted to know why. What was helping? The medications or ECT? Did I, indeed, need both?

The psychiatrist who was in charge of my outpatient care—my old friend the reptile—was unwilling to grant my request to support me while I tested myself for whether ECT was necessary. And to evaluate my state of health, perhaps granted to me by the prescription drugs I was taking.

So, without medical consent—and without medical support—I stopped ECT treatments.

I was on my own. Ripened by adversity, I was unaware that I was standing on the threshold of a dream.

My time had come.

AND NEVER
STOPS AT ALL . . .

Hope is the thing with feathers
That perches in the soul,
And sings the tune without the words,
And never stops at all.

— Emily Dickinson

The North Star is visible when facing one direction only.

I remember sitting in my mother's chair beside my bedroom window merely days after putting aside the notion of going to The Land of Dark Peace. I'll never forget that cold winter morning, January 4, 2010. I gazed in wonder at the book I'd just finished reading: *You Can Beat the Odds*. Feathers of hope gently stirred the flame of dawn, kindling the beginning of a profound transformation. My search for emotional and physical healing had exhausted me, nearly extinguishing my dream to be well. Yet there was just enough left whispering a message to my soul.

I sensed an urging—something important seeking expression.

Well before I was well, the gift of promised healing contained a nugget of passion, a mission. A responsibility to tell my story—to write a book.

In the spring of 2010 I found Jedwin Smith, author and teacher extraordinaire, through a posting on the Atlanta Writers Club website, and enrolled in his two-month workshop.

I'm perched on the edge of a black, faux-leather chair, my elbows resting on my thighs, my head bowed over a copy of the rough-as-a-pitted-dirt-road chapter I've just read out loud, held in my ice-cold hands. I'm surrounded by other writers also taking Jedwin's workshop; they're compelled into mysterious silence.

Earlier that spring, I'd tested the safety of this same group of writers and my own courage to persevere when emotions threatened to choke me; after I read what I'd written about Lyme disease ravaging my life, the silence was pregnant with mystery, too.

Just when I thought I couldn't stand the suspense any longer, the silence broke open.

Dispelling my fears of ridicule about showing my emotions, the group members delicately balanced their remarks between expressions of compassion and suggestions to help me improve.

They passed the first test.

I'm testing the same group once again, and my courage, by taking a more threatening risk, sharing fetid secrets that've rotted my insides far too long. Sweat is dripping down my back, soaking the drawstring waistband of my cotton pants. My hands, still ice cold, continue to hold pages of the chapter I've just read. A marked contrast to the silence in the room, thoughts clamor in my bowed head: *What is everyone thinking? Did I lay an egg? Will I still be liked now that everyone knows I've been a psychiatric patient? What if they think I'm a crazy person with nothing rational to say?*

I feel scared. Alone!

Something changes in the room.

I sense rather than see motion across from where I sit. Slowly, cautiously, I lift my eyes from my work.

They settle on Jedwin.

He's jerking his head from side to side like he's being repeatedly slapped hard, first on one cheek then on the other.

With glazed eyes, as though staring at something in the distance, he breaks open the silence, telling us that what I'd read had taken him back to the time when he too was a psychiatric patient. When he too was a prisoner of his own emotional darkness and agitated—restrained by a straitjacket, strapped to a bed.

Soon, another male speaks, recalling a time when doors locked behind him, too, as he was escorted into the dark recesses of a jail where he was left to wallow in depression.

Their reactions stun me at first. Then relief floods through my entire body, warming my hands. As I sit back in the chair, tears of gratitude spill from my eyes. I feel supported by their honesty—protected, even. Alone no more!

I'm vaguely aware of others speaking afterward, offering suggestions for improving my work. Some applaud my courage. I can't do much with what they say, though; I'm too full of emotions to have any room in my brain for logical processing. Yet I leave at the end of that session knowing I can trust the group with even more tender places.

I know then I will soon take an even greater risk, revealing a secret I've held for more than fifty years—since I was a sophomore in high school.

I've more business to take care of, though, before addressing *that* challenge . . .

———

I'm sitting in the reception area at the outpatient clinic of the geriatric psychiatric hospital where I was a patient. I dressed for this occasion with great deliberation. A stunning sight, my face and gray hair are framed by a vibrant, rust-colored turtleneck, layered over black, elegant slacks. Black hose, black dress flats, and a matching attaché case finish off my appearance.

I'm on a mission, waiting to see the same psychiatrist I once thought of as a disagreeable crocodile.

I've grown to like him some over the past year. Maybe that's because I've seen a glimpse of his humanity when with him for routine checks.

Once, I noticed a long, red scratch on one of his lower arms. After pointing to the scar while asking him what happened, he rotated his arm to take a look. When his eyes landed on the wound, his expression took on warmth. "My cat scratched me. She has an attitude."

Anyone who has a cat can't be all bad.

Hmm. He cares for her, in spite of her temperament.

Or maybe because she's testy.

Even though I've come to like my outpatient psychiatrist some, I'm still scared about seeing him, for this isn't a routine visit. My racing pulse speaks to that, and my fear of sparking his anger.

What if he does get mad?

Can I hang on to my power?

Complete my mission?

The Watcher responds to my concerns, working hard at settling me.

Breathe.

Take in deep, slow breaths to calm yourself.

You're in charge of your emotions.

Let your breath connect you with your powerful nature.

And just in case you need to know this: You're not waiting to be shocked by this man. He won't be standing behind a piece of equipment ready to fry your brain.

Look around you. Connect with this space.

You're in a waiting room—in control of yourself, your circumstances.

You've much to say.

Remember, you're equal to this man you're about to see. Any hierarchical status you're tempted to create in your mind is fictional. You are both human beings.

You may not have the expertise he has in his field.

You are, however, an expert about you and your recovery!

When the psychiatrist appears in the reception area to escort me to his office, I take a good look at him, silently acknowledging our equal status, then follow him with positive energy in my stride. I've taken command of my feelings. And I vibrate with the burgeoning creative prowess I'm reclaiming.

When we reach his office, he offers me a chair before he sits down on the opposite side of his dark, wood desk.

He then asks me how I'm doing—his usual question.

"Great," I say.

Straightening my back and deliberately making eye contact, I go on. "I want you to know this isn't a routine visit for a med-check. My express purpose for coming here is to tell you how I've recovered—for the record."

With that, I reach into my attaché case and take out a copy of *You Can Beat the Odds* and a document listing the research-based behavior medicine strategies described therein: diaphragmatic breathing, imagery, music, meditation. At the bottom of the page there's a bibliography of the additional resources instrumental to my healing process.[1]

After handing both items to the psychiatrist, he puts my list down then flips the book from back to front, reading the endorsements of renowned behavioral medicine specialists—Bernie Siegel, Joan Borysenko, and Anne Webster—on the cover.

While he's musing, I sit poised on the edge of my chair, like I'm waiting to catch a ball, determined to keep any words of his from penetrating me unless they pass my scrutiny.

After he lays the book on his desk, he picks up my document. His eyebrows raise when he gets partway down the list of healing strategies. Then he looks up. His gaze travels slowly across the desk, then locks onto my own. I meet him with boldness, noticing a surge of anger frosting my next remarks.

"I'm well because of the therapist who wrote *You Can Beat the Odds*—my therapist—Brenda Stockdale. She believes in my capacity to restore my mind and body. Better yet, she knows how to teach me to do just that! Using a multitude of therapeutic skills and her patient, compassionate listening to my stories of trauma, she gradually gained my trust. I felt safe in her presence. Safe enough to open up and release the long-held secrets of my past and the despair I felt from suffering chronic illness.

"And in the releasing, I eventually stabilized my emotions and my body!"

I'm poised at the edge of the chair for a counterattack.

The psychiatrist says something so maddening that I thoroughly identify with his cat's need to scratch him, only I want to dig my claws into his balls: "I prescribe meditation for my patients."

WTF!

I was his patient—in a hospital, no less—seeking his help.

Why didn't he prescribe meditation for me? And does he know about other do-no-harm techniques that could have been tried before he proposed and used ECT?

Also, what's up with a psychiatric hospital authorizing a psychiatrist to use only meds, ECT, and inane activities as therapy?

Greed? Dogma?

Disregard for a mental patient's capacity to learn emotional-management skills?

WTF!

Anger captivated my attention for a brief time, then I gathered my thoughts: "When I was an inpatient, I would have benefitted more by being taught tools like meditation to balance my emotions rather than gardening techniques!"

Shrugging his shoulders, he throws me for a loop. "I don't disagree with you. However, there was enough money to hire a horticulturist—not enough to employ a therapist."

I remain puzzled by his remark even after I leave his office. Saddened, too, by the pathos of my experiences with psychiatric mistreatment, knowing there was a do-no-harm pathway not taken when I was hospitalized and later as an outpatient. I weep, sorrow and grief spilling down my cheeks. And not just for me . . .

I've been shown my way out of insanity and sickness.

I found a therapist who held out hope for me no matter how mangled I was. One willing to be patient. One who wanted to hear my stories of trauma.

Granted, medications have helped me.

Yet they're not the answer.

And ECT couldn't shock away the truth of my past. Couldn't change my thinking.

How many others are being medicated and shocked, believing that's the only recourse, being shortchanged by experts they trust?

How many still have stories of abuse roiling their emotions because they haven't found a way to tell what happened—haven't found someone who's willing to take the time to listen?

Even more questions stoke my anger:

Why didn't the professionals treating me know that shallow breathing arouses anxiety? Why didn't they teach me that I could change my thoughts—change my brain—change my body's chemistry?

And what about the power of music to change my mood—what about that?

And exercise, too.

And the profound power of believing in me when I couldn't believe in myself?

I want to fight—for the underdog. For those who are struggling to find their way to emotional freedom in a system that has lost the belief in the power of the human spirit to heal and the need to stand beside someone while they walk through the pain of the past to reclaim the promise of the future.

My pen is my weapon of choice.

And so I write.

FREEDOM'S CHILD

Compassion illumines the path
to freedom
for a soul,
seeking the embrace of a soft and gentle peace.

—The Watcher

A predator watches, a twisted mind, honing stealth.

A twisted mind, responding to a plea from a wounded heart that weeps.

A predator watches, calculating a strike.

———

In 1958, I am a strikingly pretty, noticeably intelligent fifteen-year-old. My dark, chestnut-colored hair frames a fair face adorned with rosy cheeks. I'm spirited, sometimes funny, yet my eyes and slouched shoulders speak of a child yearning for approval—yearning for a simple love I don't know how to get from my parents.

The adult volunteer leading the small group of adolescents I meet with weekly notices my silent yearnings, marks me as prey, an easy take: I don't know I matter to anyone. I wish I felt loved, appreciated.

I signal my adoration for that leader: *I look up to you. You're special to me. I hope you like me. I want to please you so you will.*

After one of the weekly meetings, the leader I've come to idolize asks if I want a ride home.

"Yes." I bubble over with excitement, feeling honored— honored to be noticed by someone so respected and talented. "Yes, I'll call my mother to tell her she doesn't need to come and get me. I'll tell her you're going to take me home."

On the way to my house, when we're only blocks away, we turn into a dark cemetery.

I feel confused, wondering why we're stopping.

The car engine idles in the pitch-dark night.

Soft, warm hands turn my face.

My lips are covered with passion—a new kind of kiss— lingering.

"Did you like that?" I'm asked.

With my breasts tingling, my genitals flooding with moist heat, I nod my head.

A sexual predator, a woman more than twice my age, has just downed her prey.

———

The woman who kissed me in the cemetery, signaling the death of anything left in me that's sexually normal, was a respected member of the community—a trusted teacher, youth group volunteer, symphonic musician, wife, mother.

With a kiss, she downed, perpetuating her own unhealed trauma.

When she was in high school, boys had abducted and gang-raped her; she could barely walk when they dropped her off at her home, acting as if nothing had happened.

With that first darkened, passionate kiss, only a few months into my sophomore year in high school, I was seduced into a six-year-long, same-sex relationship with a woman trusted by all who knew her.

I loved her with a fierce kind of love that demanded I be with her whenever I could. I loved her with a love that was driven by raging pubescent awakenings to sexual feelings and their pleasures. I loved her with a love that was urged on by my need to be loved.

And in a perverted way, I was loved. Delighting in teaching me different things, the woman who exploited my needs, my innocence, affirmed me when I learned quickly. I felt important, smart, valued.

The true nature of our relationship was never discovered. Using my creative intellect, I became a perpetrator's ally in creating a ruse of propriety to fool my parents into giving me permission to spend time with her.

She was a masterful teacher, showing me how to ply the waters of South Florida using wind and sail. She taught me how to gently, skillfully massage her clitoris to make her come, while she did the same thing for me. Until then, I didn't know I had a clitoris. Adding to this mix of skills, she trained me in the art of surviving in the wilderness, fostering an appreciation of nature. This complex, intelligent, and damaged woman I loved also introduced me to classical music, which I grew to prize. I learned to emulate her can-do-it attitude about tackling difficult projects.

There was more.

Once, after we'd secreted ourselves in her car in a dark, isolated place to make love, she told me to comb my hands through my hair to rid them of the scent of female genitalia, so when I got home my mother wouldn't suspect my hands had been in moist places.

When she thought I was ready to learn, she introduced me to oral sex . . .

Talk about a confusing mixture—a pus-filled mess. Kind of like the rest of my childhood.

How did I ever manage to get through high school?

Being the class clown, I guess—a pretender.

Trying to hide my confusion and shame. Trying to be liked by my friends. Trying to find a way to survive my self-hatred.

Although there was no physical violence in my relationship

with the sexually abusive woman I adored, there was violence of a different sort: abuse wearing the mask of love. That mask wasn't new to me. Her eagerness to teach me about sex and to draw me into her own distorted soul continued to destroy a part of me that, looking back, I believe had been damaged in early childhood by my father.

My curiosity about sex, probably honed by factors that have never surfaced, and her sick desire to teach me about all things carnal join in a macabre partnership, destroying my natural tendency to enjoy a wholesome sexuality.

When I asked my sexual mentor about sex with men, she and her husband took me and another girl my age to see porn movies at an adult toy store. Mysteriously, I sensed I already knew about experiencing sex with a male, but I wanted to encourage her attention to continuing my sexual education.

The porn movies weren't enough.

I wanted to *feel* a penis penetrating me.

When I asked what having sex with a man *felt* like, my "teacher extraordinaire" arranged for me to have sex with her husband on a couch in their living room while her children slept in nearby bedrooms—and while she watched from a nearby hallway.

As a fifteen-year-old kid, I was incapable of seeing the tragic nature of my "mentor's" caring. I didn't know she was destroying my well-being. I didn't know her wounded soul was darkening my life in ways that bordered on sadism. And I didn't know the nature of my precious innocence.

After graduating from high school, I entered Western Carolina University in Cullowhee, North Carolina. At first, I was homesick, tempted to leave school to retreat into the arms of the woman who had abused me.

Instead, I quickly adjusted and thrived at being a college student. During the summers of my freshman and sophomore years, I worked in a nearby camp to earn spending money. I didn't return to West Palm Beach much until the summer after my junior year, when I worked there as a day camp director.

By then, my relationship with my "mentor" had changed. Even though I'd stayed in touch and had sexual encounters with her when home for holidays, I hadn't been committed to the relationship. I'd dabbled with two other lovers. One was a male student, our petting barely tamed, restrained only by my fear of getting pregnant—a sure way to incur my father's wrath and end my life as a college student. After that tie was severed, I began toying with another female partner.

When I went home during the summer following my junior year, I realized I didn't want any more to do with the woman who would still make love with me if that's what I wanted.

Because I wasn't seasoned in the art of ending relationships, when we met at the ice cream stand where I told her I didn't want to see her again, I lied about my reasons: "I don't think what we're doing is right. The Bible says so."

Even though she tried to change my mind, there was no going back. I was done.

After parting with a hug, I hastened to my mother's car I was driving, eager to put distance between us, relieved to be done with the difficult task of saying goodbye.

For a few years after that, I spoke with my twisted mentor until an intuitive part of me felt the dark, murky residue of my sexual relationship with her. Resentment and anger about what happened flourished in my soul without my understanding why. In the end, I was steadfast, refusing to make contact, even when she wrote my mother asking for my address.

———

As an adult, I'm haunted by what happened and I blame myself. Deep inside, I hide the story of my relationship with the mortally wounded woman who entered my life with a kiss of betrayal, breeding shame and self-hatred—inviting illness. I'm broken in a way I don't understand.

And as a result of my experiences, I'm often confused about my sexuality.

I never know—never will know—if I was born hetero, homo, or bisexual. I know I'm androgynous, yet I don't know how that translates to my sexual preferences. When people spew their venom about same-sex relationships, thinking the topic has nothing to do with me, they unknowingly strike my heart. At times like that, I keep quiet about my past and my doubts. Dead quiet.

A challenge I've faced as a result of my early sexual experience with a female has played out when I've sought sexual pleasures with a man. When I make love with a woman, there's always foreplay. I always come. Women know the mechanics of female orgasm, while making love with men has had varied results. Through no fault of their own, most haven't known how to pleasure me. And I've not been bold enough to tell them. Besides, I believed I needed to take care of their feelings. I often faked orgasms to make them believe they were good lovers, sacrificing my own needs.

As a young woman, I craved sexual pleasure. I sought acceptance by objectifying my body. I needed to have love expressed physically, yet I didn't have a smooth pathway for getting there. Same-sex relationships were scorned, yet that's where I experienced the most reliable sexual pleasure. Being sexual with a woman was to be in love, nothing casual. But with men, not so. In any case, sexual relationships have always spelled trouble.

I miraculously functioned well at work and with friends, although I was constantly changing intimate relationships or moving to new living places. Perhaps I thought a new place to live would rid me of the psychological agitation stoked by the inferno of pain caused by the dark side of my past.

Within eighteen years, from 1965 to 1983, I participated in two more same-sex relationships, lived in eighteen different places, and married two men.

After being married for less than two years, I ran from my first husband for reasons I didn't understand.

My second marriage?

That one was "long term": five years. Although turbulent and life-threatening, I didn't want to end that marriage until I figured I might get killed if I didn't.

In a way, my second husband was two different men: a wonderful companion and friend when he was sober, and a raging, gun-wielding, leering lunatic when he was turgid with booze. When a judge granted an uncontested divorce, I cried, feeling lucky to have escaped unharmed.

I don't remember exactly when I decided to avoid same-sex relationships. I detested the secrecy surrounding them. The fear of discovery—being scorned—outweighed their benefits.

Not so with men, or so I thought. As a "liberated" woman, I was constantly engaged in trying to find my self-worth by using my body to attract men, unwittingly hurting myself—pummeling my already wounded heart, jack-hammering insistent messages into my soul with convincing madness: "You're worthless. Your body doesn't matter—*you* don't matter. You're just a thing. Expendable."

———

In 2001, when I'm living at Sunny Hill Farm, one evening my phone rings. A friend from high school invites me to a luncheon to honor the woman who sexually exploited me when I was in high school. I haven't spoken to her for more than thirty-five years.

I'm as confused by the idea of honoring her as I am by trying to figure out how to think of her, given the disparate influences on my life. Even so, I want to see her. The time has come to break my silence. I want to talk with her about what happened between us, hoping to free myself from the anger and resentment invoking decades of silent reprisal.

When she arrives at the event honoring her, I'm saddened by what I see.

She's old—frail. Someone had to drive her there.

Walking slowly into the room, her eyes scan the group of us sitting around a large table, passing by me without recognition.

Then, her head jerks back in my direction. Her eyes question mine.

In response, I smile, stand, and walk toward her to hold her close. There's part of me that still loves her—nothing sexual, just pure compassion for both of us and our pain wrought from tragedy. I circle my arms around the goodness in her and hold her near to my heart.

While standing together, I ask if she'll let me drive her home. The urgency in her response puzzles me. "Yes. Yes, I'd like that."

After the luncheon, the minute we're both in the car, she vomits gut-wrenching misery: "I'm sorry I ruined your life. Will you forgive me?"

Taking her hand in mine, I turn to gaze into eyes streaming with tears. Choked with emotion myself, I can only love this now-frail woman sitting beside me, pleading for forgiveness. I speak from the childlike part of me that yearns to be free of resentment and anger. I speak from the childlike part of me that wants to give someone I love a wildflower.

"I forgive you."

A REUNION

In the story telling we weave together disparate and broken parts of ourselves into a courageous tapestry of grace, and in doing so, come to honor who we are because of where we've been.

—Brenda Stockdale[1]

When I'm in the midst of writing "Freedom's Child"—tough, scary business—I sometimes jump from my chair, catapulted by emotions roiling in my gut, making me want to run from the guilt and shame I feel when the long-rotting, heart-wrenching truth of my past resurfaces in my manuscript in stark detail.

When I'm in turmoil, The Watcher, still a steady presence and powerful influence, beckons me to peer into my eyes. Standing in front of a mirror, I seek my soul, listening to wise words from a heart that wants to be free of pain.

Listen up.

Pay attention to me!

One day you won't feel this way about what happened to you. I promise.

Cry! Yes, you need to cry.

Releasing your feelings—that's still your way to freedom.

Remember, you're the one in control now—a full-fledged woman in charge, not the kid who couldn't take care of herself.

I'm sure you don't want a predator's ghost to keep messing with you.

Keep writing—opening up instead of letting your past rot in shame.

You're doing a great job of healing yourself.
You're on the right track.
And one day soon, talking and writing about being abused will be like merely mentioning a dark cloud in the sky.

Even though my own wisdom soothes me, I keep looking in the mirror, sensing there's a part of me missing—the vulnerable, childlike part of me who doesn't feel loved by the woman I am. I'm still fragmented by shame and guilt; I simply can't see my long-forgotten self as an innocent fifteen-year-old child.

Seeking a way to get rid of self-persecution, my looking into my own eyes in a mirror, I pray to find a way to forgive myself— to welcome all of me into my presence. I pray to find a way that has integrity, no pretense.

And in the seeking, I find there's more to forgive.

———

When I first began to open up to my therapist about being sexually exploited, she sometimes referred to my "mentor" as a perpetrator—a criminal.

Until then, I hadn't been conscious of the fact that I'd been a criminal's victim. A victim, yes, but not a criminal's victim. News stories of priests molesting young boys made me angry, yet I didn't relate my own story to theirs. I wasn't ready to feel the pain of knowing someone I admired meant to take advantage of my neediness and innocence.

All this changed when I was doing background research for "Freedom's Child."

There's a strong academic part of me that thrives on information derived from sound investigation. Research findings in *You Can Beat the Odds*, documenting the efficacy of Brenda's mind-body healing strategies, were instrumental in my healing. They became the basis for the powerful belief that I could reclaim my health.

Searching for research-based information that would help me

understand the events of my sexual abuse was a natural next step, and exciting, even—like going to a museum to see exceptional art. A bit of a light touch I could use.

Considering the possibility that my "mentor" was a criminal was sometimes challenging; she was a complicated cauldron turgid with a stewed mixture of the horrible and the beautiful. She wasn't violent in the usual sense of the word. Even so, I search for information about female sex offenders.

And what I found was devastating.

In her book *Predators*, Anna Salter, renowned authority on sexual predators, cites a study of female sexual perpetrators, describing a category that fit my "mentor": "There is a teacher/lover group. This is not a group of . . . adult women who are eighteen or twenty and are involved with seventeen-year-olds. There was, on average, a sixteen-year age gap between offender and victim. . . . Thus, these are a group of adult women, generally in their thirties, who pretty much double the age of their victims. These women do not, in general, act sadistically."[2]

Gavin de Becker, award-winning author and expert on prediction of violence, wrote the forward to *Predators*, where he describes the chilling reality of a sexual predator's stealth, which I assume applies to both males and females: "There are two basic predatory types, the power-predator and the persuasion-predator. The power-predator charges like a bear, unmistakably committing to [her] attack. Because of this, [she] cannot easily retreat and say there was merely a misunderstanding. Accordingly [she] strikes only when [she] feels certain [she'll] prevail.

"The far more common offender is a persuasion-predator. This type of criminal is someone who looks for a vulnerable victim, someone who will allow [her] to be in control. Like a shark circling potential prey, the persuasion-predator approaches slowly and watches to see how people react to [her] advances. [She] begins a dialogue and with each favorable response [she] elicits, [she] circles closer. [She] makes a small initial investment, a low-risk strategy that allows [her] to test the waters and move on with nobody the wiser if things don't go well. [She] is a coward, a crafty one, but a coward nonetheless.

"A predator's selection of victims can be as complex and inexplicable as sexual attraction is for adults, with one important distinction: For most pedophiles, vulnerability is, all by itself, stimulating."[3]

Hmm.

Sounds too familiar: an exploratory dialogue was started by my "mentor," and with each favorable response from me, she circled closer.

A shark testing the waters.

A kiss in a dark cemetery, then: "Did you like that?"

A shark circling prey, vulnerability the blood of innocence.

At first, I was stunned by what I'd read.

Then torture overwhelmed me. I sobbed, vomiting keening wails of grief. Outrage erupted in a red-hot, scalding desire for retaliation—sputum for a devil's charm.

Fucking bitch.

What were you thinking?

I didn't need your twisted, blood-sucking love.

You were fucking sick.

You were smart.

Why weren't you smart enough to get some help for yourself?

I've paid a huge price for your "tender ministrations."

———

While I was writing "Freedom's Child," often pained by what I'd read in research findings, I receive a miraculous gift, a blessing of Divine Assurance . . .

Waiting for a Sunday service to begin, I'm sitting in the second row in the middle section of the church's sanctuary—alone. Most everyone else clusters in the back. Not me. I like to be up front, where I can see everything going on. Sometimes, though, I feel self-conscious sitting by myself.

Do people think I'm weird, sitting by myself, stuck out in the open? Do they think nobody likes me?

Shrugging my shoulders, I dismiss those notions and squiggle in the seat, settling and readying myself to stand when the music starts.

To my surprise, a gorgeous fourteen-year-old—someone I've never met—slides into the pew, scooting herself close. She leans toward me, whispering in my right ear, "I was alone at a retreat once; someone made friends with me. I'm here to be your friend— to keep you company."

Astounding! A teenage girl left her friends to come sit by me—an olde lady.

Her presence makes me teary-eyed. I feel honored, blessed beyond measure. I have no way of knowing she's yet another Earth Angel showing up in my life, a Divine messenger.

The following Sunday, this beautiful teenager joins me again. As we greet each other, our enthusiastic smiles and sparkling eyes speaking of the delight we share in our developing relationship, another strikingly pretty adolescent—an Earth Angel, too—scoots into the pew.

After the three of us sit together several Sundays, with their parents' permission, I invite them to go to lunch after church. While spending time together, then and several times after that, we share what's going on in our lives, bridging generations with a sincere interest in one another. I observe their adolescence in full flower—and their innocence.

In a quiet moment, when I'm alone after one of our times together, I'm carried back to my own long-forgotten adolescence by The Watcher:

The beautiful, eager faces of your two young friends reflect your own pretty, rosy-cheeked fifteen-year-old face. Their innocence mirrors your own innocence—unsuspecting of danger from someone you admired, from someone working with children, from someone who was a mother and wife, from someone who was skilled at masking her intentions.

The vulnerability you're seeing—feeling—in your teenage friends is a twin of your own.

You were innocent.
Innocent!

———

I remember the counsel of Joan Borysenko in her book It's Not the End of the World: "Forgiveness is for the forgiver rather than the offender. It's all about taking your life back and moving on in peace, with a little more wisdom, than you had before."[4]

With a clear vision that I was a guiltless, criminal's victim, and after processing my anger and sadness, I find myself in need of extending forgiveness, once again, to the woman who molested me.

Funny how healing from all this seems to happen in layers, the wise part of me apportioning my pain.

This time, when I'm ready to extend a pardon, my feelings run deeper. There's a richer compassion sculpted from a broader understanding of what happened to me. And what happened to the woman who molested me when she was gang-raped. This time, what I have to offer seems worth more, yet I can only speak to the memory of the woman who abused me when I forgive.

Why so?

She died from Alzheimer's within months of apologizing for what she'd done to me.

———

Before I move on, there's one thing more to do that I mustn't forget about.

There's the childlike part of me waiting in the distance—the part of me that wants to be welcomed home—the part of me that's been running from shame and guilt. The part of me that yearns to be forgiven too.

The eyes brimming with tears I see peering back at me in the mirror reflect my soul's need to be free from the shadow of abuse.

Carolyn Martin Graham

The woman I am wraps arms around my breasts, tenderly rocking the childlike part of me that's been away for so long. The woman I am speaks a gentle welcome using the flower of perfect wisdom:

My dearest Carolyn, you are so very precious, my little one.

Come to me. Come into my arms.

There, there—go ahead—snuggle close to me.

Your sweet face is so full of Light. How could anyone have hurt you?

Cry if you need to. I'll hold you tight.

You are very brave, you know. I'm in awe of your courage.

I'm proud of you, too.

I'm so glad you're still alive to tell your story.

I want you to know, you don't have to be ashamed of what happened to you.

Here, I'm kissing that guilt away forever.

We'll always be together now, no matter what happens.

I love you so. All of you.

In a little while, we'll celebrate our reunion, do our favorite thing: go for a walk in the woods to find wildflowers and butterflies—new beginnings.

FREEDOM'S CHILD
WEIGHS ANCHOR

*The artistry in cultivating courage is refined by learning to
take a well-timed step toward emotional prowess by doing
that which is compelling and ethical—in spite of fear.*

*Exercising courage erodes fear's deceptive underpinning,
extending emotional boundaries and the opportunities to
choose how one feels and acts.*

—The Watcher

My mouth feels like I've been sucking on a wad of toilet paper.

Fear knots my gut, robbing me of the ability to do anything
except mimic those surrounding me who are breathtakingly silent.

My head's bowed, held down by a weighty residue of shame
and the insecurity of new beginnings . . .

Will anyone like me now?

Wish I weren't so scared.

I stink when I'm scared like this. Sure hope no one can smell me.

My feet itch to run.

No way!

I'm sticking around.

I need feedback.

Except for my own internal reactions, the silence is pregnant
with mystery.

———

I've just finished reading "Freedom's Child" to Jedwin and other writers taking his third workshop at the beginning of 2011.

Somehow, I manage to get the courage to raise my eyes to look at Jedwin, who's sitting in an old, faded, wing-backed chair across from me. When I see his right arm and clenched fist held high in the air, signaling triumph, tears burst from my eyes.

Sagging into a snotty mess, I loosen up, readying myself for other reactions . . .

———

Reading about being sexually exploited was both scary and painful. Although I wasn't aware I was doing anything that would be perceived as extraordinary, after Jedwin lowered his raised fist, he vocally acknowledged me for my bravery.

Coming from him, that was like receiving a diamond wrapped in pure gold, for he knows courage better than most. Another person can know intimate places in my soul only if their own has worn the same garment.

Jedwin's a talented writer, teacher extraordinaire, independent thinker with a wry sense of humor, former war correspondent — all wrapped up in a heart full of compassion and a marine's well-seasoned courage.

He's the recipient of many major writing awards. In 1986, he was a Pulitzer Prize finalist for his coverage of the Eritrea-Ethiopia civil war. After I read Jedwin's book *Our Brother's Keeper*, I thought perhaps his greatest act of courage may have been exposing the truth of his own painful past and the feelings surrounding the death of his brother in the Vietnam War.

When I need to rekindle my own courage to stay grounded in openness, I draw on Jedwin's example of writing barefaced — without the mask of machismo to avoid revealing his heart's story.

No accident I found Jedwin, another Earth Angel.

No accident I started telling my story to women — and men. Mostly men.

I've never had brothers—until now.

A new thing for me, this letting males into my heart.

Through writing and sharing my past—choosing to be vulnerable—I'm unlearning the mistaken idea "all men are alike," unwittingly communicated to me by my mother in exasperated outbursts when reacting to my father's verbally violent abuses. I'm learning that men have the capacity to be compassionate and trustworthy. They can be caring and kind. Even better, I'm becoming aware that, in general, they deserve my respect—and trust. I'm coming to expect goodness in them in the same way I expect goodness in women.

Sure is bizarre that I've trusted women so much, given my experience with a female sexual predator.

She felt good and right once.

Screwy sometimes—the subconscious intricate and puzzling conclusions.

Good to bring them to light from their murky hiding places.

After I read "Freedom's Child" and looked up to see Jedwin's fist in the air, he spoke, acknowledging me for my courage once again while I was straightening up in the chair and blowing my nose. A few other writers also acknowledged my courage or offered suggestions for improving my writing skills. Most remained quiet.

Later on, when standing, ready to disband for the night, everyone walked up to me and gave me a bear hug pulsing with a warm compassion that I felt deep in my bones.

Everyone!

I then realized my belief that I'd be scorned if others knew everything about me was dragging anchor in emotional effluvia. And I came to know in a deeper way I was with writers who would treat me with tender encouragement and respect—no matter my past.

Although, I suppose, there was my part in calculating my safety before opening, there was something else going on too—Divine Mystery, Divine Light.

I'll never understand how all that works. Yet, I'm humbled by their dynamic Presence in my life, blessing me with healing direction along with my own through the incredible individuals gracing my journey.

———

I've carefully cultivated courage, gradually exposing the once-hidden truth of my adolescence. I know everyone won't react the way Jedwin and the other writers in workshops responded to my story.

Some will say, replicating some state statutes, that at age fifteen, I'd reached the age of sexual consent when I was drawn into a relationship with a woman twice my age. Some will say I'm denying a genetic predisposition to same-sex attractions and that I precipitated—consciously or subconsciously—the relationship I now decry.

No matter what happens, I now have a cadre of brothers and sisters—writers one and all—who will stand beside me while I continue to open up in different circumstances and share my experiences in *The Gift of the Circle*.

Now, I don't have to be brave and alone.

Just brave.

———

Knowing I've got lots of support, I venture forward to take care of some critical unfinished business where, once again, there's no quarter for pretense. No hiding the truth, no holding back the child in me who wants to be free from shame—the woman who intends to stand tall.

First, I square with my sister in her living room, while she sits on her couch and I in a rocker that was a favorite of our mother's. Slowly rocking back and forth comforts me, while I tell Janet the dark truth of my adolescence.

She's not surprised. For some reason, I didn't expect her to be.

Our conversation threads this way and that as we explore the tapestry of my teenage years as a victim of a sexual predator and my sister's eleven-year-old observations of what was happening. Even at that age, she felt something untoward was going on. In fact, she recalls despising my "mentor," who often came to chauffeur me somewhere for an event or to go for "ice cream and a chat."

Upon her arrival, she frequently entered our home. Even though I was anxious to leave with her, I knew not to run out to the car when she pulled into the driveway. Instead, I acted laid-back, instinctively knowing to invite her inside, all the way into the living room, to speak with my mother. Doing otherwise would have invited unwanted suspicion.

While talking to Mom, my "mentor" wore a bold presence— the shroud of deceit. We never spoke about deceiving my parents and others, yet, even at age fifteen, I knew that's what we were doing; I knew the doing was necessary to avoid dire consequences. And this complicit deceit effectively masked our shared intentions to find somewhere to secret ourselves for mutual masturbation and simultaneous orgasms.

Janet and I can only guess at my parents' thoughts while my relationship with my sexual predator was playing out. In the late 1950s, there wasn't much information about such matters. The idea that a woman could be one was unthinkable. And the idea that a child of theirs could be involved in a same-sex, criminal relationship was probably too painful to confront.

When my sister and I finish talking, I feel closer to her. There's nothing between us then except the fresh air surrounding my heart, lightened of burdens.

After speaking with Janet, I share my story with my friend Marilyn while eating an early dinner in a quiet restaurant. In response, she is caring and kind—loving me still.

For several years during my recovery from illness, I met once a week with a few individuals to pray. I wanted them to know who I was, who I really was—especially since some of the members had made disparaging remarks about same-sex relationships. When that happened, I said nothing, aware that my silence, perceived as agreement, would serve to keep my past hidden. However, stillness on the outside didn't keep me from squirming on the inside. And I wanted nothing of that pretentious, gut-oozing silence.

Either I wanted to be accepted with all of my past in tow, or not. I wanted to be loved, yet I was aware the love that was or wasn't extended to me by others was no longer a measure of my self-worth. If I was to continue to be cherished by members of the prayer group, I wanted the genesis of their feelings to be birthed in truth. And when I finally relate my story to them, even the most conservative members respond with compassion and concern, teaching me that revealing shadows sometimes has a way of inviting love.

———

As I've healed little by little from the effects of emotional and physical illness, I've faced up to their origins, knowing that being intimate with them—being fully aware of their effects on my life—is to refuse to be a victim of my past any longer. To refuse by growing my innate personal power, no matter how painful the process.

After I write "Freedom's Child" and share my story with my sister, my friend Marilyn, and others, I realize there are compelling reasons for me to schedule a trip to West Palm Beach, where I lived from the age of four until I graduated from high school.

Before scheduling a flight, I call someone who was a friend when we were in high school, intending to make arrangements to spend time together. My long-ago friend was also a member of the youth group led by the perverse woman of my adolescence. And she, too, was used by her, and, I'm ashamed to say, by me as well. Predicting my parents' thoughts, she became a decoy to deflect suspicion—nothing could be wrong if a third person was included on overnights, ostensibly to prepare for a group campout.

Even though I was a kid when I deceived my friend into thinking she was genuinely wanted on excursions with me and my "mentor," I've felt guilty ever since.

Now, I yearn to rekindle a friendship, this time based on honesty. I remember my former companion as someone gentle and talented who often found humor in simple absurdities and pleasure in quiet spaces.

As I get ready to call her, fear leaks from my forehead in beads of sweat. My icy hands can barely use the keypad on my cell phone.

The Watcher—a welcome guardian of reason—steadies me, at least for the moment:

Breathe.

Stay centered in your breath.

Your slow, deep breathing will help calm you.

You're in charge here—guardian of your soul.

Nothing said by anyone is good or bad!

You're the one who assigns meaning to words.

You're the one who decides how to react.

The phone seems to ring forever before I hear a voice—the familiar one of my one-time friend.

I'd planned to reveal the long-hidden reality of my adolescence face to face. Yet after a short time talking, telling my story right then and there seems called for. Sounding calm, I tell her the truth of my past, my gut knotted, muscles tensed, poised for an outburst of indignation.

I fear she'll call me a liar.

Instead, tears stream down my face as she says, "I'm sorry that happened to you." Sadness shades the tones of her voice. But her sadness isn't just about me.

She realized at once she had been used as a decoy. With words to that end, she reminds me about the "special" sex education experience we shared: when I told my parents I was going to see a film with her, our youth group leader, and her husband, she helped veil the truth that I was going to see a porn movie at an adult entertainment store.

While talking, I feel as though I'm crawling out from the putrid, sticky remains of roadkill.

———

When I'm in West Palm Beach, I find myself liking the one I'd misused from an authentic place. As a matter of fact, I like her so much that even if I'd never known her, I would want to. And her warm response to my visit helps me feel forgiven for mistreating her in days gone by. Releasing me of guilt that has threatened to erode the present is a gift for my journey to West Palm Beach as Freedom's Child.

My "new" friend and I may not see each other again. I hope we will, for there's something that feels good about spending time with someone who can ramble with me this way and that in the good and the bad of the past, while knowing there's no more need to expend energy covering my tracks.

———

While in West Palm Beach, I return to the tiny frame house, now unkempt, where I spent so much of my adolescence being sexually exploited. Driving—creeping—past that unpretentious, innocent-looking, white, wood-framed house is no walk in the park.

As I get close, I feel myself wanting to run from a monster that's reaching from inside my gut to grab my throat, shaking me senseless while threatening to strangle me with fear. My foot freezes, unable to move my car forward. Finally, my emotional pain erupts from eyes no longer willing to hide from my past. Tears streak my face, releasing another soiled stream of consciousness and the toxins of secrets held too long. Moments later, a mellow sort of sadness becomes like a gentle friend, holding me for a while until I take a deep breath and continue to move down the street, to gaze at the past in a way that seems as real as the little house that now captures my attention.

I look at the wooden front door leading to the living room, remembering the couch inside, positioned just to the right of the entryway, where I lay inebriated from my first experience with booze and feeling the aftershock of sexual intercourse at the inept hands of my tormentor's husband.

The bedroom windows on the front of the house remind me of many equally furtive, yet more pleasurable, sexual encounters with the woman who first taught me about all good things carnal.

Driving a few feet forward, I get a good view of the old, now saggy-roofed, wooden garage where my youth group once met and where I learned survival skills that I would one day use on wilderness excursions that would bring me pleasure—and grow me in a wholesome way.

Is anyone all bad? I don't think so.

With that, I've had enough emotional processing. Looking at the little house where I had been so deeply wounded is, indeed, painful. Yet when the last vestiges of long-suppressed shame surface, I am able to bestow a sincere benediction on *all* of the heart-rending circumstances of my adolescence. And in the benediction, I'm soothed by a final forgiving of myself for all the wrongs that are mine. A warm *knowing* bathes my soul with a compassionate understanding: I did the best I could.

And so did the woman who held my fierce adolescent heart captive, perpetrating the unhealed pain of her own past.

Wildflowers bloom in the strangest places sometimes.

I'd still give her one, if I could.

———

Yet another part of my trip to Florida takes me to a small town located near the southern tip of Lake Okeechobee. Clewiston is an old farming community surrounded by muck fields often flourishing with stalks of tall, bright-green sugar cane. Little has changed from decades ago when I camped on the nearby dike surrounding the lake.

I go to Clewiston to lunch with someone extraordinary, someone I cherished—worshipped, even—when I was a teenager. To me and my friends, she was a mentor in the highest sense, fostering the best in us, coaxing us to be all we could be. Many times, she saw in me much more potential than I could see in myself. And in the seeing, she was instrumental in nurturing the beginnings of my self-worth. I've recently come to value her role in my life even more, juxtaposing her wholesome, sincere encouragement with that of a sick mind that used my need for love and affirmation to satisfy perverse sexual needs.

I've often thought of the incredible woman I'm soon to see for the first time in more than thirty years. Every time she came to mind, gratitude for her part in my life urged me to thank her, yet I never made contact.

After I learned that she was living in Florida, and before leaving for West Palm Beach, I contacted her by phone to make arrangements to spend time together. Besides wanting to open up to her, I felt a sense of urgency about making certain I'd have the opportunity to thank her face to face. I figured she was approaching her eightieth birthday and there might not be another chance.

When we spoke on the phone, we shared in brief some highlights. For my part, I told her I was writing a book about my healing from Lyme disease as well as mental illness. And I revealed the story of my tragic adolescence that would be included.

Her reactions to my sexual abuse were puzzling.

She was a close friend of the woman who exploited me, so I thought perhaps she knew of her friend's penchant for same sex-relationships, and about ours, but she didn't. Yet my story didn't seem to shock her. In fact, her reaction was pulseless, a response I didn't question at the time.

We ended our conversation by planning to meet for lunch in

Clewiston—a halfway point between West Palm Beach and her West Coast residence.

Several days later, she called to issue an ardent admonishment: "When you said you're writing a book, you meant you're writing in a journal that you're planning to keep hidden and locked—for your eyes only—right?"

After first giving my reasons for being open, I made certain she understood that I intend to reveal the details of my past while writing *The Gift of the Circle*, that my book is not a journal, and that I don't intend to identify the name of her friend. Then we said goodbye, respectful of each other's unchanged positions, and still planning to have lunch in Clewiston.

I'm routinely early for appointments because I hate the feelings that tie me in knots when I'm late. When I arrive in Clewiston, first I find what I think is the Clewiston Inn, park my car, and walk inside to reassure myself that I'm in the right place. Suddenly, while standing in the lobby, an overwhelming desire to sleep sucks me into a vortex of oblivion.

This feels like Lyme fatigue.

Please, no. Not now.

Wait a minute.

I can't be relapsing. I don't have the other symptoms.

I'm trying to escape my feelings.

I'm grateful to hear the voice of The Watcher:

Breathe.

You've wanted this visit to happen for a long time.

I know you're feeling vulnerable, like you're a teenager again.

You're hoping your hero of the past will still see all she saw in you years ago before she knew everything.

Remember, her opinions of you will carry only the weight you attach to them.

Pay attention to what you think of yourself.

You're a woman in your own right—not a kid.

Keep breathing.

Keep your focus on the reasons you're opening up.

And remember, you've come here to express your gratitude, to pay homage to someone who planted the seeds of self-worth in your soul. Focus on that.

I'll be right here if you need me . . .

———

Before my long-ago hero arrived at the Clewiston Inn, I was dealing with the fear of facing her with my now transparent past disclosed. Now that I'm back in Georgia, writing and thinking about the last part of the conversation I had at the Clewiston Inn, my feelings are much different.

Once I overcame the pull of sleep that was trying to suck me into the maw of avoidance, I wondered if I'd recognize my once-revered model.

I did, the second she stepped into the lobby: a wrinkled version of her former self, just like me. We hugged in greeting, like old times.

After we selected food from a buffet, we spent a leisurely lunch sharing in depth about our lives and those important to us.

As with everyone I know, she'd had her share of painful—even tragic—emotional challenges and stellar achievements.

While we were talking about ourselves, I became aware that I no longer felt like a kid. I'd relaxed, using my breath to ground me in the present. To feel like the woman I had become. The fact that my companion seemed happy to be with me also helped. When the time seemed right, I thanked her in simple terms for the significant contributions she'd made to my life.

Her reaction disappointed me. She didn't seem to understand the profound nature of my gratitude. Maybe my words weren't adequate. Maybe I misread her response. Or maybe she was distracted by her own thoughts.

When we were nearing the end of our time together, she once again admonished me to keep silent about her deceased friend's part in my life, voicing concern for living family members and the potential for emotional pain they might feel at learning someone they may have loved was a sexual predator.

I didn't tell my erstwhile hero—again—my reasons for telling the truth of my past, nor that I don't intend to reveal her friend's identity. I didn't ask how she would have felt if her friend had taken advantage of her own daughter. And I didn't tell her how my life has been affected, the very reason sexual exploitation of a minor is, indeed, a criminal offense.

What was she thinking?

Maybe that I was a consenting adult at age fifteen.

Hmm, then why would she worry about her dead friend's reputation?

She's a brainy woman, well-read, with an honorary doctorate.

But odd—her priorities.

What about parents and authorities needing to know this stuff to protect children?

And what about me?

She didn't seem to care about how I was affected by her friend's "ministrations." There's something awry in her reactions—irreconcilable.

Something, I guess, I'll never figure out . . .

Although I was piqued by remembering what I think was a misguided admonition, I was grateful we'd met; we parted amiably enough, but I was left with questions and unsettling feelings as a result of her suffocating counsel.

————

Usually, when I think of Florida, I don't think of the still troubling luncheon at the Clewiston Inn, and I don't think of a land mass. Instead, I think of water.

I've spent the majority of my leisure time either swimming, sailing, or canoeing—even living *on* Florida's waters for five years, either in a houseboat or sailboat.

Perhaps there's no wonder the recent counsel I received during that lunch has a way of taking me back to the days when I was a mariner at the helm, tacking against the wind . . .

I've owned or co-owned a wide variety of sailboats. Being at the helm of each one taught me practical lessons—wrapped in symbolism—about taking charge of reaching a destination while tacking against ever-changing wind. Made in New York, my first sailing craft was a thirteen-foot aluminum canoe outfitted with a short aluminum mast, a lateen-rigged, blue-and-white-striped mainsail, and a sideboard to counteract side-slipping. She took me exploring on the rivers and lakes of Florida's St. Johns River. In fact, she stayed tied to the side of my houseboat, close at hand for adventurous excursions.

Something a bit more complicated, a twenty-one-foot English-made, fiberglass longboat, entered my life in the mid-1970s when I lived on Stock Island in a trailer with my second husband. Our co-owned longboat was a yawl, outfitted with oak masts, three lateen-rigged, tanbark sails, and a centerboard to help keep her on course. She was a perfect boat for sailing to outlying islands off the Keys, where we beached her to snorkel.

Then there was *Trivet*.

Trivet was a vintage, thirty-foot deep-water sloop, built in Solomons, Maryland, in 1935, also purchased in the mid-1970s and co-owned with my second husband. She was all wood and brass. Her spruce mast reached forty-two feet into the sky to support a tanbark mainsail. With her tons of lead in the keel to keep her balanced under sail and on course, she drew eight feet of water. When I took my turn at her helm, one hand on the smooth, varnished tiller, the other grasping the mainsail sheet, I tacked back and forth against the wind, keeping *Trivet* on a predetermined compass course, often referring to nautical charts close at hand. I at once felt her power under sail, and her vulnerability; she wasn't designed for navigating shallow waters. Sailing her off course could have resulted in grounding—or worse.

―――

Remembering my sailing days, The Watcher takes the helm,

teaching me about myself, balancing my emotions—keeping me steady while I capture or spill wind to keep opening and writing *The Gift of the Circle*:

Now that you've written about that conversation at the Clewiston Inn, I see that you're angry.

No. I'm pissed.

Angry. No need for drama.

Asking you to keep silent wasn't the worst response you could have had. Tame, as a matter of fact.

At your own admission, you chose not to elaborate on your reasons for opening up to your one-time hero.

No one can possibly know everything another person has learned from personal experience.

In fact, you may have missed an opportunity to educate someone with your heart who has the capacity to understand more than most.

However, even if you'd tried, that may not have changed a thing.

You can't go back to find out.

Continue to honor the woman who counseled silence and forgive her for what you see as a shortfall.

You've acknowledged your anger.

Let go, now, of feelings that aren't working in your favor.

Truth sometimes carries the potential to hurt others, even though there's no malice intended. And emotional pain is part of authenticity in relationships. With this discomfort comes the opportunity to learn from experience, whether one is the storyteller or the listener. And revelation is flush with the invitation to forgive and extend compassion, family members of a sexual predator notwithstanding.

Anger at the admonishment to keep quiet at first irked me, becoming a fiery underpinning for continuing to be transparent.

In the end, The Watcher, still commanding the helm, counsels from the heart of wisdom:

You've considered the consequences of opening up—and for keeping secrets. Reviewed research. Assessed your own experiences. Charted your course.

Keep your hand on the tiller. Continue to take charge of your destiny. Expect changes. Expect challenges.

The ever-changing wind won't always be at your back.

Trust the process you've chosen for yourself, even when wind tries to blow you off course.

Your intentions and your breathwork will continue to function like a deep-water keel to balance you.

While opinions from others are sometimes worth considering, in the end you have to come to your own conclusions about matters important to you.

Humans can, indeed, have radical differences of opinion when considering the same issue.

Approval or disapproval of others can't be your rudder.

Using the right timing, capture wind that propels you forward; spill the wind you don't need.

Keep grasping the tiller and mainsail sheet—your keel in deep water.

Hold fast to your destiny. Stay on course—compassion and integrity your compass.

You've spent a lot of time and effort learning to write. And learning to balance your emotions when you've revisited—again and again—painful experiences.

You're writing The Gift of the Circle *to continue your own healing.*

And don't forget what you read in You Can Beat the Odds: *Like you, adults who suffered abuse or neglect as children are 150 percent more likely to develop serious illness than others. And that's only the beginning—for those who suffered from multiple types of childhood trauma, the risk of disease escalates exponentientially.*[1]

Spreading the word about those powerful research outcomes is reason enough to do what you're doing.

There's more, though.

Informing parents, authorities, and those organizations offering youth groups is critical. Female sexual predators, wearing the mask of decency, do, indeed, exist. They abide in all economic levels of communities; they are masters of deceit, and the effects of their abuse are life-shattering—and life-threatening.[2]

You're ringing the alarm to protect innocent children!

You're now well on your way to sustained mental and physical health. Although everyone's past and healing journey will be unique, you're here to say, with undeniable authenticity, healing—and learning—from unimaginable insults to body and mind, no matter what they are, is possible.

Wildflowers do, indeed, grow, from seeds in the dirt.

MOMMA. MOM. MOTHER. ETHEL MARTIN GRAHAM. IN MEMORIAM.

Golden rays of sun speak of mist and early dawn.

In the glow of a new day, there stands my mother, regal in a velvet robe of muted rose.

I go to her.

With tenderness, I drape a garland of fresh mint leaves around her neck, scenting the Aire with my newfound love for her.

Mom, I wish you were as close as you seem.

Feeling you nearby makes me want to cry. I've missed you more than you could imagine.

Does that sound strange, coming from me?

My feelings about you have changed so much.

Before I tell you anything else, I know you'd want to know about "your two girls"—Janet and me.

We're both doing fine!

I'm completely well now. Janet can tell you about her life herself. She's happier than ever.

Mom, you and I haven't connected in years. On April 25, 2005, when we last spoke, I was critically ill with Lyme disease, being dosed with voluminous quantities of antibiotics through a port in my chest.

The day you died, I was walking to the shower in the afternoon, wrapped in a towel. You called then—not like you. Normally you waited until after dinner, so I didn't expect to hear your voice when I picked up the phone. You were bursting with enthusiasm about your day—bridge in the morning, lunch with your friends. Still vibrant and healthy at age ninety-three.

You didn't call to tell me about your day, though. You called for reasons you may not have understood completely: "Keep fighting. Don't give up, Carolyn."

"I won't, Momma," was the best I could say, my voice flat with depression. We said goodbye, acknowledging that we'd talk that evening.

Later, Janet and I were sitting in her family room watching TV, waiting for your usual call.

When I answered the phone, sometime after five, I expected to hear your voice.

I didn't.

You were gone, Momma.

Gone.

Even though the nurse from the continuing care village where you lived told me you'd died without a struggle, my feelings knotted into a mess of grief-darkened gratitude. I was grateful you didn't suffer, but I couldn't believe I'd never see you again. Yet nothing I felt then came close to the unspeakable grief I felt the year before you died—the day before I left for Georgia.

Rebecca—you remember my friend Rebecca. She drove me to your apartment that day because I was too sick to drive myself.

That was only part of the story.

I wanted her with me because I couldn't bear to be by myself saying goodbye to you. Even though I'd told you and everyone else I'd be staying with Janet for just a short while, I knew in my gut that wasn't true.

Do you remember our last moments together?

I'll never forget them.

Rebecca took pictures of the two of us. I could barely bend my lips into a smile.

Even all these years later, looking at those pictures makes my heart ache. In those reflections of trauma, I look as sick as I was—emaciated. Your eyes seem to speak of heart-wrenching concern for your sick child.

After Rebecca took pictures, she and I walked behind you in your motorized chair, down the hallway outside your apartment to the double doors leading to the sidewalk.

You pushed the button on the wall to open them.

I can still see you now, Mom, sitting on the sidewalk, your snow-white hair and pearl earrings framing your face, still rosy-cheeked and pretty even at your age. Teal and lavender flowers on your blouse and matching teal pants spoke of the pride you took in caring for yourself.

Unable to avoid leaving, I leaned over and wrapped my arms around you, snuggling your cheek. You reached up with one of your hands to grasp my forearm—the touch of warmth and caring so natural to you.

When I stood up to turn away, lumps of grief filled my throat. I choked them down, miming bravery I didn't feel.

You didn't cry. Neither did I. That was so unlike both of us.

Were you trying to make my leaving as easy as possible for me?

That's what I was trying to do for you.

After Rebecca and I got in her car, she backed out of the parking space and spun the car around, facing the exit to the parking lot.

Slowly, her car moved forward, toward what I saw as the bleak death-maw of my future.

As the car passed by where you were sitting, we waved goodbye.

Then I turned my head away from you, only to turn back and wave to you one last time.

When you were out of sight, the feelings I'd shoved down my throat erupted.

Doubling over, I vomited heaving emotions. A primal wail of grief signaled what I sensed was the death of our time together.

My relationship with you was sometimes troublesome, at least from my point of view, so I didn't understand why leaving you made me feel so wretched.

Sometimes I wish I knew how you really felt about me—not just that day when we said goodbye, but at other times in my life.

When I got divorced—twice.

When I had ten cats.

Did you think I'd lied to you about farting—my word, certainly not yours—when you confronted me about the overwhelming stench you smelled in the department store that day we were shopping for stockings?

What about the time I told you I was going to a nudist colony?

And when I received my diploma for my master's degree?

What did you think of me when I was struggling to survive after Lyme shattered my life?

I won't presume to know any of your feelings; now I can't find out.

So this will just have to be a one-sided event—something we both have to accept.

Let me start by telling you something I remember from years ago. Something that's puzzled me throughout my life.

When I was in kindergarten, each of us children made a plaster-of-Paris handprint as a gift to our mothers for Mother's Day. I painted mine pink.

Only I didn't give my tiny handprint to you.

Instead, when I got home, I walked upstairs and gave my Mother's Day love gift to the nurse living above us.

Did that hurt your feelings?

Mine would have been hurt if I'd been in your shoes.

You know, Mom, for decades I've often wondered why at such a young age I turned away from you like that—why I didn't like you.

Does that surprise you?

The truth is, you were likeable. Your life was rich with long-standing friendships.

I never could figure out why I didn't like you too.

Until now.

Before I go into that, there's something I need you to tell you that might not seem related. I'm sorry to be so abrupt, but I need to get something off my mind so what I say later will make sense.

I was sexually exploited when I was in high school.

Did you suspect then that something untoward was happening between me and my youth group leader?

You told me more than once how masculine she looked—an observation that felt loaded. Your eyes told me you felt like you were on to something.

I could go on and on about that; maybe someday I will, but I don't want to get stalled right now.

Let me just say, I've spent lots of time in therapy healing from the ill effects of my sex offender's misguided attention. And in preparing to write and speak about the heinous effects, I found a piece of revolutionary information that led me to understand why I distanced myself from you— why I couldn't like you, not just that I didn't.

Before I read to you the quote written by abuse experts, I've got one more thing to say.

Dad was abusive. He was sometimes Father, mostly Dad—never safe enough to be Daddy.

When I was just a small child, after Dad beat me with a belt or razor strap for making a simple mistake, I often sought solace in your arms. While holding me close, you tried to console me: "Your father loves you."

Love isn't found in misdirected rage. Never!

A few years before Dad died, you confided to me and Janet that you were afraid he was going to kill you. Until then, you wouldn't acknowledge his violent streak. And you wouldn't own up to the fact that his physical and verbal assaults on me and Janet were destructive.

For once, you won't argue about that.

When Janet and I were little, Dad was the all-powerful physical and verbal aggressor. You were the weak one—too afraid of his reprisals to protect yourself or us. The only way you could get back at him was by using passive-aggressive tactics; behind his back, you accused him of being insane. In front of us kids, you scolded him for impropriety as if he were your naughty child.

Now that I've had my say about that, I'm ready to read.

This passage is what compelled me to reach out to you: "The abused child can identify with either the aggressive, powerful perpetrator or the weak, passive, but usually equally angry, partner. Living in a home with continual passive and active rage, the child is like a sponge, absorbing the high levels of resentment. The child will tend to identify with the powerful aggressor, as if to say, 'I'll become like him . . . so no one can ever hurt me again.' In addition, the child tends to rebel against internalization of the weak parent, who is despised for not protecting the child."[1]

When I was a little girl, I identified with Dad because I saw him as a slave owner. That slave was you.

In my child's mind, I thought becoming like him was the way to survive. The way to protect myself from harm—the best way I knew.

If Dad loved you, I never saw that. He treated you as if you were stupid—and so did I. He couldn't be emotionally close to you. I patterned myself after him in my own way—rebelling against you, refusing to be drawn into your love for me.

I felt that if I let you love me, you'd rub off on me and I'd become like you—a slave to incessant abuse. If I let you in, I'd never escape from the part of me that's like you—the part that struggles with the death grip of powerlessness.

I can fix what I can understand.

After I read that passage I just shared with you, I knew in an instant that, from the time I was a young child, I'd barricaded my heart against the love you extended to me.

I understood why I could never see the good in you that others were drawn to.

I don't blame you or Dad for anything that went on in our home. You did the best you could; so did he.

No, that's not a trite statement. Given the effects of your own past at work every time you acted, you did the best you could.

That said, Mom, I'm still on a journey of forgiving Dad. Suspecting that someone brutalized him when he was a little boy helps.

I don't have to struggle to forgive you. I do have difficulty forgiving myself for withholding the love and respect you so deserved. So, I guess I'll have to work on accepting that I did the best I could, just like you and Dad did.

The feelings that erupted in a wail of grief that day we said goodbye outside your apartment in 2005 spoke of my love for you, which was more than I could ever have imagined. Now I understand why my grief was overpowering. Also, ever since I've figured out that I mimicked Dad's feelings about you until the day you died, the wall of fear and resentment I'd built between us has evaporated. I see how wonderful you were in so many ways. I see you like others saw you.

You were at the top end of bright, Mom.

Do you think Dad resented you because you had a college degree and he didn't?

Books were a huge part of your leisure time—autobiographies, memoirs, and other nonfiction works. If my memory serves me, you seldom read fiction. You subscribed to the New Yorker *until the day you died, voracious reader that you were.*

Being smart is minor unless someone thinks you're stupid. And you were the most resilient person I've ever met, even-tempered beyond belief.

Fear sometimes took you to out-of-control places, though. I'm like that too. Anxiety can run rampant in me. When I see that part of you in me, I understand now how you felt and wish I hadn't been so critical of you when unreasonable fear drove you to the point of despair.

Yes, most of the time, you were kind and loving—and generous.

Because you cared about leaving "your girls" some of your assets, I was able to get well. My healing from Lyme disease and emotional turmoil was expensive. Insurance wouldn't pay for the treatments that were instrumental in my recovery.

In the end, your legacy of generosity, expressed by leaving your assets to me and Janet, was the source for my healing.

I could keep going, Mom. The list is endless now that I've released the need to keep you out of my heart.

I wish I could have seen how wonderful you were before you died. I'd give anything to get one of your big hugs right now. You never held back when you wrapped me in your arms to hold me close.

Even though I can't have exactly what I want, I can feel your presence and see your goodness in other ways. When I look into the mirror, your kind smile is my own. When I find your humor in the way I get tickled at a simple irony, your easy, robust laughter rings the air.

Best of all, Mom, I get to feel something much like your ample hug when Janet wraps me in her arms. I see your love for me reflected in her eyes.

So, Mom, I sense the time has come for us to say goodbye.

I guess you feel like that too, because I feel your presence wafting in the mist now.

Yet the scent of mint—signaling a new understanding between us—lingers in the Aire.

And my heart is warm with a luminescent glow, forgiveness for your errant child.

I hope you're happy wherever you are, Mom.

You deserve to be.

And if I could, I'd give you a bouquet of wildflowers and hold your hand.

I love you, Momma.

AFFIRMING
THE STRANGER

The time will come
when, with elation
you will greet yourself arriving
at your own door, in your own mirror
and each will smile at the other's welcome . . .

—Derek Walcott

Who am I now?

Disease filched my identity.

Maybe.

Profession, house in the woods, income . . .

Was that really me?

I thought so—a stranger to my intricate, talented self, unaware of my urge to bloom.

When I couldn't experience my best—flexible and unrestricted by boundaries of circumstance—others mirrored my nature, reflecting what they saw in me.

Quite literally, those who loved me bestowed healing, voiced in the form of authentic affirmations.

Affirmations.

When they are sincere, they vibrate with the unmistakable energy of truth. They speak the language of well-being, reflecting the majesty of who we are—who I am.

Spoken in the form of well-timed praise, affirmations act as positive reinforcements endowed with the potential to shape behavior.

Applause, an especially potent type of affirmation, inspires the body and mind to create conditions ripe for miracles.

When I applauded my immune system in front of a mirror, clapping and cheering my phagocytes for their stellar performance, all my cells responded, transforming my body's chemistry and nudging my immune system into peak performance.[2, 3]

A few times, after sharing my journey of recovery with large audiences, I was stunned by resounding, standing ovations. Until then, I'd never been affirmed with that kind of unified, energetic empathy.

Each time an applauding audience rose to stand, I cried. Nothing I'd experienced in the way of tributes had ever moved me so, and I wondered why.

Probably because the responses touch me in a deep, lonely place—one that sometimes felt no one could possibly understand my suffering.

These rounds of applause connected me to the empathy of others like nothing else had. Their heartfelt responses told of their own stories that connected us, speaking in the language of compassion for my own. I wished everyone could experience such an affirmation, for I believe all people have a story of survival worthy of one.

When I was struggling to find my way home to well-being—someone eager to find a new way to be—such affirmations revealed a pathway out of self-hatred, shame, and a feeling of worthlessness, dark places bereft of solace.

Attempting to reconstruct my broken life when I was with my therapist, Brenda, I shared pictures and stories from my past. At times, her responses astounded me. I continue to cherish the time she exclaimed, "You're a Renaissance woman!" On rare occasions, I'd secretly thought so myself, yet I'd never have given voice to my thoughts.

For someone as renowned as my therapist to do just that, and to persistently affirm me in other ways, was, quite literally, life-giving—trailheads from which to start my many-faceted journey toward wholeness.

Nevertheless, I still have trouble sharing such tributes to me when telling my story. Oppressive mores haunt me, telling me in rattle-brained voices that I shouldn't share the joy I've felt when I've been honored.

Fie on mores that make no sense.

———

When I began writing *The Gift of the Circle*, I never imagined the profound effects sharing my work would have on my healing process.

Working in solitude was the beginning. Sharing what I'd written in public followed. Then came the pinnacle of my healing experience as a writer—the responses.

Jedwin's were monumental. More than once his thumbs-up for my courage emboldened me to continue telling my truth in spite of fear. To disgorge the poison of secrets.

"I am speechless. Praising your courage merely isn't strong enough—you have the guts of a marine, which is something I seldom say. This is beautifully written—priceless," he wrote in red at the end of "A Reunion."

Through Jedwin's reflections, I unwrap who I am and say hello to myself. I salute my grit.

Semper Fi, Jedwin.

On a scientific note, related to comments about mirroring in *The Neuroscience of Human Relationships*, by Louis Cozolino: while I learned new ways to think about myself, mirroring thoughts of others, I began creating virgin neurological pathways in my brain.[4]

As I practiced saluting my grit and other positive attributes that others affirmed, I often acknowledged Norman Doidge's comment in The Brain That Changes Itself, solidifying my understanding of the biology I'm manifesting: "The brain that wires together, fires together. The brain that wires apart, fires apart."[5]

So, I have focused more on acknowledging the positive aspects of myself, strengthening new neurological pathways. And, because I have refused to nourish thoughts that are destructive, their unused thought patterns—neurological pathways—are gradually disappearing.

I'm shaping a new reality for myself. Changing my brain, even.

I've got the best seat in the house—attending the play I create.

What's said to me matters.

What's said to anyone matters.

More than I'd realized.

———

When I left Florida to live with my sister in Georgia, I said agonizing, tearful goodbyes to friends who'd been part of my life for decades. They'd enriched me with their unique, authentic, and sometimes mischievous personalities, as well as their ever-present love.

With Lyme disease sucking my energy and anxiety tormenting me, I wasn't motivated to reach out to make new friends. At the tiniest effort to extend myself—to go beyond the constricted, agoraphobic boundaries anxiety prescribed—fear spiked, nailing me to my terror. Loneliness shriveled my world, adding to my emotional agony.

When I was well enough to recreate my life, making friends was more important than ever before. I found that shadows enhance beauty. And the loss of something precious magnifies the value. While making new friends and staying in touch with my friends of many decades, I cherish them all the more, their worth made supreme by the shadows of my past.

———

One evening in 2013, as I prepared to read aloud a revised version of "Freedom's Child"—a chapter I hadn't shared in two years—shallow breathing and icy-cold hands told of the fear knotting my guts. Making up the majority of those attending Jedwin's workshop were some of my newfound, female friends.

Can I do this?

I have to.

No stopping now.

My new friends will soon know I've been sexually stimulated by other women.

Will they now think my affection toward them has ulterior motives?

Will they still be comfortable with my hugs?

Will they still like me?

Breaking through the wall of fear, I read. Although I swallowed near-choking emotions while tears were running down my cheeks, especially near the end of the chapter, I finished reading "Freedom's Child." After a brief pause to catch my breath, I raised my eyes to look across the table. Two of the friends I was afraid of losing met my gaze. Before I could look further, they were on their feet, walking around the table, arms outstretched. Their hugs took me into their still-present love, dissolving my worries.

As if that weren't enough, one of them sent me an email at 3:55 a.m.: *Just a quick note to tell you how touched I was to be a part of your inner circle at the writing group last night as you shared your story of innocence lost. You are one of the bravest and most generous people I know. Your capacity for caring for others—even those who've hurt you—is inspirational. I know your journey will help others who have been through terrible things. Keep writing. Keep sharing! Your story is important. I found a quote from* Let's Take the Long Way Home *by Gail Caldwell that I thought would move you: "I know now that we never get over great losses; we absorb them, and they carve us into different, often kinder, creatures."*

Early in my journey as a writer, healing in ways I couldn't have imagined, a male kindred spirit affectionately known to me as the Bent Rim emailed me, blessing me beyond measure:

Yo Carolyn,

I apologize I didn't get a chance to chime in much the other day in class because I was starting to lose my voice.

But a few things:

I have a hard time reconciling where you were once with where you are now and that's a huge fucking compliment. In addition, this may sound shallow and trivial, but by your stepping up, baring your soul, and sharing your travails and challenges, you make writing about my own journey ten times easier.

I'm glad you've chosen life and are among the living. You are an inspiration.

Your buddy and President of the Bent Rim Association.

———

Choosing life.

That is what I did that one unforgettable day sitting at a red light, eyeing a bottle of pills, considering my options . . .

Thinking tentatively, *Maybe there's a better way to work with anxiety and other challenges. Maybe killing myself isn't necessary. Maybe I can find another way out of my suffering.*

And so I did with the direction of Divine Timing and Grace. With Earth Angels by my side.

And so I did.

While Jedwin's been the foremost male influence on my healing through writing, Rosemary Daniell has been his female counterpart.

Sometimes I get stuck, feeling tired of disciplining myself to write. Sometimes I balk at the idea of dealing with painful emotions. Sometimes I forget why I started to write my legacy.

When I'm with Rosemary, I see a glimmer of myself. As I feel the power of her femininity, I sense my own. When she acknowledges feeling a "thrill in the truth," I know she understands why I intend to be wide open.

More than that, Rosemary inspires me to reveal my inner world unencumbered by unnecessary filters.

Occasionally, I scheduled an appointment with Rosemary, sending her portions of my manuscript for editing weeks ahead of our planned time together.

On one of those occasions, she attached a note at the end of my work written with purple ink on bright-pink paper. Her inspirational words, kept visible on a bulletin board beside my desk, encourage me when I struggle to write: "Carolyn, reading this brought tears into my eyes more than once! I believe this book will be a memoir/spiritual guide that will help many, many people."

And so I live.

And so I write.

And so I learn to value myself, mirroring who I am to the stranger who for so long yearned to know herself as others do.

IN THE RAW—
A SERIAL PRACTICUM

The Squeebs.
That's what grips my body when terror strikes.
I splatter yesterday's eats all over my tail feathers
and other indiscriminate places.

Once, on a day when snow covered the ground,
I glanced down from my perch in a tree,
my wee tiny eyes drawn to a long, dark form
lying flat against the white-covered earth.
A snake!

The Squeebs attacked.
I sounded an alarm.
Chirp! Chirp! Chirp!
Nearby birds paid no attention.
My wee tiny brain wondered why.
Confused, I looked once again at the form in the snow.
Then, I understood why my feathered friends weren't afraid, too.

What I feared was a snake
was merely a stick darkened by rot.

Silly bird, me.
I wonder,
do I create my own reality?

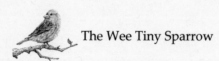

The Wee Tiny Sparrow

EPISODE ONE

My swollen brains are being squeezed into painful confinement by an insidious, unrelenting pressure. Irritated, throbbing, they threaten to burst from my skull. Words hide, held hostage in hot, foggy gray matter, making the formation of thoughts a challenge. Writing chapters for *The Gift of the Circle* is impossible.

I feel like I'm dragging an anchor that's getting weightier by the day. A stagnant, dense fatigue and the sorrow of remembered vitality pull me into my bed for too many hours. I'm unable to refresh myself with sleep.

I've stopped eating raw vegetables and fruits because they torture my stomach—like I've swallowed battery acid. Although there's no visible sign of irritation, I feel like someone is piercing my tongue with hot needles.

While I'm running errands I can't park my car evenly between lines no matter how hard I try. A perverse dilemma, as is the spilling of a full cup of hot coffee all over a checkout counter. Too often, I'm dropping things at inopportune moments. Suppressed fear and intestinal inflammation explodes undigested food into the toilet and haphazard places, with contempt for modesty.

At the beginning of the summer of 2012, after witnessing my body's escalating torment for several weeks, I break through the steely armor of denial and finally admit I'm sick again. Neurological Lyme disease is hammering me into a pulpy mess of dysfunction and despair.

I've been taking an antidepressant to keep anxiety within normal limits. For times when I've needed something stronger, I've supplemented my prescription drug with music and exercise, changing my body's chemistry and reversing my emotions in short order.

But, in the face of Lyme, none of that quells my stampeding terror. I'm certain I'll be sucked deep into the black maw of catastrophe.

Disease will ravage my life—again—and steal my soul.

Disability will strike me useless.

My loft. I'll lose my loft—be dependent on others just like before.
I can't do this.
I can't!

Rabid with worry, I twist any hope for wide thinking into a tangled mass of thorns and ice, silencing the voice of The Watcher.

All my hard-won calm using diaphragmatic breathing, all the skills I've honed at practicing behavior medicine, and my belief that I have the intrinsic resources to heal myself go down the toilet with my undigested food.

In my logic-weakened state, I make an illogical and potentially destructive decision.

I must be hospitalized.
I must.
Now!

Pacing and sweating, I call to ask for a bed at the psychiatric hospital where, a few years before, I was treated for anxiety and depression with electroconvulsive shock therapy.

And assuredly will be again, if I'm admitted.

Even so, from my deranged perspective, shock treatments seem like a walk in the park compared to the misery of screeching panic.

And certainly better than using suicide to end my agony.

The unfortunate reality, for me, is that agreeing to shock treatments again would be like drying dishes with a wet, filthy rag. Beyond pointless. They didn't stop my habitual, destructive thought patterns in the past. They won't now, yet I'm out of touch with pragmatism.

Although muted for now, The Watcher observes, nonetheless, while I continue to stoke my terror with the wailing winds of remembered tragedy, exacerbating Lyme symptoms—compromising my immune system. Yet, unknowingly, I wear the armor of Divine Protection. After asking for a hospital bed, I hear unbelievable words: "There are no beds available in the psychiatric unit and won't be for at least a week."

Wondering how I can survive that long, I email my therapist

to let her know what's going on, something I should have done long before now. Then I call my sister, Janet, to tell her.

My sister's response is insightful. Because she knows I've refused to take benzodiazepines since my challenging withdrawal from them several years ago, she treads with caution when she speaks: "Will you take a benzo of mine if I bring one to you?"

"Yes. Yes, maybe that will help me."

Merely twenty minutes after taking the Ativan, I'm sitting on my oh-so-comfortable living room couch, leaning against the squishy corduroy back, my left arm draped across the top, the other resting on a soft pillow at my side—cocooned in physical comfort and emotional ease.

In that brief period of time, using a tiny pill, my body's chemistry is transformed. Anxiety disappears like a raging, dark cloud that empties rain into the earth.

Janet and I marvel at how quickly the Ativan changed my body's chemistry and my world—and how much my panic attack mimicked those of our mother's.

After I say goodbye to my sister at the door to my loft, I email my therapist to tell her what's just happened—to let her know I'm doing better. Returning to my couch, I settle again into squishy comfort, now receptive to The Watcher's sage words:

You just learned a mighty lesson. Right?

Don't be hard on yourself, though.

Lyme is scary business for you. Your reaction is completely under-standable. Common, even, for someone who's experienced the trauma of chronic illness.

Even so, learning from what happened is important. Acknowledge that you could have made an unfortunate decision when you were in a froth.

And remember that you've healed yourself before.

You can do so again.

Now, get going, sister!

And so I do.

For a few weeks, even after using music, exercise, and some other mind-body medicine strategies to calm myself, I often stay stuck in a state of heightened alert, like a soldier who believes an unseen sniper with a cocked gun lurks nearby. With the slightest twinge of a Lyme symptom, my muscles jerk into tense surveillance and I escalate into panic again.

When I tell Brenda what's happening, she introduces me to Ashok Gupta's work as a potential antidote. Intrigued and hopeful, I google him for information, discovering that he is a well-known British researcher and therapist who has developed a set of behavioral medicine strategies to help those suffering with chronic fatigue syndrome/myalgic encephalomyelitis and fibromyalgia. Intrigued, I purchase his interactive DVDs.[1] When engaging with their content, I substitute the word "Lyme" when he refers to other conditions, refashioning his videos into powerful healing resources tailored to my situation. With diligent use of Dr. Gupta's methods I learn to relax my vigilance and quickly subdue my anxiety, a monumental achievement!

Using Ashok Gupta's strategies and the same behavior medicine techniques I activated two years before, along with the limited use of homeopathies, I'm able to stabilize my mind and body within a few weeks, optimizing my immune system.

As a result, I rebound with surprising speed.

———

EPISODE TWO

Fall colors and cool breezes herald the beginning of a day perfect for hiking with an old friend. My brisk pace to my car reflects excitement about the forthcoming adventure as I begin the hour-long drive to her home.

Along the way, miles of interstate slip by, sheathed by sixteen-wheelers, white lines, and billboards. Music, radiating with the light of an angel's heart, fills my car, and gratitude spills from my eyes. Wonder at my wellness humbles me.

Once again, all is well.
Once again I'm free.

Free to play in the woods with a cherished companion.

When I arrive at my friend's home, we chat for a few moments in her driveway, then I stow my gear in the back seat of her car. Soon, we're on the way to a state park with her at the wheel.

After arriving and parking, we get out of the car and gaze at a vibrant blue sky decorated with a rust-toned ombré of fall leaves. From a distance, a river bounding down a rocky gorge calls out, inviting us to spend time nearby—to relish the day and our time together. We are both filled with anticipation, eager to yield to the pleasures so naturally extended to us.

As my enthusiasm builds, I'm unaware that things are about to take an abrupt turn. I'm clueless that my friend is about to teach me a profound lesson, becoming like a renowned expert, summarizing a textbook chapter using live media. I don't suspect my friend will soon surprise me, bestowing me with a gift: a sequel to Episode One of my unintentional practicum that will soon bring about the downfall of anxiety's tyranny in my life.

Unsuspecting, I don gear from the back seat of the car while my friend opens the trunk. She lays her purse and keys on the trunk bed, then retrieves a water bottle and a few other items. When I join her at the back of the car, I too place my purse near hers.

In a split second, our plans shatter into broken expectations: using her right arm, my friend slams the trunk door closed.

"My keys. My keys are locked in the trunk," my friend cries, while wringing her hands. Repeatedly, she begs for deliverance. Her feet jerk up and down as if she's standing with raw, bare feet on the fiery coals of hell.

The Watcher arrives in an instant, observing with fascination— a judgment-free observation.

This experience is amazing. You're seeing a mirror image of yourself—your panic that silenced my wisdom just months ago.

Although the circumstances are different, the script's the same.

Your friend has become a marionette, her power given over to the loudmouthed, knee-jerking despot: unnecessary fear.

You know the feeling all too well!

Certain I will ease my friend's misery, I offer a solution that seems simple: "I have roadside service. We'll call for a locksmith. I've had to do that more than once. The worst that can happen is a broken window."

At that, she calms a little. Encouraged by seeing her feelings tempered and knowing there'll be at least an hour's wait for a locksmith, I suggest we hike first, then call for help after we're through.

That idea is a colossal flop. My friend insists on calling for help *now*.

Because both of our cell phones are locked in the trunk, we go to the state park office, where I call for a locksmith as my friend breathes down my neck, holding on to her hands, barely able to restrain herself from grabbing the phone.

Afterward, we return to the car for a long wait. My friend is too stirred up to sit on the curb and chat, so we pace around the parking lot until the locksmith finally arrives. Then, using a specialized tool, he snakes into the car through the top of the driver's side window. He unlocks the door, presses a latch, and opens the trunk—within minutes.

Piece of cake!

———

EPISODE THREE

I gaze upward through a delicate mesh of lime-green leaves, noticing dusk garnishing an unblemished blue sky. Cooling breezes whisper a tentative farewell to another spring day.

With affection, I glance down at my dog Willow as we reach the exit to the trail where we've been hiking for a few hours.

As the two of us ramble, Willow, her nose close to the earth, gobbles up the scents she tracks back and forth. Once in a while, she gets a whiff of something mysterious that grabs her attention, lifting her twitching nose in the air to search for clues of their origin.

On the other hand, I'm captivated by the sight of exquisite wildflowers blooming this time of year. They most often don shades of pink, violet, and red, inviting me to pause and peer deeply into their vivid personalities using my jeweler's loupe that hangs from a neck cord.

Now that another fascinating walk is over, hunger pangs make me eager to get home to eat. My evening ritual beckons me too: a jigsaw puzzle in progress on my tablet, meditation, then savoring a yummy book or two until I can't keep my eyes open.

When hiking with Willow, I wear a two-pocket, cotton work apron that ties around my waist. On the left side I store my cell phone and compass. In the other, I keep a roll of poop bags and training treats. Before leaving the trailhead today, I attached my car keys to the right apron string with a carabiner. When we get to my car, I reach for them to open the passenger side to let Willow in.

They're not there.

Ahhh, man.

Now what?

They must've fallen off my apron string—somewhere on the trail.

Shit fire!

Panic whipping me like a savage demon, I command Willow to heel, then spin around with her at my left, held tight to my side, and charge into the woods, retracing my steps, with impending darkness chasing us. Pummeling the earth, sweat dripping down my back, I keep Willow's leash as taut as my neck and shoulders.

After a few minutes, The Watcher somehow manages to wedge into my consciousness:

Wait a minute. You may never find your keys. Their weight could have sunken them into the leaves—hiding them forever. Anyway, at home, you have duplicates of every single one. And Janet has a spare key to your loft she won't mind bringing to you.

Someone will come get you and Willow. Staying out here, where you'll soon be in the dark, isn't safe.

With that wise counsel, I inhale deep, slow, calming breaths.

My shoulders drop, letting go of their neck grip. I loosen Willow's lead, then release her from the heel command, turn around, and walk back to the car. I sit on the curb near the passenger side with Willow lying on the grass beside me while I call a friend to ask for a ride home. I can hear the smile in her voice as she repeats the directions to our location.

While we're waiting for our ride, a woman with two dogs arrives to hike, even though dusk is settling. As she walks toward the trailhead, flashlight in hand, she tells me how pretty Willow is. I think nothing more of our encounter.

My friend arrives, surprising me all over again with her cheer, dispelling my fear that I'm being a bother. While we're on the way to her home, I call Janet to tell her what's going on and to ask her to bring me her loft key. Without hesitation, she tells me she'll come right away—a forty-five-minute drive.

Within minutes of talking to Janet, I answer a call from an unidentified number. "I found your car keys," an unfamiliar voice announces.

"Say that again."

"I found your car keys."

"You did? Cool!"

I'm so amazed I don't even ask who's calling before I blurt out another question: "Where were they?"

"Beside one of the trail-map posts."

"How did you know they were mine?"

"I remembered seeing you and your dog sitting beside the car in the parking lot and figured out what had happened."

"How did you get my phone number?"

"I used the car key I found to unlock your car, opened your glove box, and saw your name and phone number on a piece of paper.

"I have to go now, so I'm leaving your car unlocked and your keys under the floor mat on the driver's side."

"Thank you. Thank you so much!"

I'm so astounded by what's happened, I don't even get my benefactor's name.

———

After the conclusion of the third episode of my practicum, The Watcher has much to say.

First, let me thank you for this opportunity to wax eloquent—my favorite pastime, second only to watching.

To that end, I hope I've something meaningful to offer you about your probing question: "Do you make your own reality?"

That's a complicated and deep inquiry for an amateur philosopher like me.

There's been great debate among famous philosophers about the nature of reality. I'm not going to enter into that fray. My thoughts will be related to emotions as we experience them in our lives. And the premise for my considerations will be based on what I've learned from the Professor Extraordinaire—recent experience.

Before I get to the meat of the matter, let me remind you that feelings are important aspects of being human. They shape our growth, and when they're released with skill in well-timed circumstances, they facilitate healing. When they are suppressed, they have the potential to prompt disease states.

Fear is no exception.

Fear is designed to alert us to real danger. To even be life-saving.

When you misconstrue circumstances as life-threatening when they're not, you create havoc. Anxiety roils your guts, as in the condition you've named "The Squeebs" (a clever and unforgettable designation, I might add).

I'm certain you understand mistaken fears more clearly now after progressing through that amazing, well-timed practicum of yours.

Let me repeat myself for emphasis: there's nothing wrong with feeling fear when you're in real danger.

In your world, though, run-for-your-life circumstances are, in fact, rare.

Sometimes, becoming aware of what's actually occurring in a given moment takes practice. I think you realize that now. In fact, during that last episode with the Squeebs, you executed a dramatic turnaround in the way you handled something that scared you. And isn't that the way of practicums—meaningful learning in the raw?

When you were charging up the trail in a real froth about losing your keys, you suddenly became aware that something was awry with what you were doing. Then you halted yourself to do something critical to being reasonable: you took a deep breath and brought yourself into the present.

And that's when you started to distinguish between a throat-cutting death threat and one that merely felt that way.

Then you engaged a mantra of sorts, something Brenda taught you: "Pause. Breathe. Reflect. Choose."

Remember? You paused, even when you were in a volatile emotional state. You took a deep, slow breath that relaxed you, opening your ears to my voice. You were then able to hear my wise counsel.

Afterward, you made a decision that worked to your benefit. One that would have worked even if someone hadn't found your keys. Calming yourself to come into the moment to make a rational decision supported your immune system as well.

So, let's return to your original question: do you choose your own reality?

You'll never be able to choose all the circumstances that manifest in your life.

From what I can tell, though, you can choose your reactions to them, genetics notwithstanding. In fact, there's research saying you can learn to affect the outcome of genetic predispositions—even the expression of anxiety.

By now, I know you realize how different your experience with Lyme could have been if you'd learned years ago what you know now. Once in a while, I've noticed that you acknowledge sadness about that. Yet you've quickly found your way to feeling something much different.

As you've discovered, chronic illness can be both a challenge and an opportunity.

Remember what you used to think about that fiery red ring on your abdomen? The one encircling the Lyme-carrying tick bite—an ominous sign of impending doom, or so you thought? You even stashed drugs to eventually escape the maw of the tragedy you believed was a certainty.

And now?

That red ring has changed as much as you have—morphed into a circular, cloud-white scar—a mark you call "The Gift of the Circle."

You've journeyed from the maw of death to reclaim a life rich with meaning and purpose. You're writing and teaching others about our bodies' natural tendency to heal, while celebrating your own healing journey.

You and your sister have grown closer.

You found your friend Marilyn at the hand of near death.

Then there's your therapist, Brenda—she saved your life. And she's still teaching you how to fulfill her wish for you: "May you find majesty in every journey."

And best of all, because of a tick bite, you've found the love of your life—yourself.

You've learned to savor your time here. To live dancing with the heart of simple things. To appreciate the shadow of mortality that makes each moment precious.

There's so much more. Certainly, more blessings than you ever imagined possible.

Yes, in light of all that, I have to say, as far as emotions are concerned, you do, indeed, create your own reality.

OLDE

Olde birds rock!

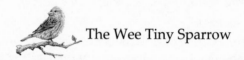 The Wee Tiny Sparrow

I'm olde—well-seasoned.

Recently, when riding through an upscale district north of Atlanta, I noticed an unusual number of designators ending in "e," adding a certain panache to the area: Bottle Shoppe, Towne Realty, Olde Roswell.

Olde plays a chord of mirth in my bones. Given my penchant for playing with words, I couldn't wait to get home to look for definitions. In the meanwhile, I decided to add an "e" to the adjective describing my "older than dirt" physical and emotional status, adding the ring of class.

In the two digital dictionaries I use, olde has one standard definition and one that's curious and rife with infinite possibilities: "Pseudoarchaic variant spelling of old," is the first.[1] The second meaning begs for mischief: "No Dictionary Results."[2]

With a bit of playful misbehavior tickling my sense of humor, I use both to describe my current seasoned status: "Olde— pseudoarchaic and without pigeonholed boundaries." I'm intentionally creating a unique pathway through my aging process now that I'm feeling so much better.

Yes, I'm experiencing some diminished non-disease-related

capabilities; however, I don't want to fall prey to the general cultural expectations underestimating and devaluing the aged. Indeed, I'm olde, hoping to stay open for opportunities to express meaning and purpose. At my best, I feel and act childlike.

I still get excited about playing with a new toy, I still like being consoled by a dog, letting Willow lick my face when my feelings are hurt, and I still like to feel someone's warm hand hold one of mine, saying silently, "I love you."

Eyes of the olde, my childlike eyes, sparkling, laughing, peering through holes in wrinkled skin.

Eyes of the olde, my childlike eyes, speak of times past when my body frolicked in the sun.

And life had no end.

Eyes of the olde, my childlike eyes, speak the wisdom of the ancients, the wisdom of the children.

Eyes of the olde, my childlike eyes, beckon a journey to the Aethers, where my soul will fly with raptor's wings on the breathless winds of infinite tomorrows.

I've noticed the eyes of the olde in others peering through wrinkled skin. Yet I don't realize mine are like theirs until my sister takes a picture of me.

More than my eyes, I'm startled by the myriad of wrinkles in the face smiling at me in the digital imprint.

I don't smile back. Rather, I rush to the bathroom mirror to examine myself.

Wrinkles carved all over my face clearly reveal my age; they've even etched folds in my earlobes.

How did this happen to me?

My journey with illness must have taken me way far away from myself.

I can't make a connection with the woman in the mirror. I don't understand why not.

Maybe this isn't really me.

There's so much more to me than wrinkles.

Maybe my heart will find peace in knowing that.

The wisdom sculpted by my meditation practice and my past,

rich with blessings and sorrows, often soothes me. Wisdom molds my compassion for others my age too.

I like that.

And I like knowing the mental energy I use for crafting creative expressions in my chair at the computer keyboard are gradually replacing the once energetic expressions of my body.

All that seems so right to me, like a meant-to-be design of the Universe. While my body is wearing down, my soul is enriched by an intuitive knowing—a natural transition.

Even though I know slowing down physically is natural, I sometimes feel sadness, like when I'm acutely aware there's no way now I can ride a fully loaded, gear-packed bicycle on a five-hundred-mile trip.

When I go into a bicycle shop for a gift certificate for someone who can do that, the unique smells of the shop make me long for a more youthful body.

Years ago, on a hot summer's day, I sat in the shade of an ancient oak tree with an ancient, wrinkled woman sitting beside me. Her old dog was lying at our feet. As she nodded toward her graying, furry companion, she said in a matter-of-fact way, "He'll be goin' on one day soon."

Now that I'm well and my life is full of expectation, I'm not eager to "go on," although I understand that I will. Being part of several age-ranged groups helps me to experience the full continuum of life and my impending end as a matter of course.

I wasn't afraid to die when I attempted suicide. I'm not afraid to die now. Rather, I'm afraid of what the dying process might present to me in the way of challenges.

And I'm unsettled by an odd twist in my conditioning. During my entire life, I've taken care of "eating the lima beans on my plate" before getting dessert. As a routine of my past, I've done the hard things first, getting them out of the way before "playing."

I can't do that with this dying thing, which frustrates me.

When I'm aware of the fear I have about the dying process, I'm saddened when I remember my psychiatric hospitalizations in a center specializing in late-life depression. Surrounded by old people, all of us suffered.

Ire still bites at the anomalies. We were never in a professionally facilitated therapy group, where we could share our feelings. Where we could develop compassion for each other. Where we could laugh at ourselves. Where we could heal together by telling our stories.

I free myself more easily now from the rage fueled by that injustice. My writing is my way of seeking resolution in becoming, perhaps, an agent of change.

Anger at anything can't root these days. I'm more inclined to focus on the funny things that happen, like the time I walked into a convenience store one day to get favorite my treats. Mimicking my past. I made a beeline to the sweets, selecting one fireball and two pieces of bubble gum.

At the checkout counter, I placed my delights in front of an aging cashier, eager eyes and wrinkled smile belying my apparent age.

"For your grandchildren?" the cashier asked.

My right index finger poked at my chest, telling her the truth.

She tilted her head to one side, placed a hand over her mouth, and looked up at me with mischief in her eyes, telling me she, too, knew about being a little kid in an old package.

I don't get this thing about being an "adult." I rather like being a child of wisdom and play, especially now that I'm not sick.

In *Growing Young*, Ashley Montagu made a statement I read thirty years ago, one that has more significance to me under the current circumstances: "As a consequence of the unique evolutionary history of our species, we are designed to fulfill the bountiful promise of the child; to grow and develop as children rather than into the kind of adults we have been taught to believe we ought to become. . . . We are, by every confirmable measure, designed to continue, throughout our lives, to grow and develop in the traits so conspicuously exhibited by the child."[3]

Even though I am forever childlike, my body shows signs of

aging other than wrinkled skin. Indeed, they strike me funny—sometimes . . .

My flaccid, once-firm breasts sag like flat, wide-mouthed balloons only partially filled with water. When unimpeded by a brassiere, they hang so far down they appear to be begging my navel to nurse. That being said, the right one's more eager to seek her destiny than the left. An adage plays in my funny bones. An aging woman's body parts and real estate have something in common: location is everything.

Recently I've discovered a type of contraption that architects cleavage, albeit wrinkled: a push-up brassiere. Yet entering one of them at my age is an acquired talent. First, I bend over, letting my breasts hang perpendicular to my body. Then, orchestrating the brassiere with finesse, I put my arms through the straps and place the underwired cups at my breasts. Taking the dangling ends of the back straps in my hands, I reach behind me and secure them.

That's not all, though. The last maneuver mashes my flaccid breasts to my chest. They bulge beneath the underwire, pinning them to my rib cage. Alas, my breasts are no longer round and firm enough to fall naturally into the cups.

The *coup de maître*, the master stroke?

I reach down with my right hand and scoop up my left breast and place her into the left cup. Then, with my left hand, I do the same thing with my right breast.

The result is a high-chested, wrinkled cleavage I'm proud to wear.

Not to leave behind something else that's happened, the geology of my buttocks has changed radically. The once round, firm cheeks appear to have caved into my intergluteal cleft, or butt crack, for those less inclined to be scientific.

Body hairs are doing odd things, too. My pubic area is balding. But I've grown a hair that, when left untrimmed, sticks out of the left side of my ear, prompting me to wonder if one of the hairs from below my navel migrated to my ear in an obtuse expression of freedom.

With regret, I report that the aging process, the residual effects of neurological Lyme disease, or the drug I take to mollify anxiety has adversely affected my orgasms. That's merely a guess, as no one I know talks about orgasms. So I don't know what's normal for someone my age. Orgasms still feel good, but they aren't the powerful bursts of unrestrained pleasure they once were. Now, their intensity is no more than the pleasure of having a morsel of dark chocolate flood my taste buds. "Music, art, literature, food. Passion is the fire within us all. Passion for creativity, innovation, perfection. Daring, perseverance, flair, brilliance. The genius spark that is born of love," reads the label on the bar. "And we're passionate about chocolate." These days, so am I.

On another note, nowadays "dealing with an issue" means loosening sphincter muscles have leaked an unbidden substance from my body, making for all kinds of adventures I'd rather not have. Expressions of guttural discontent from my anus are no longer dry. They leave behind skid marks and dirty laundry, signaling their passage. Despite doing frequent Kegel exercises, if my bladder gets a wee bit full, a mere sneeze causes my clothes and my pride to be soaked in urine.

All that said, for a seventy-year-olde, I'm in great shape.

PASSAGES

The kaleidoscope of human experience is boundless.
Miracles are borne in the mystery of Divine Light,
shimmering in the wilderness.

        —The Watcher

After canoeing solo for a week, I find myself standing on a muddy bank of Utah's Green River, northwest of the Confluence, or so I think. The fifteen-foot aluminum canoe I've paddled downriver for more than fifty miles is beside me, loaded with necessities for primitive camping in the backcountry of Canyonlands National Park.

I've just run through a stretch of unexpected turbulent water. In a matter of seconds, a surge of rushing water lifted my aluminum canoe into the air, shot my craft downhill, and then slammed the port side against a giant gray boulder on shore

Now that I'm safe, I'm irritated.

All my pushing and shoving with every ounce of strength I have hasn't freed my canoe. I'm tired, and in a hurry to get farther downriver to meet an outfitter's jet boat at the Confluence for the trip back to Moab. I can unload the canoe to lighten the load for maneuverability. Yet I'm too impatient to take the time, and too agitated to think clearly.

Because I've been preoccupied with efforts to get back on the water, I haven't paid attention to my surroundings. When taking a break from trying to free my canoe, I stand up, arch my back, stretching, and look around. Two large, yellow rafts resting on the shore a short distance away, and a small group of people standing nearby, grab my attention.

Someone leaves the group to walk toward me along the white sand of the boulder-strewn riverbank. While waiting for him to get near enough to speak, I find myself hoping that whoever's coming will help me get unstuck.

I also consider my appearance—ill-suited for greeting a stranger. My tan, floppy, wide-brimmed hat, stained by red-brown river silt, is held in place with a chinstrap, snugged extra tight to keep the wind from robbing me of protection from the sun. Although my eyes are shaded, my nose is exposed and red, burned despite the white, zinc-based sun block I've smeared there every day. Around my neck, a bright orange-and-yellow bandanna drips water down my chest and back. The temperature has been at least one hundred degrees for more than an hour, and as a matter of routine, a little while before going through the turbulent water that landed me on the beach, I'd dunked both my hat and bandanna in the river, then put each back in place, dripping cold, muddy water to cool me.

My world-class knobby knees, scratched and red from kneeling on grit to paddle, glare from beneath the hem of my saggy-rumped shorts. In the early-morning hours, sipping coffee before launching myself on the river, I sat on a wet bank—a mixture of dark-gray clay and red-brown sand—where I'd camped the night before. The remains of the bank left on the back of my shorts insinuate a fecal accident. After shoving off from the muddy shore this morning, clumps of riverbank clung to the straps of my water sandals. They're still there, along with dirty toenails, adding to my charm.

To protect my arms from the sun, I have on a well-traveled, once-white, long-sleeved knit shirt with undeniable character—olde like me. The crew neckline is raveled and frayed, cuffs split at the seams, the arms also stained by rust-colored river mud like everything else I have on. Over that sassy sun protector I wear a short-sleeved, rust-colored T-shirt proclaiming an undeniable reality: "Older Than Dirt." Today, I'm celebrating my seventieth birthday—June 24, 2013, in my *haute couture*, most certainly off grid.

I wonder if the young man now standing before me thinks so, too, when he asks, "What are you doing here?"

———

Five days earlier, I pushed my rented seventeen-foot aluminum canoe into the fast-moving currents of a turgid Green River, beginning my fourth solo canoe journey in Utah's Canyonlands . . .

Dip. Pull. Push away. Feather. Arc.
Dip. Pull. Push away. Feather. Arc.

While kneeling on the floor of the canoe, I reach forward along the right side, dip the eight-inch-wide blade of my lightweight wooden paddle into the water, then pull with my hands positioned on the shaft and handle back toward the stern and beyond my torso, propelling me and my canoe downriver. Before lifting the blade out of the water to execute the next stroke, I make a slight push-away motion with the blade to counteract the canoe's tendency to veer left from the preceding pulling motion; in so doing, I keep the canoe pointing straight downstream— without switching sides to paddle. After pushing away just enough to point the bow in the right direction, I lift the paddle out of the water and feather the blade parallel to the river's surface, reducing wind resistance. Arcing the paddle in a sweeping semicircle, I reach forward to begin again the silent motion.

Thus, I ply Utah's Green River with my paddle, Kayenta. She carries the name of a rock formation in the Canyonlands, where I now journey solo on a fifty-mile excursion in the solitude of back-country for the third time. With no watch, no digital devices—just a pencil, writing tablet, and my slow, deep breathing—I pulse with my surroundings, synchronizing my days with the rhythms of the river and the canyons.

I feel as though I've been summoned here once again. I wanted to come to the Green River this time to celebrate the end of seven decades of robust living. To celebrate my continuing emotional and physical well-being. And to usher in a new way to be in this world.

I'm poised for something mysterious and profound to happen.

I'm certain there's a spiritual reason that has beckoned me here, although I don't know what it could be. I recall the way I felt three years ago when, at the end of my river trip, flute music echoed in the canyons. I knew Divine Destiny had called me to be there for that serenade—to be there to celebrate my healing journey, and my readiness to seek even more well-being while gratitude for the opportunity spilled from my eyes.

Since receiving The Gift of the Circle on January 4, 2010, I've journeyed, homeward bound, seeking wholeness.

I know I'm close to finding my way there. I don't feel shame when speaking openly about being sexually abused or my experiences in psychiatric hospitals. I express the newfound love I feel for myself by nourishing my body with quality food and creating time for respite. And I've cleaned up the emotional detritus leftover from childhood trauma.

An experience awaits me on the eve of my seventieth birthday, a passage into the rest of my life, the final stretch of a magnificent, though challenging, journey.

To the Confluence! *Dip. Pull. Push away. Feather. Arc.*

———

All six expeditions, three solo including this one, in the back-country of Canyonlands National Park have invoked similar teachings. Each has taught me more about working through my fears while taking calculated risks, building confidence in myself, and manifesting in my off-river life. Each has added to my skill at pursuing my dreams in spite of the fears that want to rob me of the privilege.

On the day of launching for this excursion, when I faced the Green River still swollen with spring runoff from the Rockies, I didn't have to talk myself into going on the water. Yes, a tinge of fear surfaced when I first shoved off. But once I felt the first pull of Kayenta against the water, that fear transformed into assurance.

Even so, unexpected fears surprise me.

One of those wears a mask of deceit I've never seen here before, posing as an old and feeble me, taunting me about becoming seventy. I'm too often tempted to question my skills and strength merely because I'm well-advanced in years.

When that happens, The Watcher is quick to intervene:

Avoid limiting your expectations.

Preconceived notions of what to expect at age seventy are not useful.

Base the evaluation of your capabilities on your experiences — right here, right now.

Your upper body strength is good. Your paddling is taking you downriver where you want to go. Applaud your mental and physical strength.

You're taking precautions — wearing your flotation device when needed, getting off the river when the wind threatens your safety, keeping your canoe pointed downstream and into the wind-driven waves.

Look around. You're fine!

The Watcher's prompting becomes a mantra, settling me when age-related fears try to bully me.

Another unsettling fear is bothersome, too: I can't explain the gut-tingling dread that haunts me when I'm on the water and there's nothing alarming happening. Especially in the mornings, trepidation nags me, coming on soon after I've launched myself on the river. The Watcher attempts to assuage my feelings:

Is there wind threatening you now?

No.

Are you moving fast enough to get you to the Confluence to meet the Tex's Riverways boat on time?

Yes.

Will you be okay if you need to camp an extra night out here?

Yes. I have enough water and plenty of food for several additional days on the river.

Despite wise coaching, the same inexplicable fear haunts me most mornings and erupts other times while I'm paddling. Although the bouts don't persist, they're troubling.

———

Birds and a few animals, or their footprints engraved on muddy riverbanks, remind me I'm not alone in this pristine wilderness.

The first night out, I camp along a canyon inlet created by high water—snowmelt—ebbing, yet still flowing into the river from the Rockies to the north. When paddling back to the river the next morning, a beaver escorts me on the port side of the canoe, gliding in the glassy silence of dawn with only his head breaking the water, raising a gentle, V-shaped wake. When we reach the river, the beaver lifts a wide, thick, rounded tail into the air. *Slap!* With that crisp goodbye, he disappears underwater. Feeling a connection with the majesty of boundless expectations, I go on my way, relishing the soft breezes cooling my skin, whispering greetings for a new day.

One morning, when I beach my canoe on a wet, muddy beach to eat breakfast, I see fresh footprints—signs of mule deer and coyote, who came to drink during the night. Routinely, at dusk, bats flitter about catching airborne insects while silhouetted against the pale blue-and-coral ombré of radiant sunsets.

While preparing my camp one afternoon, I see a rabbit nearby, frozen in place, eyes speaking of fear. Often, squirrels entertain me, scurrying this way and that on the limbs of an infrequent cottonwood tree. Bright-green collared lizards frequently acknowledge my presence, pumping their upper bodies up and down on rocks or the sandy banks I pass.

As I'm beginning to stir in the mornings just before dawn, birds chirp overhead in low-lying branches, announcing the arrival of the sun soon to paint a golden glow low in the east.

Like never before, black-chinned female hummingbirds grace me with their presence. At first, I think they're merely attracted by the orange-and-yellow scarf I wear around my neck. Yet every evening, long after my scarf is off and out of sight, they come humming near the opening to my tent. I think of them as special messengers, telling me I'm loved, a special guest in the Canyonlands.

Most of the people I see are in the distance, remarkable merely because being near others here in the backcountry is rare. The number of people on the river is controlled by Canyonlands National Park to preserve the environment and to provide solitude for those like me, seeking the rare opportunity to be alone.

After launching on the first day, I lunch a few miles downriver with a group who put in the water the same time I did. After they leave the inlet to the canyon where we ate, I pitch my tent there to stay for the night. I see no one else until the evening of the second day, when I glimpse a couple far to the south of me bathing nude in the river.

I'm completely alone during the third day until fixing dinner on a rocky beach, protected from the wind by a tamarisk hedge. A park ranger arrives in a motorized pontoon boat and stops to check my backcountry permit. No one appears for most of the fourth day; in the late afternoon a group of adolescents and adults pass by. They struggle to paddle against the same high winds that forced me to stop. Their energy, youth, and numbers at the paddle keep them moving forward when I couldn't budge.

In a pre-launch briefing, an employee of the outfitter I used issued a warning: "Wind can create three-foot—and four-foot—standing waves in the canyons; they move a lot of weight. If the wind gets strong, stop. Get off the river. Take a hike. Wait until things calm down before you go on." Indeed, high winds plague me every afternoon, a consistent pattern of weather I've never experienced here. Temperatures above one hundred and gale-force winds blowing against the current mark this solo journey in the Canyonlands as my most challenging.

Early every morning, gentle winds ripple the river. They brush my skin off and on while I paddle, reminding me that nothing ever stays the same. Reminding me to be flexible—to work with what nature delivers in the way of lessons. To pay attention to The Watcher, who so loves this part of the universe.

Winds and emotions—alike in many ways.

A certain kind of energy seems to power both. Unseen—evident only by expression: Leaves rustle in a tree. Fingers tap on a table.

Wind, emotions—both with the power to calm, both with the power to destroy.

Both can offer renewal and hope.

Wind and emotions—ever changing.

But, a major difference marks them.

You can't control the wind.

You can take charge of your emotions.

———

There's no time for musing when the sun rises high in the afternoon sky, heating the canyon walls, provoking the wind to bellow in gusts.

Gusty winds, bending trees and shrubs growing along the shoreline, signal me to move close to the lee side of the river, thinking of the pre-launch warning. I hold on to branches, bowing my head to keep desert sand from stinging my face while the wind howls. When there is a pause in the uproar, I paddle a short distance, struggling to make headway.

Always, by early afternoon, I'm forced to stop. When the sun's rays scorch the canyons, heating the metal on my canoe hot enough to burn my fingers, constant, stiff winds agitate against the current, kicking up white caps. A few times I try to paddle against the afternoon turmoil, only to get blown back up the river at a fast clip. Places with enough level ground to pitch even my compact tent are scarce.

When snowmelt, flowing down from the Rockies into the Canyonlands, begins to ebb, the water level on the Green River recedes, revealing sandy beaches—campsites. That's just beginning to happen, inch by inch, but not enough to offer many good places to spend the night. And when I'm threatened by facing a standing wall of water, I can't keep paddling to find a good spot.

When I can no longer budge forward, I begin searching for just a spit of land to pitch my tent. Inching myself forward, pulling my loaded canoe using overhanging branches of shrubs, I keep going until I find a shaded sliver of land. After pitching my tent—twice with half the floor angled up a slope—I bathe myself, wash the clothes I've worn that day, and don those I cleaned the day before.

I spend hours gazing at the beauty surrounding me—or meandering in my thoughts—until I get hungry for dinner. The changing angles of lacy tree-branch shadows and the blunt, rounded shadow of the canoe's bow intercepting the sun's rays fascinate me. In the silence of the wilderness, they tell of passing time and where the sun will set, orienting me. I relish the simple nature of my experience.

I don't write much when I stop for the day. I'm too tired.

Climbing or hiking in the canyons after I set up camp is nothing I want to do, either. By afternoon, the sun broils the canyon floors. When I walk on them for even a short distance, they blast their heat onto my body, rapidly evaporating any water I've poured on myself as a coolant. Without moisture on my skin, I feel fried and so uncomfortable that all I want to do is retreat to the shade near the river.

Each day when I paddle, using my mind and body to work with my windy environment and my age-related fears, I feel the reality of my progress toward physical and emotional healing. Even though I have some gut-tingling fear taunting me when I'm on the water, even when they persist, they don't overpower me.

While entraining to the rhythm of the wilderness with my

mind and body, The Watcher, accompanied by the canyons and the river, proclaims my hard-won emotional mastery.

You're in command of your feelings now.

The power and timing in your stroke are so like the way you're working with emotions: the symbolic maneuvering in a challenging environment.

You're so not a victim of circumstances.

Never have been. You merely thought you were.

And you're no longer a victim of sexual abuse. You're speaking out now. Letting go of the shame that held you bondage.

You're in capable hands—your hands.

Trust yourself!

When considering those points, I'm certain they're the summation of my lessons from this land of metaphor.

I'm way off base.

This master pedagogue is far from done with me.

Even considering the short time I have left on the Green River, there's more—much more—this wilderness plans to teach me.

Dip. Pull. Push away. Feather. Arc.

———

When the stillness of the Canyonlands' backcountry absorbs my attention, I orchestrate my days using only what's happening around me, harmonizing my own needs with the rhythms of the wilderness.

Every morning, I sit near my tent, heating water in a fire-retardant, neon-green sleeved container that rests on the burner of my propane gas stove. When the water comes to a rumbling boil, I lift the container and pour hot liquid into a dark-blue-and-white-specked metal coffee cup. The scent of Italian roast instant coffee rises in the steam, inviting pleasure. Listening to the birds chip overhead while appreciating cool morning temperatures, I make and sip two cups of brew, in no rush to depart.

After I've finished coffee, I strike camp. When all my things are stored tidily in the canoe, I survey the situation, making necessary adjustments to balance the load.

Standing aside, I ready myself for each day. Because I've frequently been haunted by an inexplicable fear when waterborne, I pause to ask for Divine Protection before I push offshore. Lifting my face to the sky, I spread my arms wide, opening my palms in supplication:

May I make wise decisions when making my way downriver.

May I be protected.

May I be safe.

After I've canoed for a while, hunger predictably strikes. I find an inviting spot to stop for breakfast. Once in a while, a white beach hosts me, where I sit on sand leaning against the side of my canoe, eating. Most often, though, I dine while floating in a shallow spot near the shore under the shade of tamarisk bushes.

I eat an assortment of the same things for breakfast and lunch: protein bars or powdered protein mixed with water, dried goat milk, vanilla, and stevia; assorted nuts, pumpkin and sunflower seeds, and dried cranberries; dehydrated kale and string beans prepared for me by my sister before I left for Utah.

My dinner doesn't vary, either. Even so, I look forward to the robust flavors that burst in my mouth when I satisfy a grabby hunger, egged on by energetic paddling.

Preparations begin with sautéing fresh, minced garlic in oily sesame tahini, using a small frying pan and my stove. When the garlic's toasted to a golden brown, infusing my surroundings with a mouth-watering aroma, I add canned beans to simmer, juice and all. While that's cooking, I slice a red bell pepper into wide strips on a tiny bamboo cutting board. I squeeze fresh lemon juice into the bubbling hot mixture I've poured into a bowl that matches my coffee cup. Hot sauce adds the final touch. Salivating, I spoon the bean mixture into my mouth with pepper slices, adding their flavor and crunchy texture to the mix.

For dessert, I pinch off a bit of halvah to nibble. Taking my time, I savor the flavor of sesame flour, sweetened with honey.

Soon after I wash my dishes in river water, using a multi-purpose bucket and biodegradable soap, the sun finally drops behind the canyons. Relinquishing torment, the blistering heat yields to the cool, soothing temperatures of desert nights. Like me, the wind responds with relief, slowing down for a much-needed rest.

Before crawling into my tent to sleep under the twinkling stars and the moon soon to be full, I tie a knot in a rope hanging from a canoe thwart, signaling the end of another day. Silence embraces me and my surroundings, except for a hummingbird hovering at the door of my tent.

———

With the rhythmic stroking of my paddle, I've canoed downriver for four days now.

Early in the afternoon, high winds force me to stop and set up camp on a sliver of muddy bank.

While the sun fades in the west, I begin preparing dinner, enjoying my waterfront accommodations on this last night on the river.

A hummingbird comes and hovers at eye level.

At first I pay little attention to her.

She's insistent, though.

Remaining close to my face, humming, flittering, and humming, she insists that I acknowledge her presence.

I stop what I'm doing. After laying aside cutting board, garlic, and knife, I turn my attention in her direction to *be* with her. Our eyes seem magnetized, mine hazel, hers black and sparkling.

As I look deeper into hers, I know we connect. In the instant that happens, I know we've bonded in a way we both understand.

I begin a conversation. "You're so pretty. I'm glad you came to be with me."

"Chirp, chirp, chirp," is her whisper-soft response, a message speaking of mutual appreciation.

For a time the hummingbird perches next to me on a root protruding from the ground. I'm touched by her quiet gesture of trust. Awed too. Although I know hummingbirds must rest or stop their busy search for nectar to sit on eggs, I've never seen a hummingbird motionless.

While this tiny, energetic bird sits beside me in the stillness of the evening, I resonate with our common ground:

The need to eat.

To have a safe place to land.

For companions.

We share The Sacred in silent wonder.

———

The next morning, I sit on the sliver of mud and sand where I camped the night before, sipping coffee. As I begin my fifth and last day in the backcountry, chilly breezes whisper against my cheek. Birds chirp above my head. The Green River glides by with the silence of glass, reflecting the majesty of the canyons across from where I sit.

I pick up my topographical river maps, trying to figure out exactly where I am.

I've had trouble more than once locating myself. For some reason, I've underestimated the distance traveled with my strong, efficient paddling. I've been able to place myself with certainty only when arriving at a familiar landmark.

The day before yesterday I camped across the river from Turks Head. Yesterday I passed Jasper Canyon, a place where I've overnighted on other river trips.

After passing Jasper Canyon, which is about ten miles from the Confluence, I wasn't certain how far I paddled before stopping for the day. No matter, I figured: *There's less than ten miles between me and the Confluence. I'm sure I've plenty time to meet the Tex's Riverways jet boat at eleven a.m.*

Eagerness to get going prompts me to put aside my river guide.

If I put some muscle behind my stroke, I can get to the Confluence on time with no trouble.

Piece of cake.

After taking one last sip of coffee, I stow my supplies and gear in the canoe.

For a reason I still don't understand, once again I feel the mysterious, gut-tingling fear that's so often haunted me on the water. Now that fear roils in my gut before I even go on the river—so strongly I want to cling to the shore.

I'm impatient with myself because I don't see anything to be concerned about. And, I'm eager to get to the Confluence. So, shrugging my shoulders, I prepare to shove off the bank in spite of the way I feel. With the bow of the canoe facing downriver, my hands gripping the gunwales, my right foot positioned in the center of the canoe near the stern, left leg poised to thrust me onto the river, I feel energy surging, ready to push me onward.

Then I come to an abrupt halt.

Yikes, I've forgotten to ask for my well-being.

Should I take the time?

With this feeling churning in my gut, I'd better!

I get out of the canoe, then pull her onto the shore; standing beside my dependable vessel of aluminum, with arms outstretched I, once again, beseech Divine Grace.

May I be protected.

May I be safe.

May I be safe!

Fearful still, yet knowing I've done the best I can to take care of myself, I push me and my canoe onto the river, bow pointed toward the Confluence.

Dip. Pull. Push away. Feather. Arc.

———

Today, the gut-tingling unease lingers longer than usual.

While paddling, my mind adrift, I notice something strange—
and unsettling. I can't visualize myself at the Confluence.

I've been there before—five other times. I can even recall the
unique formation of the gray shale topography at the junction of
the Green and Colorado rivers. Yet I can't call up the image of
myself planting my feet on the sandy shore, paddle in hand,
feeling triumph like I have before.

Am I having a premonition?

Is something bad going to happen?

Is that the reason for the fear I've been unable to explain?

*Too many of my friends, my sister, even Brenda, issued unprece-
dented concern before I left: "Be safe."*

Were they on to something?

Dip. Pull. Push away. Feather. Arc.

———

Propelling myself downriver, I paddle without a break during
the early-morning hours, intent on arriving at the Confluence by
eleven a.m., often recalling my magical encounter with the hummingbird.

In fact, I imagine writing about my experience with her.
Playing with words and plying the waterway, I stoke my forward
passage.

Something prompts me to pause paddling and "writing."

For a few moments I pay casual attention to the rock formations.

They tell me I must be nearing the Confluence.

Even so, I still can't picture myself landing there.

And I'm still unable to position myself. Frustrated because I
can't match my surroundings to the topographical representa-
tions of the terrain, I throw my booklet of maps onto the floor of
the canoe.

The reason I couldn't get a reference point?

In my concerted effort to arrive at the Confluence on time, I'd powered myself downriver much faster than I thought possible. And, imaginary writing took me far away from the present and the task of identifying my stopping point.

Dip. Pull. Push away. Feather. Arc.

———

By midmorning, even though I know I've got to be close, I still can't picture myself putting my feet on the white sandy beach of the Confluence. To reassure myself, I run a few checkpoints through my mind.

I just passed the group of adults and young, strong adolescents who passed me yesterday.

If wind and waves threaten to stop me, I know they'll tow me.

If I capsize, I can swim to shore, hang on to branches, and they'll rescue me.

If I lose my rental canoe and toilet, I have the resources to pay for them.

My stuff is easily replaced.

Figuring there's nothing to stop me from reaching my destination, I get excited. Exhilaration replaces my fear.

I "write" with fervor, telling about this entire time on the river, moving words around, reconstructing sentences. I'm engrossed— riveted to an artistic process when I should be paying attention to my surroundings. I'm simply not present when I pass the Confluence.

Without knowing what's happening, I propel myself onto the Colorado River and into Cataract Canyon, where dangerous rapids await my imminent arrival.

Dip. Pull. Push away. Feather. Arc.

On my left, I see a sign with bold red letters at the top: Danger Cataract Canyon. I think the sign's merely warning me that I'm approaching the Colorado River, since, without my glasses, I can't read the smaller letters telling me I'm about to be sucked into white water.

Thinking I'm still on the Green River but getting closer to the Confluence, I'm puzzled that I don't see my familiar landing spot. *Dip. Pull. Push away. Feather. Arc.*
Partway 'round a bend in the river, I hear a ferocious roar. *Dip.*
I stop paddling.
Noisy water. Where's that coming from?
Cautious, I inch a little farther.
Pull. Push away. Feather. Arc.
The full measure of the threat ahead explodes into view.

Thundering, roiling waves crash against boulders and rocks choking the river's passage. In a flash of misguided logic, I think a geological event has occurred, confirming a disclaimer in the introduction to my Canyonlands maps: "River channels change frequently, sometimes within a few hours. Rocks, sandbars or other obstructions may suddenly be laid in."[1]

I'm not afraid of what I see ahead, for I think I handled this kind of challenge already when I ran the Slide three years before.

However, I *am* fully present now. Watchful. No more "writing."

The current strengthens, sucking me faster and faster into the turbulent water.

While I still have time, I search for the best way to pass through the obstacle ahead.

To the right, near the river's edge, I see my only chance at safe passage.

I kneel into the bottom of the canoe and switch my paddle to my left side. With all my strength, I pull my paddle through the water to counteract the current that's pulling me sideways, threatening to broadside the hull into the thrashing waves.
Dip. Pull with everything you have. Push away. Feather. Arc.
Again.
Fast.
Pull hard!
I paddle until I can't control the canoe.

Thrusting the paddle under a thwart, I sit all the way back on my heels, and grab hold of the gunwales for balance.

With the hull slightly angled toward the shore on the right, one wave after another slams into the metal sides, jerking me back and forth, sending spray and froth shooting into the air.

In a final act of authority, the waves and current lift my canoe.

Bow forward, the hull is propelled onto the beach, the keel driven into mud and sand, the port side wedged against a large gray boulder, preventing any possible forward motion, protecting me from disaster downriver.

The guide, the one I saw walking toward me on the beach when I took a break from trying to get my canoe unstuck, has just introduced himself and asked me what I'm doing here.

"I'm headed for the Confluence to meet a jet boat at eleven a.m."

"You passed the Confluence two or three miles back. You just ran Brown Betty—Class Three rapids. You're in Cataract Canyon," he announces with a big grin spreading across his face and his eyes dancing with wonder.

"No way."

The guide nods in confirmation.

"I can camp here. I've plenty of food and water for a few days. Do you have a communication device to call the outfitter to let them know what's happened?" I blurt, feeling the need to appear logical.

Turning to face the people standing by the yellow rafts downriver, and pointing his head in their direction, my soon-to-be rescuer is adamant: "We can't leave you stranded here like that. I need to talk with the group to figure out what to do."

When we arrive at the rafts, a fellow river guide and friend reaches over the hull of the raft in which he's standing to introduce himself. My escort then steps into the same raft to confer with his friend, their conversation muted by winds and Brown Betty roaring in the background. While they consult, I present myself to the four passengers on the expedition.

I quickly forget their names, yet each person is memorable. The only woman is French, distinguishable by her accent. One portly man tells me he has a gimpy hip; another has glossy, curly black hair adorning a young, lean frame. Another sports sun-seasoned wrinkles and distinguished, silver-gray tresses.

We talk for a few minutes until one of the guides interrupts, announcing the solution to my predicament: "There's a trail along the canyon cliff, leading back toward Spanish Bottom, the southernmost pickup point before Brown Betty. We've contacted the outfitter to let them know we're on our way to meet them. We're going to carry your canoe . . ."

Nodding ascent, I'm polite, yet all business—all the while in the process of unwrapping a magnificent birthday gift, one I was destined to receive.

The young man who found me on the beach hops out of the raft and heads toward my canoe, his passengers following close behind.

I stay back, watching the other guide secure gear inside the raft; when everything's in place, he bends over to pick up a long-sleeved, cobalt-blue shirt. After he puts his arms in the sleeves, he begins buttoning the front while I wonder aloud, "Does that have UV protection?"

"No, I always take this with me on expeditions. This was my cousin's."

"What happened to him?"

Eyes filled with sadness foretell the one-word story: "Suicide."

Pain stabs my heart too. "I'm sorry."

In that simple exchange, I'm reminded that every breath I breathe is a gift of life and hope. Tears of gratitude fill my eyes in the face of a profound truth: if I'd succeeded at killing myself, the grief I see in this young man's eyes would have come from the eyes of those who love me. I feel grateful that I'm still here. That we're still together. And that we can share the gratitude that comes from knowing we were spared the grief from a tragic loss.

———

With the nobility of archangels and the potent directive of example, the river guides, both young enough to be my *great-grandsons*, start unloading my canoe. Their passengers follow their lead, silence reigning. When the canoe is empty, Matthew and Andrew hoist the hot metal hull, positioning the gunwales on their shoulders. I don the backpack containing my clothes and pick up my paddle, Kayenta, and the dry-seal bag protecting my camera while watching others already carrying everything else. Everything. A box with food and cooking gear; plastic gallon jugs full of water; stainless-steel toilet; toilet seat; bucket holding soap and toiletries; tent; deflated, rolled-up air mattress; mesh bag with sponge and scoop for bailing; fire pan; and my bag of trash—even my trash.

Despite the scorching heat and gusting winds, the guides, the French woman, and the gray-haired man disappear from view on a narrow trail winding up the sandy, rock-strewn cliff ahead. The man with the gimpy hip stays in the rear carrying two gallons of water and a few other items—more than his share of the load. The dark-haired man stays close behind me, becoming a shepherd, guarding me from danger.

As we walk, the distance between those in the lead and me lengthens, describing the difference in age and fitness. While navigating with the sun beating down, they're energetic. They're sure-footed, confident. On the other hand, I'm worn out. My legs are unsteady. Besides that, I'm scared. To me, the cliffside trail is treacherous, threatening.

My shepherd is much younger than I am—perhaps in his thirties—self-assured, respectful, asking if he can put a hand on my shoulder to reassure me. I feel honored by his presence, cherished beyond measure.

When we're high on the cliff, I chance a look over my right shoulder, seeing mere inches between me and a splat against the rocks on a roiling Brown Betty. I suck in my breath.

Adamant, The Watcher instructs:

This is no time to give in to your feelings.

Fear unbalances your body.

*Rivet your eyes to the trail. Look for the next place to put a foot—
that's all!*

Sensitive to what's happening with me, my black-haired
shepherd extends an arm around my right side. "I've got you
covered. You're fine. I'm watching your back."

My foot falters. This son of Gaia takes hold of my right forearm,
ensuring I don't fall.

When my thigh muscles quiver with exertion and I don't think
I have the strength to go on, I wonder aloud how much longer we
have to walk, then correct myself: "There's no point in asking a
question like that. I just have to put one foot in front of another.
We'll get there soon enough."

"Like life," my dark-haired companion remarks.

"Mmhmm."

We come to a steep crest in the trail partially blocked by a fallen
boulder. There's little room for a foot and no room for error. Wind
catches the blade of Kayenta, threatening to sail me off the cliff. I
hand my paddle to the man with the gimpy hip, and then crawl
up the trail using my hands to steady me. Somehow my nimble-
footed shepherd finds room to stand beside me, letting me handle
the challenge while guarding my progress.

After we reach the crest, I slide down a steep descent on my
rump; my thigh muscles can't support a downhill effort in an
upright position. At the bottom of the drop, I struggle, attempting
to stand. I can't. With a graceful movement, a danseur of sorts, my
shepherd steps around in front of me. Taking my right arm that's
extended to him, he leans back against my weight and tugs as I
try to push myself up. Grunting with the effort, I can't budge.

I'm not going to be carried the rest of the way to Spanish Bottom.

I've got to finish this walk—on my own two feet!

Summoning all the strength I have, we try again. My weight
now seems disembodied. Even so, somehow I manage to stand,
legs wobbly.

One of the guides appears ahead of us as I prepare to walk

forward. "You have just a little more climbing, then the trail levels off and descends to Spanish Bottom. You're almost there."

To get a head start back to the rafts so he'll arrive with the rest of the passengers, the man with the gimpy hip hands my stuff off to the guide, and waves goodbye. I want to hug him. He's dear to me now. The trail is too narrow for me to change my position. So a thank-you and a wave is all I can give him as he turns to walk toward the rafts.

Andrew and my shepherd escort me the rest of the way to Spanish Bottom.

I'm breathless and spent when we finally get there; the canoe and all my stuff has already been loaded onto the outfitter's jet boat, now waiting for me to board. The generous, extraordinary individuals who shouldered the weight of my things when I couldn't surround me.

One by one I gaze at them all. Awe at what they've just done for me renders me speechless. Putting my arm around the one who found me on the beach, I look into his eyes and burst into tears.

"What's wrong? You're safe now. The jet boat's here."

Although I'm too emotional to be coherent or to grasp the full significance of what's just happened, I do the best I can. "There's nothing wrong! I simply feel enormous gratitude. Today is my birthday. Today I'm seventy."

In disbelief, he interrupts, "You're not *that* old."

"Oh, yes I am. Indeed, I'm seventy years old. You and your friend are young enough to be my great-grandsons.

"You've just delivered an unforgettable birthday gift. You carried all my stuff. All my stuff—even my trash," I blubber, sweeping my arm to include everyone in the circle.

My hero repeats what he said before. "We couldn't leave you stranded."

"Oh, but you could have. Each one of you had a choice. You chose to help me. That speaks to your noble character."

My escorts and I hug once more.

While they shout, "Happy birthday," I walk toward the jet boat. Making an "elegant" departure, I scoot down steep, sandy steps on my rump. When my feet touch the shore, I stand, walk a few feet, then step onto the flat deck of the jet boat's bow. Sitting on a nearby bench, I face my Earth Angels, all gleaming with smiles and still shouting, "Happy birthday!" We blow kisses to each other until my heroes disappear behind shrubs and rocks to return to the rafts.

Jet boat engines roar.

When we're underway, and before picking up more paddlers returning to Moab, Devon, co-owner of Tex's Riverways, slides into the empty space on the bench beside me, leaving an employee to pilot the boat. I think he's come to mess up my day—to scold me for going beyond the Confluence.

"Did you underestimate the distance you'd traveled this morning?"

"Yes. But that's only part of the story. My mind was pre-occupied with a flurry of imaginary writing about my time on the river."

Nodding, he acknowledges my meaning, then continues. "In twenty-three years, the time I've owned this outfitting company and supported self-guided tours, only three—including you—did the same thing. One went more rapids than you before she could swim to shore. Did you capsize?"

"No!"

"You're the only one who didn't."

With that, Devon raises a high-five.

Grinning from ear to ear, I respond with a crisp salute to myself.

Devon slides out of the bench, returning to the bow. Wind blows against my face as the jet boat makes wide sweeps, gliding back and forth across the river, seeking deep water. While profound insights flood me, tears of gratitude stream down my cheeks:

The part of you that cherishes being on the water, the part of you that knows how to navigate dangerous waves, the part of you that has the expertise to paddle yourself in the wilderness, all were gifted to you by those in your past who harmed you most—your father and the woman who exploited you sexually.

As a young child, I fished with my father in the ocean on his unpretentious boats. When going to and from the sea, he navigated through the often turbulent Palm Beach inlet. Surrounded by walls of water too high to see anything else, he warned me over and over again about the importance of keeping the bow of a boat into the waves to avoid going broadside and capsizing.

The woman who molested me honed my skills in a canoe, refining the use of a paddle to direct my course.

Your safe passage through Brown Betty was an apology of sorts, a way to make up for destruction, a way to balance things.

While feeling the effects of a benediction on my past, my deep, rhythmic breathing pulses along with the easy sway of the jet boat gliding back and forth across the river.

Metaphor tells of more lessons from the wilderness.

You were a child from death and shadow, borne on the river of life, landing on an unknown shore.

Know this: when you are lost, someone will find you.

Perfect strangers will share your burdens. Earth Angels, shepherds, will protect you from danger when you falter.

Just like when you were sick.

Someone will always be there for you.

Always.

My musings drape me in jewel-toned shades of trust, my birthday present.

A powerful sense of feeling loved cradles my need to feel safe in this wilderness.

The dazzling desert sunlight sparkling on the river speaks of hope.

In this time of wonder, my mother comes to mind.

I imagine us gazing into each other's knowing eyes. Understanding casts a newfound warmth between us.

I'm well, Mom.

She smiles, a mother's smile of gratitude for her once-sick child.

I acknowledge my mother for her financial generosity that helped me find my way to help and wholeness.

I marvel at the canyons of my soul sculpted by tragedy, arraying my vision with splendor. Peaks of glistening triumph sparkle in the Aire. The majesty of who I've become because of my past dazzles me.

I lift my shirt, exposing my naked belly emblazoned with a scar. A perfect circle, once a fiery red wreath of pain and sorrow, now transformed into a symbol of compassion and gratitude. A permanent reminder that the most tragic of circumstances offer the opportunity to experience miracles and the greatest of teachings.

As my imaginings soar, a red-tailed hawk paints the future with hope, circling higher and higher in the blue, cloudless desert sky.

Upon my shoulder, a humble, earth-toned sparrow comes to rest, a symbol of resurrection and simple wisdom.

Hovering by my eyes, a hummingbird peers into my soul, reminding me of my interconnectedness to all who share the earth.

Those who love me surround me, singing joyful praises for my newfound wealth. Their music fills the Aire with angels' song.

In a grand pas de deux with Divine Healing Light, I'm lifted high and spun around, then lowered gently to the ground to face the threshold of my future.

My feet are eager to be moving.

There's much for me to do.

And so I dance.

And so I dance!

A Few More Things . . .

I'm no longer celibate. In 2017, I moved from Georgia to North Carolina to be with my person. She's kind, generous, and runs in deep currents, often finding humor in the simple that sometimes bubbles up into robust snorts and throaty guffaws. Our relationship has stretched her limits of goodness and my own, fostering growth in both of us. While cradled in the hard-won safety of our partnership, I've experienced the eruption into the present of my past sexual abuse. Although painful, the remembrance of horrors provided me the opportunity to continue my healing journey, and to, once again, find compassion strengthened for myself and others.

When writing "Olde," I told of my orgasmic experiences as being merely like those I had when savoring a piece of fine dark chocolate. They must have been tempered, then, by the aftermath of physical and mental trauma and the antidepressant I was taking. As a high note, at the age of seventy-six, I report that they now explode into pulsations of rapture that were beyond my wildest imagination. Indeed, they sometimes prompt me to explode into gales of unrestrained laughter.

So, what about Lyme disease?

On January 4, 2020, I was ten years out from the day I found my pathway to healing. Although I relapsed during the early stages of my recovery, I've not experienced symptoms for years. Besides knowing robust physical health, my mental health is in fine shape too.

What's happened to The Watcher?

That part of my consciousness has evolved into an ever-present sense of wise awareness that is one with the present moment and no longer speaks to me from a separate space.

Will I go back to Utah's Green River?

I'd like to return in 2023, the year of my eightieth birthday, if both my body and mind are working well enough to handle the *terrain*. If I'm able to go, I'll hire a guide, one who will keep an eye on me and yet stay far enough in the distance to offer me the illusion of being alone.

Anything else?

Yes.

I was recently certified to teach a research-based model of compassion training. I'm actively seeking opportunities to share this powerful agent of change for a troubled world. And, I'd welcome in-person or web-based speaking engagements about any facet of my story. Let me know if I can be helpful by reaching out to me at majesty.journey@gmail.com.

Thank you for traveling with me for a while.

May you know love and peace. And may you find hope in The Wee Tiny Sparrow's morning song.

Namaste!

Acknowledgments

When I've read acknowledgments written by authors who included countless individuals, I've often wondered if they were being authentic.

I now know they were, for I've many to thank too.

My gratitude for those who saved me from myself is included in my story, so my remarks here are focused on those who helped me with my writing.

From the beginning of my attempts to write with feeling, Rosemary Daniell and Jedwin Smith, both award-winning authors, inspired my raw integrity with their own indomitable courage to be frank. As to developing my skill with words, no matter how much of a mess I made when learning to write, they found an authentic way to encourage me to keep on going.

For the mixture of emotional support and editorial suggestions from my fellow writers, I'm so appreciative. From my heart that can't say enough, I thank Mari Ann Steffanelli, Susan Jimison, Ann Wainscott Sargeant, Roy Richardson, Shane Etter, Chuck Clark, Shean Hastings, Angela Durden, Jim Butorac, Stan Waits, Jane Shirley, Lisa Story, and Faison Covington.

I debated about whether to seek publishing in the traditional manner or to self-publish. In the end, I've relished having the ultimate control over my work that self-publishing has afforded me, and now I can't imagine working any other way. Book Logix, a company offering quality support for all stages of the publishing process, has provided me with a high degree of professional services, underpinned by the intention to help me enhance my storytelling.

'Tis indeed true: writing a book takes a village.

References

FROLICKING IN THE FRINGES

[1] Simon, Sidney, Leland Howe, and Howard Kerschenbaum. *Values Clarification.* 1999. 3. Print.

THE NAKED TRUTH

[1] Lewis, C. Day. In Messner, Reinhold. (October 1981). "At My Limit." *National Geographic* 160, 4. 566.

THE WARRIOR TAKES FLIGHT

[1] Logue, Christopher. *Ode to the Dodo.* London: Jonathan Cape Ltd. 1981. 96. Print.
[2] Stockdale, Brenda. *You Can Beat the Odds.* Boulder: Sentient Publications. 2009. Print.
[3] Burns, David. *The Feeling Good Handbook.* Revised. New York: Penguin Group. 1999. Print.

ON EAGLE'S WINGS

[1] Stockdale, Brenda. *You Can Beat the Odds.* Boulder: Sentient Publications. 2009. 267. Print.

TENDER MESSAGES

[1] Montagu, Ashley. *Touching.* New York: Harper. 1986. 6. Print.
[2] Montagu, Ashley. *Touching.* New York: Harper. 1986. xv. Print.
[3] Cozolino, Louis. *The Neuroscience of Human Relationships.* New York: W. W. Norton. and Company. 2006. 311. Print.

Carolyn Martin Graham

CEREMONIES OF THE HEART

[1] Gibran, Kahlil. *The Prophet*. New York: Alfred A. Knopf. 1962. 12. Print.
[2] Stockdale, Brenda. *You Can Beat the Odds*. Boulder: Sentient Publications. 2009. 18. Print.

FREEDOM BECKONS

[1] Stockdale, Brenda. *You Can Beat the Odds*. Boulder: Sentient Publications. 2009. 189–199. Print.
[2] Stockdale, Brenda. *You Can Beat the Odds*. Boulder: Sentient Publications. 2009. 156–160. Print.
[3] Stockdale, Brenda. *You Can Beat the Odds*. Boulder: Sentient Publications. 2009. 161. Print.
[4] Stockdale, Brenda. *You Can Beat the Odds*. Boulder: Sentient Publications. 2009. 162. Print.

ENTRAINING WITH AWARENESS

[1] Stockdale, Brenda. *You Can Beat the Odds*. Boulder: Sentient Publications. 2009. Print.
[2] Lipton, Bruce. *The Biology of Belief*. New York: Hay House. 2005. 111. Print.
[3] Stockdale, Brenda. *You Can Beat the Odds*. Boulder: Sentient Publications. 2009. 18. Print.
[4] Goldstein, Joseph, and Jack Kornfield. *Seeking the Heart of Wisdom*. Boston: Shambhala Publications. 1987. 13. Print.
[5] Goldstein, Joseph, and Jack Kornfield. *Seeking the Heart of Wisdom*. Boston: Shambhala Publications. 1987. 14. Print.
[6] Kabat-Zinn, Jon. *Mindfulness for Beginners*. Sounds True. 2006. CD.
[7] Stockdale, Brenda. *You Can Beat the Odds*. Boulder: Sentient Publications. 2009. 220–221. Print.

TO SHOOT A BIRD—OR NOT

1 Stockdale, Brenda. *You Can Beat the Odds.* Boulder: Sentient Publications. 2009. 54–62. Print.
2 Stockdale, Brenda. *You Can Beat the Odds.* Boulder: Sentient Publications. 2009. 65. Print.
3 Stockdale, Brenda. *You Can Beat the Odds.* Boulder: Sentient Publications. 2009. 56. Print.

UNIVERSAL LANGUAGES

1 Stockdale, Brenda. *You Can Beat the Odds.* Boulder: Sentient Publications. 2009. 103. Print.
2 Stockdale, Brenda. *You Can Beat the Odds.* Boulder: Sentient Publications. 2009. 104–115. Print.
3 Stockdale, Brenda. *You Can Beat the Odds.* Boulder: Sentient Publications. 2009. 29. Print.
4 Stockdale, Brenda. *You Can Beat the Odds.* Boulder: Sentient Publications. 2009. 122. Print.
5 Montagu, Ashley. *Growing Young.* New York: McGraw Hill. 1981. 192. Print.
6 Stockdale, Brenda. *You Can Beat the Odds.* Boulder: Sentient Publications. 2009. 122. Print.
7 Stockdale, Brenda. *You Can Beat the Odds.* Boulder: Sentient Publications. 2009. 124. Print.

THE CARESS OF COMPASSION

1 James, William. *The Varieties of Religious Experience* (Harvard University, 1902). Quoted in *Healing Trauma,* by Daniel Siegel and Marion Solomon. New York: W. W. Norton. 239. Print.

SUSPENDING DISBELIEF

1 Stockdale, Brenda. *You Can Beat the Odds.* Boulder: Sentient Publications. 2009. 75–81. Print.
2 Stockdale, Brenda. *You Can Beat the Odds.* Boulder: Sentient Publications. 2009. 76. Print.

[3] Stockdale, Brenda. *You Can Beat the Odds*. Boulder: Sentient Publications. 2009. 83–87. Print.

[4] Lipton, Bruce. *The Biology of Belief*. New York: Hay House. 2005. 107–111. Print.

[5] Stockdale, Brenda. *You Can Beat the Odds*. Boulder: Sentient Publications. 2009. 83–87. Print.

THE ART OF LETTING GO

[1] Pennebaker, James. *Opening Up*. New York: The Guilford Press. 1990. 36. Print.

[2] Pennebaker, James. *Opening Up*. New York: The Guilford Press. 1990. 37. Print.

[3] Pennebaker, James. *Opening Up*. New York: The Guilford Press. 1990. 37. Print.

[4] Pennebaker, James. *Opening Up*. New York: The Guilford Press. 1990. 197. Print.

[5] Stockdale, Brenda. *You Can Beat the Odds*. Boulder: Sentient Publications. 2009. 165. Print.

IN THE CARE OF ANGELS

[1] Hay, Louise. *Power Thought Cards*. Carlsbad: Hay House. 1999. Print.

[2] Stockdale, Brenda. *You Can Beat the Odds*. Boulder: Sentient Publications. 2009. 147. Print.

[3] Stockdale, Brenda. *You Can Beat the Odds*. Boulder: Sentient Publications. 2009. 147. Print.

[4] Stockdale, Brenda. *You Can Beat the Odds*. Boulder: Sentient Publications. 2009. 118–119. Print.

FLEXING WITH VARIABLES

[1] Stockdale, Brenda. *You Can Beat the Odds*. Boulder: Sentient Publications. 2009. 199–202. Print.

[2] Stockdale, Brenda. *You Can Beat the Odds*. Boulder: Sentient Publications. 2009. 199–202. Print.

[3] Stockdale, Brenda. *You Can Beat the Odds*. Boulder: Sentient Publications. 2009. 199–202. Print.

[4-10] All are from the Resilience Quiz reprinted in *You Can Beat the Odds* with permission from the developer, Al Siebert, PhD. All references to the quotes are on page 201 of *YCBTO*.

PRESENT TENSE

[1] Santorelli, Saki. *Heal Thy Self*. New York: Three Rivers Press. 1999. 16. Print.

A FLEDGLING

[1] Daniell, Rosemary. *The Woman Who Spilled Words All Over Herself*. Winchester: Faber and Faber. 1997. xiii. Print.

[2] Daniell, Rosemary. *Secrets of the Zona Rosa*. New York: Henry Holt and Company. 2006. xv–xvii. Print.

PRACTICING

[1] Doidge, Norman. *The Brain That Changes Itself*. New York: Penguin Books. 2007. 174. Print.

BONES IN THE DESERT

[1] Siegel, Daniel J. *The Mindful Brain*. New York: W. W. Norton and Company. 2007. 327. Print.

[2] Goldstein, Joseph, and Kornfield, Jack. *Seeking the Heart of Wisdom*. Boston: Shambhala Publications. 1987. Print.

PREPARING FOR FREEDOM

[1] Stockdale, Brenda. *You Can Beat the Odds*. Boulder: Sentient Publications. 2009. 75. Print.

SEEDS IN THE DIRT

[1] Andre, Linda. *Doctors of Deception*. New Brunswick: Rutgers University Press. 2009. 37–39. Print.

[2] Andre, Linda. *Doctors of Deception.* New Brunswick: Rutgers University Press. 2009. 29. Print.

[3] Andre, Linda. *Doctors of Deception.* New Brunswick: Rutgers University Press. 2009. 29. Print.

[4] Andre, Linda. *Doctors of Deception.* New Brunswick: Rutgers University Press. 2009. 271. Print.

[5] Andre, Linda. *Doctors of Deception.* New Brunswick: Rutgers University Press. 2009. 97. Print.

[6] US Department of Health and Human Services. *Mental Health: A Report of the Surgeon General.* Rockville, MD: US Department of Health and Human Services, Substance Abuse and Mental Health Services Administration, Center for Mental Health Services, National Institutes of Health, National Institute of Mental Health. 1999. 259. Print.

AND NEVER STOPS AT ALL . . .

[1] Stockdale, Brenda. *You Can Beat the Odds.* Boulder: Sentient Publications. 2009. Print. The following includes a beginning page reference in *You Can Beat the Odds* where more information can be found for each immune-system strategy I included on my to-do list:

Imagery. 73
Stream-of-Consciousness Journaling. 165
Affirmations. 147
Music. 101
Exercise. 206
Mindfulness Meditation. 220
Autogenics/Psychoacoustics. 101

Additions to the above list based on my unique needs were devotions, supplements, and reading something relevant to mind-body medicine that will both educate and inspire me. For instance, *The Biology of Belief* by Bruce Lipton, *The Brain That Changes Itself* by Norman Doidge, and *The Mindful Brain* by Daniel Siegel.

A REUNION

[1] Stockdale, Brenda. *You Can Beat the Odds*. Boulder: Sentient Publications. 2009. 164. Print.

[2] Salter, Anna. *Predators*. Cambridge: Basic Books. 2004. 78. Print.

[3] Salter, Anna. *Predators*. Cambridge: Basic Books. 2004. xi. Print.

[4] Borysenko, Joan. *It's Not the End of the World*. Carlsbad: Hay House. 2009. 60. Print.

FREEDOM'S CHILD WEIGHS ANCHOR

[1] Stockdale, Brenda. *You Can Beat the Odds*. Boulder: Sentient Publications. 2009. 159. Print

[2] Duncan, Karen. *Female Sexual Predators*. Santa Barbara: Praeger. 2010. Print.

MOMMA. MOM. MOTHER. ETHEL MARTIN GRAHAM. IN MEMORIAM.

[1] Schwartz, Mark, Lori Galperin, and William Masters. "Sexual Trauma within the Context of Traumatic and Inescapable Stress, Neglect, and Poisonous Pedagogy." In *Adult Survivors of Sexual Abuse*, edited by Mic Hunter. Thousand Oaks: Sage Publications. 1995. 16. Print.

AFFIRMING THE STRANGER

[1] Walcott, Derek. "Love after Love." In *Collected Poems, 1948–1984*. New York: Farrar, Straus & Giroux. 1986. Print.

[2] Lipton, Bruce. *The Biology of Belief*. Carlsbad: Hay House. 2005. Print.

[3] Stockdale, Brenda. *You Can Beat the Odds*. Boulder: Sentient Publications. 2009. Print.

[4] Cozolino, Louis. *The Neuroscience of Human Relationships*. New York: W. W. Norton and Company. 2006. Print.

[5] Doidge, Norman. *The Brain That Changes Itself*. New York: Penguin Books. 2007. 174. Print.

IN THE RAW—A SERIAL PRACTICUM

[1] Available at www.guptaprogram.com.

OLDE

[1] Version 2.3.0 (239.1) Copyright © 2005–2019 Apple Inc. All rights reserved. This came from an app that was on my Apple Mac upon purchase.
[2] Dictionary.com, s.v. "olde." Accessed December 5, 2019. https://www.dictionary.com/noresult?term=olde&s=t.
[3] Montagu, Ashley. *Growing Young.* New York: McGraw Hill. 1981. 117. Print.

PASSAGES

[1] *Canyonlands River Guide.* 2nd ed. Evergreen: Westwater Books. 1992. 17. Print.

About the Author

Carolyn Martin Graham was an educator by profession, a teacher at heart. Currently she is a speaker, sharing her inspiring story of healing. She is also an instructor of Cognitively Based Compassion Training®, certified by the Center of Contemplative Science and Compassion Based Ethics at Emory University.